ANALYSIS OF
RIGID FRAMES

ANALYSIS

OF

RIGID FRAMES

(AN APPLICATION OF SLOPE DEFLECTION)

BY

A. AMIRIKIAN, C. E.

Principal Engineer
Bureau of Yards and Docks
Navy Department
Washington, D. C.

M·D·K

UNITED STATES
GOVERNMENT PRINTING OFFICE
WASHINGTON : 1942

NAVY DEPARTMENT,
BUREAU OF YARDS AND DOCKS,
Washington, D. C., March 24, 1942.

This treatise on rigid frame analysis is a compilation of a series of 44 articles by the author, previously having appeared as technical supplements to the Bureau News Memorandum.

These articles were written primarily for the benefit of the Bureau's technical personnel, as an aid in the design of continuous structures. However, the demand in excess of the limited supply of mimeograph reprints has made it necessary to republish the articles in book form.

In this national emergency, when conservation of all structural materials is a paramount necessity, the importance of modern methods of analysis, as a means of realizing appreciable savings in materials, cannot be overemphasized. To this end, this book is presented as a contribution to National Defense as well as to engineering literature.

B. MOREELL,
Rear Admiral (CEC), U. S. N.,
Chief of Bureau.

PREFACE

During the past decade great progress has been made in the field of continuous structures. With the increased use of welding, as now extensively utilized in a large variety of steel framings, few structures, built of steel or reinforced concrete, could justly be classified outside the scope of rigid framing.

This progress in construction technique has placed special emphasis on the importance of the quality of design. Faulty analysis or a design based on ready-made, easily-applied, rule-of-thumb methods of computation can no longer be tolerated—from the standpoint of economy as well as of structural adequacy.

A rigidly connected framing constitutes an elastic unity. For a satisfactory design, we must have a clear concept of its elastic behavior under loading. Fortunately, an understanding of such an action is not as difficult or complex as is generally assumed, provided the designer is willing to do a little exploration in the fundamentals of the theory involved. The purpose of this book is to provide an opportunity for such an exploration to one undertaking the study of statically indeterminate structures.

For convenient study, the book is divided into four parts. Part I deals with the fundamentals of elastic deformation and the principles of *slope deflection*. Part II contains the analysis of continuous beams and simple framing, including a simplified method of solution of simultaneous equations. Part III presents a broad and original application of *slope deflection* to the analysis of frames involving side sway, covering a large group of bents representative of modern building framing. Part IV consists of a detailed discussion of some factors of analysis of minor importance in design.

Unlike many works of this character, where the practical application is only incidental to the theory, here, in nearly all cases, the analysis of each particular type of bent, and the derived formulae, constitute a systematized presentation of an actual framing problem, in connection with the design of a definite project in the Bureau.

The many illustrative examples and numerous working problems, answers of which are given at the end of the book, render it particularly suitable as a reference text for self-study. The author has used the material in his special classes for engineers and obtained good results. It has also been used by several universities for post-graduate courses in structural framing.

The author is greatly indebted to Rear Admiral B. Moreell, Chief of the Bureau, and to Capt. C. A. Trexel, Director of Planning and Design, for their interest in the work and for many helpful suggestions. The opportunity of this task is traceable directly to their inspiring leadership in the field of continuous frames and welded structures.

Messrs. E. R. Slade and E. G. Odley of the Bureau's Designing Engineers' staff checked the solution of the majority of the illustrative examples and the answers to the problems and rendered valuable assistance in the final preparation of the book.

A. AMIRIKIAN.

Washington, D. C.,
March 1942.

CONTENTS

Chapter II

SLOPE DEFLECTION

PART II—FRAMES WITHOUT SIDE SWAY

Chapter I

DIRECT METHOD OF SOLUTION

Chapter II

SOLUTION BY APPROXIMATIONS

PART III—FRAMES INVOLVING SIDE SWAY

Chapter I

RECTANGULAR BENTS

Chapter II

TRAPEZOIDAL BENTS

Chapter III

VIERENDEEL TRUSSES

Chapter IV

GABLE BENTS

Chapter V

LEAN-TO BENTS

Chapter VI

HIP BENTS

Chapter VII

BENTS OF IRREGULAR OUTLINE

PART IV—SUPPLEMENTARY CONSIDERATIONS

NOTATIONS

$A, B, C \ldots$ 4 E times true values of deflection angles θ_A, θ_B, θ_C ..., at joints
        $A, B, C \ldots$: $A=4E\theta_A$; $B=4E\theta_B$; $C=4E\theta_C \ldots$

$\overline{A}$ Area of simple beam bending moment diagram.

$\overline{A}_1$ Modified area of simple beam bending moment diagram.

A_c Cross sectional area of member.

E Modulus of elasticity in tension and compression.

F Concentrated horizontal load.

F_A Joint coefficient, equal to the sum of the stiffness factors of all
         members meeting at joint A.

FM_{AB} Fixed-end moment at end A of member AB.

G Modulus of elasticity in shear.

H Horizontal component of reaction; horizontal shear at joint.

HM_{AB} Fixed-end moment at end A of member AB when end B is hinged.

I Moment of inertia of member.

K Stiffness ratio of member, $K=\dfrac{I}{L}$.

L Length of member.

M Bending moment.

$\overline{M}_A$ Moment at center A_1 of support A.

M_{AB} Moment at end A of member AB.

M'_{AB} Moment transmitted through joint A of member AB.

P Concentrated vertical load.

Q_A Sum of load constants in the joint expression for joint A.

$\overline{Q}$ Modified area of shear diagram due to external loading.

R Simplified deflection term or deflection, $R=\dfrac{6E\Delta}{L}$.

S Total cross-sectional shear.

V Vertical component of reaction.   Vertical shear at joint.

V'_A Simple end reaction at face of support A due to external loading.

V_{AB} Shear couple corresponding to end moments M_{AB} and M_{BA}.

c Distance of concentrated horizontal load, F, from joint.

e Distance of concentrated vertical load, P, from joint.

f Rise of gable.

f_A Coefficient of deflection angle A in a joint equation.

f_{AB} Coefficient of correction to be multiplied by successive values of A
         to obtain corresponding increments of B.

h Height of story or vertical leg of gable bent.

k Cross-sectional constant of shearing deformation.

l Length of span.

m Ratio of spread of legs of trapezoidal bent to distance between
         legs at base.

n Ratio of spread of legs of trapezoidal bent to length of top member.

p Area of modified moment diagram for a span length of unity and a
         restraint moment at the left support equal to unity.

q	Area of modified moment diagram for a span length of unity and a restraint moment at the right support equal to unity.
	Sum of the load constants in shear expression used in solution for R values.
$\bar{q}$	Modified area of shear diagram for a span length of unity and a unit shear.
r	Radius of gyration of cross-section of member.
u	Centroid distance of area p from left support.
v	Centroid distance of area q from right support.
w	Intensity of uniform loading per linear foot.
x, y	Rectangular coordinates.
$\bar{x}$	Centroid distance of area $\bar{A}$ from right support.
$\bar{x}_1$	Centroid distance of modified area $\bar{A}_1$ from right support.
α, β	Simplified connection constants for member AB: $\alpha = 2\,EK\lambda_A$; $\beta = 2\,EK\lambda_B$.
γ	Unit shearing deformation, $\gamma = \dfrac{\tau}{G}$.
Δ, δ	Deflection of joint or of a point on a member from its original position.
$\bar{\epsilon}$	Unit strain or elongation.
ϵ	Total strain in element δx in length.
$\theta_A, \theta_B, \theta_C \ldots$	True deflection angles, in radians, at joints $A, B, C \ldots$
λ_A	Connection constant or "slip" of connection of joint A due to the transfer of a unit moment, $\lambda = \dfrac{\theta'_A - \theta_A}{M'_{AB}}$.
μ	Poisson's ratio.
ρ	Radius of curvature.
σ	Unit tensile or compressive stress.
τ	Unit shearing stress.

ANALYSIS OF RIGID FRAMES

(AN APPLICATION OF SLOPE DEFLECTION)

PART I. FUNDAMENTAL RELATIONS

CHAPTER I

MOMENT AREA THEORY

1. Elastic Curve and Radius of Curvature.—The neutral axis of a beam in bending takes the form of a curve, referred to as the elastic curve of the beam, composed of a series of small arcs with varying radii.

The radius of curvature at any location along the length of this curve is a function of the moment M at the section, the moment of inertia I of the cross section, and the modulus of elasticity E of the material.

The simple relation between these terms is readily obtained from Fig. 1, which represents a segment of dx in length, cut from a beam

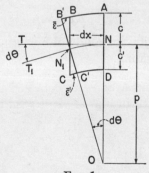

FIG. 1.

subjected to bending. Here the parallel lines AD and BC indicate the two sections limiting the segment dx in the free position of the beam. During bending, the top fibers stretch by an amount $\bar{\epsilon}$ and the point B moves into B'; likewise, due to contraction $\bar{\epsilon}'$ of the bottom fibers, the point C moves into C'. There is no change in length at the neutral axis. Then the inclined line $B'C'$ indicates the position of BC

1

in bending, relative to AB; and the line ON, obtained by the intersection of the extended lines AD and $B'C'$, represents the radius of curvature ρ for the segment dx. From symmetry of the triangles N_1BB' and ONN_1 we have:

$$\frac{\bar{\epsilon}}{c}=\frac{dx}{\rho}, \dots\dots\dots\dots \quad (1)$$

c being the distance of the outermost fiber from the neutral axis. But $\bar{\epsilon}$ is the total strain at B, corresponding to the length dx and to a unit fiber stress σ at the same point, and may be expressed

$$\bar{\epsilon}=\frac{dx\sigma}{E}=\frac{dxMc}{EI} \dots\dots\dots\dots \quad (2)$$

Substitution of this value of $\bar{\epsilon}$ in eq. (1) will give

$$\frac{Mdx}{EI}=\frac{dx}{\rho};$$

or,

$$\frac{M}{EI}=\frac{1}{\rho} \dots\dots\dots\dots\dots \quad (3)$$

Eq. (3) is the fundamental expression for curvature. In this equation the ratio $\dfrac{dx}{\rho}$ represents the tangent of the angle NON_1, and since it is a very small angle, the tangent may be replaced by the angle itself. The resulting equation,

$$d\theta=\frac{M}{EI}dx, \dots\dots\dots\dots \quad (4)$$

is the important expression for angle of curvature or deflection angle of a beam segment in bending.

2. Properties of Moment Area.—An enlarged and much exaggerated view of this angle is shown in Fig. 2. It is seen that the central angle

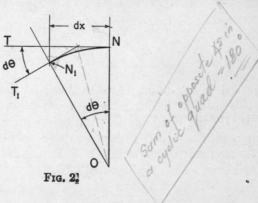

Fig. 2.

3. Deflection Angle.—Since the tangents are drawn to the curved or deflected position of the neutral axis, the angles of these tangents with respect to the unstrained position of the axis are called deflection angles, and, hence, the angle made by two tangents represents the change in deflection angle between the two points on the elastic curve.

To determine the change in deflection angle between two points, it is necessary, therefore, to compute the area of the $\frac{M}{EI}$·diagram between the points desired. This area may be considered as a transformed moment diagram in which moments are replaced by their $\frac{M}{EI}$ values.

Consider, for example, the cantilever beam shown in Fig. 4. The cross section of the beam is constant and the supported end is held fixed

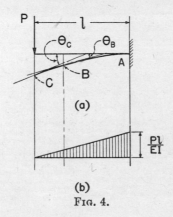

(a)

(b)

FIG. 4.

in the wall. The moment of inertia being constant, the $\frac{M}{EI}$ diagram in (b) is of the same shape as the moment diagram due to the concentrated load P at the free end. That part of the beam which is built into the wall is restrained and the neutral axis for that portion remains a straight line, coinciding with the tangent to the elastic curve at the support. Then the area of the $\frac{M}{EI}$ diagram between the support A and any other point B on the span, representing the change in deflection angle between the two corresponding points on the elastic curve, indicates also the slope or deflection angle of the tangent to the elastic curve at B, with reference to the horizontal tangent at A. Accordingly, for the deflection angle at the free end we have:

$$\theta_c = \frac{Pl}{EI} \cdot \frac{l}{2} = \frac{Pl^2}{2\,EI}.$$

NON_1 is equal to the angle made by the lines TN an
tangent to the curve NN_1—representing the bent p
neutral axis of the beam—at the ends N and N_1, res
may, therefore, define the angle of curvature of a be;
bending as the angle formed by two end tangents of t
senting the neutral axis of the segment.

The angle $d\theta$ in Fig. 2 corresponds to a small length
ing moment M which is assumed to be constant along
similarly small segment dx_1 has been added in Fig. 3.

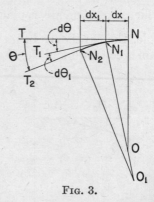

FIG. 3.

moment of the latter segment be indicated by M_1, th
curvature becomes

$$d\theta_1 = \frac{M_1 dx_1}{EI};$$

and for the total angle, corresponding to the curve NN
by the end tangents TN and T_2N_2, we have:

$$\theta = d\theta + d\theta_1 = \frac{Mdx}{EI} + \frac{M_1 dx_1}{EI};$$

or,

$$\theta = \int \frac{Mdx}{EI} \quad \cdots \cdots$$

Eq. (5) defines the first principle of moment area
the angle formed by the tangents drawn at any tw
elastic curve, representing the neutral axis of a bea;
equal to the sum of the areas of small $\frac{M}{EI}$ strips contai
two points.

4. Deflections.—It was stated above that the elastic curve of a beam in bending may be considered a series of small arcs with varying curvature. Fig. 5 represents this conception, as applied to a portion

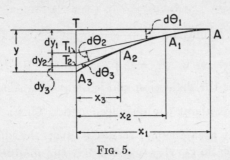

FIG. 5.

of a cantilever beam. Here the line TA represents both the unstrained position of the beam and the tangent to the elastic curve at A, and the curve AA_3, its bent or deflected position. The chords AA_1, A_1A_2 and A_2A_3, corresponding to the three small arcs of the curve, will coincide with the tangents at A_1, A_2 and A_3, respectively, if the arcs are made very small. Then the intercept of two consecutive tangents on a line, drawn normal to the unstrained position of the beam, may be taken as the tangent of the arc corresponding to the angle made by the two tangents. Thus, for the intercept T_1T_2, taken on the line TA_3, we can write:

$$dy_2 = x_2 d\theta_2; \quad \ldots \ldots \ldots \ldots (6)$$

or, substituting the value of $d\theta_2$ from (4),

$$dy_2 = \frac{x_2 M_2 dx}{EI_2}; \quad \ldots \ldots \ldots \ldots (7)$$

M_2 and I_2 being the moment and the moment of inertia, respectively, between A_1 and A_2. Similarly,

$$dy_1 = \frac{x_1 M_1 dx}{EI_1},$$

and

$$dy_3 = \frac{x_3 M_3 dx}{EI_3}.$$

But the sum of dy_1, dy_2 and dy_3 represents the displacement of the point A_3 from the tangent at A; denoted by y,

$$y = dy_1 + dy_2 + dy_3 = \frac{x_1 M_1 dx}{EI_1} + \frac{x_2 M_2 dx}{EI_2} + \frac{x_3 M_3 dx}{EI_3} \quad \ldots \ldots (7a)$$

Likewise, for the sum of $dy_2 + dy_3$, representing the displacement of the same point from the tangent at A_1, we have:

$$dy_2 + dy_3 = \frac{x_2 M_2 dx}{EI_2} + \frac{x_3 M_3 dx}{EI_3} \quad \ldots \ldots \quad (7b)$$

Eqs. (7a) and (7b) may be expressed in the general form

$$\Delta = \int \frac{Mxdx}{EI}, \quad \ldots \ldots \ldots \ldots \quad (8)$$

where Δ denotes the deflection and is defined as the sum of moments of small $\frac{M}{EI}$ areas about the displaced end. This is the second principle of moment area theory, restated thus: the displacement of a point on the elastic curve—representing the neutral axis of a beam in bending—from the tangent at another point on the curve, measured normal to the unstrained position, is equal to the moment of the area of the $\frac{M}{EI}$ diagram included between the two points, taken about the first point.

It is to be noted that the displacement becomes the true deflection of a point on the elastic curve if the reference tangent coincides with the unstrained position of the axis. The following example will serve for illustration:

ILLUSTRATIVE EXAMPLE

A cantilever beam of span l (Fig. 6) is subjected to a concentrated load P, applied at the free end. Assuming the moment of inertia of the section constant and the beam fixed at the support, determine:

(a) The deflection of the free end C with respect to the tangent of the elastic curve at midspan;

(b) The true deflection of the free end.

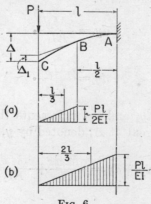

FIG. 6.

Solution: Since the I of the beam is constant, the $\dfrac{M}{EI}$ diagram is a triangle, and the areas corresponding to (a) and (b) are $\dfrac{Pl^2}{8EI}$ and $\dfrac{Pl^2}{2EI}$, respectively. Then for the deflection in (a) we have:

$$\Delta_1 = \frac{Pl^2}{8EI} \cdot \frac{l}{3} = \frac{Pl^3}{24EI}.$$

Similarly, for the deflection in (b),

$$\Delta = \frac{Pl^2}{2EI} \cdot \frac{2}{3}l = \frac{Pl^3}{3EI}.$$

PROBLEMS

1. Determine the vertical displacement of the end C in the above example (Fig. 6) from the midspan point B.

2. The load P in Fig. 6 is moved from the end to point B. Determine:
   (a) Change in deflection angle between points B and C;
   (b) Deflection angle at B;
   (c) Deflections Δ^1 and Δ.

CONJUGATE BEAM

5. Conjugate Beam of Deflection.—In the preceding examples of cantilever beams the deflection angle at any point on the elastic curve was readily obtained from the reference tangent at the support. In the case of simply supported beams it is necessary to locate a point on the elastic curve where the tangent is horizontal, or parallel to the unstrained position of the beam, in order to determine the inclination of any other tangent along the axis.

Consider, for example, the beam shown in Fig. 7. The ends are

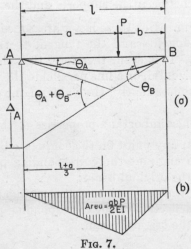

Fig. 7.

freely supported, the moment of inertia is constant, and a concentrated load P is applied at a distance a from the left support. The area of the $\frac{M}{EI}$ diagram in (b), representing the angle made by the two end tangents, or the sum of deflection angles at the two supports, is equal to $\frac{abP}{2EI}$. The moment of this area about A gives the deflection of the left support from the tangent at the right support. Denoting this deflection by Δ_A,

$$\Delta_A = \frac{abP}{2EI} \cdot \frac{(l+a)}{3} \quad \ldots \ldots \ldots \ldots \quad (9)$$

and dividing it by the span l, we will obtain the tangent of the deflection angle at B or the deflection angle θ_B (since the angle is very small and unlike the exaggerated view in the figure). Then,

$$\frac{\Delta_A}{l} = \theta_B = \frac{abP}{2EI} \cdot \frac{(l+a)}{3l} \quad \ldots \ldots \ldots \quad (10)$$

The right side of eq. (10) represents the reaction at the support B due to an imaginary loading of the $\frac{M}{EI}$ diagram over the span l. We may call the beam under the loading "conjugate beam of deflection," or simply "conjugate beam."

6. Properties of Conjugate Beam.—It is to be noted that the deflection angles θ_A and θ_B in Fig. 7 (a) are formed by the end tangents to the elastic curve and a horizontal line indicating the unstrained position of the beam. Since these two angles are equal to the respective reactions of the conjugate beam, their values are given by the $\frac{M}{EI}$ areas contained between the supports and the point of zero shear of the conjugate beam. But these latter areas measure also the angles made by the end tangents and the tangent to the elastic curve at point of zero shear. It is seen, therefore, that the tangent at point of zero shear is a horizontal, or a line parallel to the unstrained position of the beam, and, consequently, the value of the deflection angle at this point is zero.

There are two other important properties of the conjugate beam:

(1) The shear at any point on the conjugate beam is equal to the deflection angle at the corresponding point on the elastic curve of the original beam;

(2) The moment at any point on the conjugate beam represents the true deflection of the corresponding point on the elastic curve of the original beam.

Obviously, (1) is a restatement of values of deflection angles as referred to a horizontal tangent, and may easily be seen from Fig. 8.

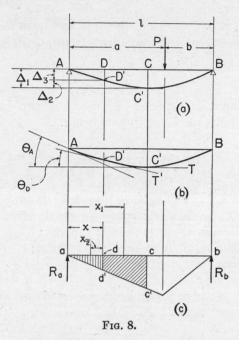

FIG. 8.

The elastic curve of this simply supported beam, shown in (b), can be considered as that of two cantilvers joined at C', and having a common horizontal tangent at the same point. Since C' is the point of zero shear of the conjugate beam, then the portion acc' of the $\frac{M}{EI}$ diagram in (c) represents the reaction R_A at the left support or the deflection angle at A of the original beam. The deflection angle at any point D' on the elastic curve is given by the area $cc'dd'$ of the $\frac{M}{EI}$ diagram, and may be expressed

$$\theta_{D'} = \text{area } acc' - \text{area } add'$$
$$= R_A - \text{area } add';$$

which is the shear at D of the conjugate beam.

The demonstration of (2) is equally simple. Let the deflections of the points A and D', shown in (a), from the tangent at C' be denoted by Δ_1 and Δ_2, respectively. Then the true deflection Δ_3 of the point D'—given by the distance DD' in (a)—is equal to the difference of the deflections of the points A and D' on the elastic curve from the reference tangent at C', or

$$\Delta_3 = \Delta_1 - \Delta_2 \quad . \quad . \quad . \quad . \quad . \quad . \quad . \quad . \quad . \quad . \quad . \quad (a)$$

The values of Δ_1 and Δ_2, obtained from the definition of deflections, are:
$$\Delta_1 = \text{area } acc' \cdot x_1,$$
$$\Delta_2 = \text{area } acc' \ (x_1 - x) + \text{area } add' \cdot x_2;$$
in which x_1 is the c. g. distance of the area acc' from the left support, and x_2 the c. g. distance of the area add' from D. Substituting these values in eq. (a), we have:
$$\Delta_3 = \text{area } acc' \cdot x - \text{area } add' \cdot x_2$$
$$= R_A \cdot x - \text{area } add' \cdot x_2;$$
which is the moment expression of a point D, located at a distance x from the left support, of the conjugate beam.

ILLUSTRATIVE EXAMPLES

1. A simply supported beam of span l is subjected to a concentrated load P, placed at a distance a from the left support. Assuming that the I of the cross section is constant, obtain the following:
    (a) The deflection angle at the left support;
    (b) The deflection angle at the right support;
    (c) The deflection under the load.

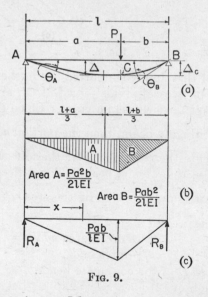

FIG. 9.

Solution: The area of the $\dfrac{M}{EI}$ diagram in Fig. 9(b), representing the conjugate beam loading, is equal to $\dfrac{Pab}{2EI}$, and the distances of its centroid from left and right supports are $\dfrac{l+a}{3}$ and $\dfrac{l+b}{3}$, respectively.

Then,

$$(a) \quad \theta_A = R_A = \frac{Pab}{2EI} \cdot \frac{(l+b)}{3l} = \frac{Pb(l^2-b^2)}{6lEI}.$$

$$(b) \quad \theta_B = R_B = \frac{Pab}{2EI} \cdot \frac{(l+a)}{3l} = \frac{Pa(l^2-a^2)}{6lEI}.$$

$$(c) \quad \Delta_C = R_A a - \text{area } A \frac{a}{3}$$

$$= \frac{Pab(2ab)}{6lEI} = \frac{Pa^2b^2}{3lEI}.$$

2. Assuming $a > b$, determine the point of maximum deflection of the beam in the preceding example.

Solution: The point of maximum deflection of the original beam corresponds to the point of zero shear in the conjugate beam. The moment area between the left support and a point at a distance x from the left support (Fig. 9(c)) is equal to $\dfrac{Pbx^2}{2lEI}$. Then,

$$R_A - \frac{Pbx^2}{2lEI} = 0,$$

$$\frac{Pb(l^2-b^2)}{6lEI} - \frac{Pbx^2}{2lEI} = 0,$$

and

$$x = \sqrt{\frac{(l^2-b^2)}{3}}.$$

PROBLEMS

3. Determine the following for the beam shown in Fig. 9:

    (a) The change in deflection angle between points A and C;
    (b) The deflection angle at point C;
    (c) The maximum deflection of the beam.

4. A simply supported beam of span l (Fig. 10) is subjected to two concentrated loads, placed at the quarter points of the span. The cross section of the beam

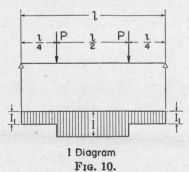

I Diagram

Fig. 10.

is variable, the I for the middle half of the span being equal to twice the I for the end quarters. Denoting the loads by P, and the moments of inertia at the ends by I_1, compute the following:

(a) The deflection angle at the supports;
(b) The deflection angle at the load points;
(c) The true deflection at the load points;
(d) The true deflection at the center of the span.

7. Sign of Deflection Angle.—The sign of a deflection angle is determined from the direction of rotation of the tangent to the elastic curve. If the rotation, with respect to the unstrained position of the member, is clockwise, the sign of the deflection angle is considered positive $(+)$; and if the rotation is counterclockwise, the sign is negative $(-)$.

Refer, for example, to the simply supported beam shown in Fig. 11. Under the downward load P, applied at midspan, the elastic curve of

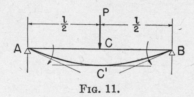

Fig. 11.

the beam assumes the position $AC'B$. The tangent drawn at the left support represents a clockwise rotation with respect to the line AB and, accordingly, the deflection angle at A is positive. Moving along the curve toward C', the tangent retains its clockwise rotation and the value of the deflection angle diminishes, becoming zero at C' where the tangent takes a horizontal position. Beyond the point C' the rotation of the tangent is counterclockwise, and the value of the deflection angle increases from zero at C' to a maximum at the right support. It is seen, therefore, that the deflection angle is positive at any point on the curve between A and C' and negative between C' and B.

This convention of sign is in agreement with that for shear of the conjugate beam; the shear in that case being considered to be positive when the vertical shear couple rotates in a clockwise direction—as in the left half of the span—and negative, when the rotation of the vertical shear couple is counterclockwise—as in the portion of the span between zero shear and the right support.

8. Sign of Deflection.—The deflection of a point on the elastic curve, from the tangent drawn at another point, is considered to be positive (+), if the line joining the two points is rotated in a clockwise direction with respect to the original position of the beam. According to this definition the deflection of the free end of a cantilever beam, subjected to a downward loading, may be either positive or negative, depending on whether the free end is located to the right or to the left of the support. Likewise, the deflections of the two ends of the simply supported beam shown in Fig. 11, with respect to the tangent at C', are of opposite sign, being (+) for A and (−) for B.

9. Deflection Angles and Deflections in Continuous Beams.—When a beam is continuous over its supports, the loading in a span produces moments not only within the span but also at the supports. In obtaining deflection angles and deflections in a continuous beam, one must, therefore, consider both the simple beam moment diagram of the span and the moment diagrams resulting from the moments at the supports.

The simplest example of a continuous beam is a beam cantilevering over its supports, as shown in Fig. 12 (*a*). If the loads P_1 and P_2 in the end spans be temporarily omitted, the middle span under the load P will act as a simple beam, having zero moment at the supports B and C and a single conjugate beam loading—shown in Fig. 12 (*b*). Due to the deflection angles θ_{B1} and θ_{C1}, points A and D will rise by the rotations of the lines BA and CD, and the new positions of the latter lines will coincide with the respective tangents to the elastic curve at the supports. Accordingly, the angles ABA_1 and DCD_1 measure the deflection angles θ_{B1} and θ_{C1}, respectively, and for the deflections of the points A_1 and D_1 we have:

$$\overline{AA_1} = l_1\theta_{B1} = +\frac{Pl^2 l_1}{16EI} \cdot \quad \cdots \cdots \quad (a)$$

and

$$\overline{DD_1} = l_2\theta_{C1} = -\frac{Pl^2 l_2}{16EI} \cdot \quad \cdots \cdots \quad (b)$$

Now the load P_1 is restored in the first span. As a result, both points A_1 and D_1 move downward into positions A_2 and D_2, Fig. 12 (*c*), and the deflection angles θ_{B1} and θ_{C1} decrease to θ_{B2} and θ_{C2}. The moment at the support B equals P_1l_1 while that at the support C

remains zero. The triangular conjugate beam loading (the moment of inertia is assumed to be constant) in the span BC, corresponding to the load P_1, produces deflection angles at the supports, with signs opposite to those for the loading shown in Fig. 12 (b). Denoting the

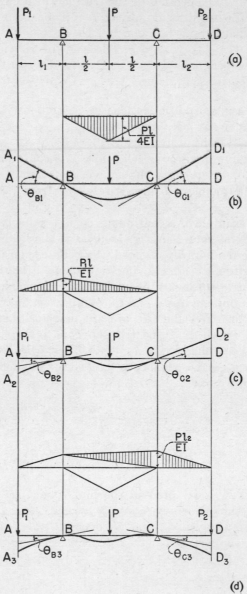

Fig. 12.

moment P_1l_1 at B by M_B, the values of the deflection angles, resulting from P and P_1, are:

$$\theta_{B2} = +\frac{Pl^2}{16EI} - \frac{l}{3EI}M_B \quad . \quad . \quad . \quad . \quad . \quad . \quad . \quad (c)$$

and

$$\theta_{C2} = -\frac{Pl^2}{16EI} + \frac{l}{6EI}M_B \quad . \quad . \quad . \quad . \quad . \quad . \quad . \quad (d)$$

Similarly, the load P_2, with a moment of $P_2l_2(=M_C)$, produces the deflection angles $-\dfrac{l}{6EI}M_C$ and $+\dfrac{l}{3EI}M_C$ at supports B and C. Then, for the values of resultant deflection angles, corresponding to the loads P, P_1 and P_2, Fig. 12 (d), we have:

$$EI\theta_{B3} = +\frac{Pl^2}{16} - \frac{l}{3}M_B - \frac{l}{6}M_C \; , \quad . \quad . \quad . \quad . \quad . \quad (e)$$

$$EI\theta_{C3} = -\frac{Pl^2}{16} + \frac{l}{6}M_B + \frac{l}{3}M_C \quad . \quad . \quad . \quad . \quad . \quad . \quad (f)$$

10. Sign of Moment.—Having established a sign convention for deflection angles and deflections, it now remains to define the sign of moments. From eqs. (c) to (f) it is seen that for a given moment at a support, producing fiber stresses of the same sign through the span, the deflection angles at the two supports assume opposite signs. It is further noted that if sections are cut through the beam just to the right of the left support and to the left of the right support, the resisting moments of the internal fiber stresses acting upon the two sections tend to rotate the respective ends in the same direction as the rotation of the tangents to the elastic curve, drawn at the two supports. Consistent with this action, a moment is considered to be positive (+), when its resisting moment, as defined above, rotates in a clockwise direction; and negative (−), if the rotation of the resisting moment is counterclockwise. Accordingly, the sign of the moment at the support B in Fig. 12 is (+) at the left of the support, and (−) at the right of the support.

Differentiation between the two moments at a support is provided in notation by two subscripts; the first letter indicating the joint or support under consideration, and the second letter its direction. Thus, the moment at the left of support B (Fig. 12) is indicated by the symbol M_{BA} and that at the right by M_{BC}. Likewise, the notation of moment at C, in the span BC, is M_{CB}.

ILLUSTRATIVE EXAMPLES

1. What is the maximum deflection in the span BC, Fig. 13? The moment of inertia of the beam is assumed to be constant.

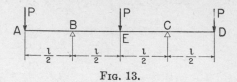

FIG. 13.

Solution: The conjugate beam reaction at B, due to moments M_{BC} and M_{CB}, equals $-\dfrac{Pl^2}{4EI}$; and the moment of the conjugate beam at the center line of the span is equal to the deflection resulting from the end loads P, or,

$$\Delta_1 = -\frac{Pl^3}{16EI}.$$

For the simple beam deflection, under the load P, we have:

$$\Delta_2 = +\frac{Pl^3}{48EI}.$$

The resultant maximum deflection of the span BC is then given by $\Delta_1 + \Delta_2$, or,

$$\Delta = \Delta_1 + \Delta_2 = -\frac{Pl^3}{16EI} + \frac{Pl^3}{48EI} = -\frac{Pl^3}{24EI}.$$

The $(-)$ sign indicating that the line BE rotates counterclockwise about the support B, resulting in an upward deflection for the point E.

2. A two-legged rigid bent is hinged at the bases, and subjected to a vertical load P (Fig. 14), placed at the middle of the top strut. The EI is assumed to be constant and equal to unity for all three members of the bent. Compute:

   (a) The spread of the legs, assuming one of the hinges mounted on rollers;

   (b) The magnitude of the horizontal reactions at the base required to move the displaced hinge to its original position.

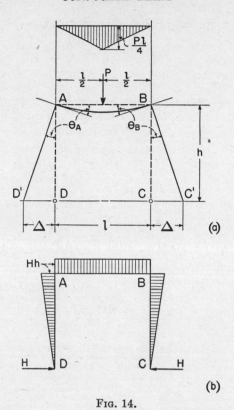

FIG. 14.

Solution: (*a*) The deflection angles at A and B, resulting from the simple beam $\dfrac{M}{EI}$ diagram of P in the span AB, Fig. 14 (*a*), are:

$$\theta_A = +\frac{Pl^2}{16}, \qquad \theta_B = -\frac{Pl^2}{16};$$

and the corresponding displacements of points C and D,

$$\overline{CC'} = h\theta_B = -\Delta = -\frac{Pl^2h}{16},$$

$$\overline{DD'} = h\theta_A = +\Delta = +\frac{Pl^2h}{16}.$$

(The negative sign of $\overline{CC'}$ indicates that the leg BC rotates counterclockwise, that is, the displacement of C is in opposite direction to that of D.)

Then, the total spread of the legs equals 2Δ, or,

$$2\Delta = 2 \cdot \frac{Pl^2 h}{16} = \frac{Pl^2 h}{8}.$$

(b) The bending moments in the members of the bent, produced by the reactions H, are shown in Fig. 14 (b). Denoting by Δ_1 and Δ_2 the two displacements of the point D with respect to A—the former being the sway of the leg caused by the deflection angle at A of the constant moment Hh in the span AB and the latter the deflection due to the triangular loading on the leg AD—we have:

$$\Delta_1 = -\frac{Hh l h}{2} = -\frac{Hh^2 l}{2},$$

$$\Delta_2 = -\frac{Hh^2}{2} \cdot \frac{2}{3} h = -\frac{Hh^3}{3}.$$

Equating the sum of Δ_1, Δ_2 and the displacement Δ of the point D in (a)—the resultant displacement—to zero, and solving for H,

$$-\frac{Hh^2 l}{2} - \frac{Hh^3}{3} + \frac{Pl^2 h}{16} = 0,$$

$$H = \frac{3Pl^2}{8h(3l+2h)}.$$

PROBLEMS

5. Determine (a) and (b) in example 2, Fig. 14, by replacing the concentrated load P with a uniformly distributed load W.
   Compute also:
   (c) Moment at the middle of span AB;
   (d) Maximum deflection in the span AB.

6. A beam of constant cross section is simply supported at the left support (Fig. 15) and continuous over the right support. There are two concentrated loads P, placed at the center of the first span and at the end of the overhang.

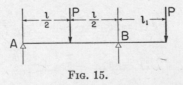

FIG. 15.

Indicating the length of the first span by l, and the length of the cantilever by l_1, determine:
   (a) An expression for deflection angle at the left support;
   (b) An expression for deflection angle at the right support;
   (c) Value of l_1 in terms of l to make (b)$=0$;
   (d) Maximum deflection in the first span in accordance with (c).

FIXED-END MOMENTS

11. Definition of Fixed-end Moment.—In obtaining deflection angles at the supports of a simply supported beam it was necessary to draw the $\frac{M}{EI}$ diagram or loading of the conjugate beam and compute the two reactions. It was also seen in Art. 9 that when making the simple span continuous over one or both supports, by addition of one or two cantilever spans, subjected to loading of the same direction as that of the original span, moments were produced at the supports and through the span, resulting in deflection angles of opposite sign to those for the simple beam. Since these latter moments are functions of the loadings or span lengths of the cantilevers, they can be made equal to any desired magnitude and thus modify values of deflection angles of the simple span. That particular value of such a moment at a support, which will produce a deflection angle at the same support equal and of opposite sign to that resulting from the simple span— while the two supports remain at the same level, is called the fixed-end moment of the beam for that end. Obviously, the value of the fixed-end moment at a support is not only dependent on the loading and moment of inertia of the beam, but also on the magnitude of moment for restraint condition at the other support. The action of the fixed-end moment at a support is that that of nullifying the deflection angle produced by the bending moment of the simply supported beam, or restraining the tangent to the elastic curve at the support against rotation from the unstrained position. Each of the various cases will be discussed and values of the fixed-end moments determined separately.

12. Constant Moment of Inertia, Symmetrical Loading, Both Ends of Member Restrained.—The beam shown in Fig. 16 (a) will serve as an example for this case. Because of symmetry in loading, the fixed-end moment to be applied at A is equal and, in accordance with our sign convention, of opposite sign to the fixed-end moment at the support B. Denoting the area of the simple beam bending moment diagram in Fig. 16 (b) by $\overline{A}$, the corresponding deflection angle at the support B is given by the expression for reaction of the conjugate beam:

$$\theta_{B1} = -\frac{\overline{A}}{2EI} \quad . \quad . \quad . \quad . \quad . \quad . \quad . \quad (11)$$

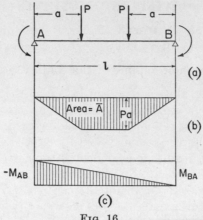

Fɪɢ. 16.

Similarly, the deflection angle at the same support resulting from end moments M_{AB} and M_{BA} in Fig. 16 (c) equals

$$\theta_{B2} = \frac{l}{3EI} M_{BA} + \frac{l}{6EI} M_{AB}$$

$$= \frac{l}{2EI} M_{BA} \ldots \ldots \ldots \ldots \ldots (11a)$$

(It is to be noted that both the negative end moment M_{AB} and the positive end moment M_{BA} produce positive deflection angles at support B, hence the positive signs in the substitution in eq. (11a).)

By definition of fixed-end moment, the end moment M_{BA} in eq. (11a) must be of such magnitude as to make the sum of deflection angles θ_{B1} and θ_{B2} equal to zero; thus,

$$\theta_B = \theta_{B1} + \theta_{B2} = -\frac{\overline{A}}{2EI} + \frac{l}{2EI} M_{BA} = 0 \ldots \ldots \ldots (11b)$$

Denoting this particular value of M_{BA} by FM_{BA}, FM being the symbol of fixed-end moment when both ends of the member are restrained, we have:

$$FM_{BA} = +\frac{\overline{A}}{l} \ldots \ldots \ldots \ldots (12)$$

Likewise, noting that $M_{BA} = -M_{AB}$,

$$FM_{AB} = -\frac{\overline{A}}{l} \ldots \ldots \ldots \ldots (12a)$$

For two loads, as shown in Fig. 16, we have:

$$\overline{A} = Pa^2 + Pa(l-2a) = Pa(l-a);$$

and

$$FM = \pm \frac{Pa}{l}(l-a) \ldots \ldots \ldots (12b)$$

For a single load P, at midspan, we have:

$$\overline{A} = \frac{Pl^2}{8}; \qquad FM = \pm \frac{Pl}{8}; \ldots \ldots (12c)$$

and for a uniform load of w per lineal foot,

$$\overline{A} = \frac{wl^2}{8} \cdot \frac{2}{3}l = \frac{wl^3}{12}; \qquad FM = \pm \frac{wl^2}{12} \ldots \ldots (12d)$$

13. Constant Moment of Inertia, Symmetrical Loading, One End of Member Restrained and the Other Hinged.—The beam shown in Fig. 17

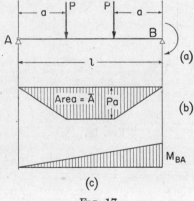

FIG. 17.

(a) is continuous over support B and hinged at A.   As in the preceding case, the deflection angle at the support B, corresponding to the simple beam bending moment diagram shown in Fig. 17 (b) and the tapering moment diagram of M_{BA} shown in Fig. 17 (c), equals the reaction of the conjugate beam:

$$\theta_B = -\frac{\overline{A}}{2EI} + \frac{l}{3EI}M_{BA} \ldots \ldots \ldots (13)$$

The value of the fixed-end moment at B is then obtained by equating expression (13) to zero:

$$HM_{BA} = +\frac{3}{2} \cdot \frac{\overline{A}}{l}; \ldots \ldots \ldots (14)$$

in which HM is the symbol of fixed-end moment at one end of a member the other end of which is free to rotate.

By comparison of eqs. (12) and (14), it is seen that the value of fixed-end moment in this case is one and one-half times the corresponding value of the preceding case, in which both ends of the member were fixed.

14. Constant Moment of Inertia, Unsymmetrical Loading, Both Ends of Member Restrained.—Fig. 18 (*a*) represents a beam subjected

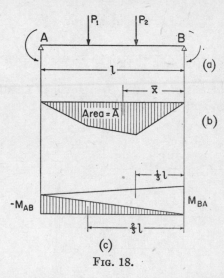

Fig. 18.

to a system of loading P. Let $\overline{A}$ indicate the area of the simple beam bending moment diagram, Fig. 18 (*b*), and $\bar{x}$ the distance of its centroid from the right support. For the deflection angles at the supports A and B, corresponding to the reactions of the conjugate beam with loadings shown in Fig. 18 (*b*) and (*c*), we have:

$$\theta_A = +\frac{\bar{x}}{lEI}\overline{A} - \frac{l}{3EI}M_{AB} - \frac{l}{6EI}M_{BA}, \quad \ldots \quad (15)$$

$$\theta_B = -\frac{(l-\bar{x})}{lEI}\overline{A} + \frac{l}{6EI}M_{AB} + \frac{l}{3EI}M_{BA} \quad \ldots \quad (15a)$$

Equating expressions (15) and (15a) to zero and solving simultaneously for the two end moments, we have:

$$FM_{AB} = -\frac{2\overline{A}}{l^2}(3\bar{x}-l), \quad \ldots \ldots \ldots \quad (16)$$

$$FM_{BA} = +\frac{2\overline{A}}{l^2}(2l-3\bar{x}) \quad \ldots \ldots \ldots \quad (16a)$$

Eqs. (16) and (16*a*) are the general expressions of fixed-end moment for a beam with constant moment of inertia, and restrained at both ends. By substituting $\dfrac{l}{2}$ for $\bar{x}$, these expressions become identical with those for the symmetrical case, given by eqs. (12) and (12*a*) in Art. 12.

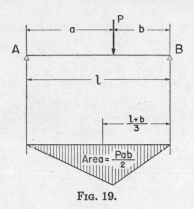

FIG. 19.

For a single load P, placed at a distance b from the right support (Fig. 19), $\overline{A}$ equals $\dfrac{Pab}{2}$, and $\bar{x}=\dfrac{l+b}{3}$. With these substitutions eqs. (16) and (16*a*) take the respective forms

$$FM_{AB}=-\frac{Pab^2}{l^2}, \quad \ldots \ldots \ldots \ldots \quad (17)$$

$$FM_{BA}=+\frac{Pa^2b}{l^2} \quad \ldots \ldots \ldots \ldots \quad (17a)$$

These latter expressions may also be used to obtain fixed-end moments for a series of concentrated loads, and for a uniform load occupying only a portion of the span. For other loadings, graphical solution of values of A and $\bar{x}$ and determination of fixed-end moments by the general expressions (16) and (16*a*) may be found more convenient.

15. Constant Moment of Inertia, Unsymmetrical Loading, One End of Member Restrained and the Other Hinged.—The beam shown in Fig. 20(*a*) is assumed to be hinged at A and continuous over the support B. Similar to the preceding cases, the value of the deflection

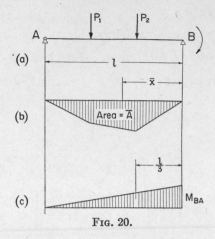

FIG. 20.

angle at B, corresponding to the moment diagrams shown in Fig. 20(b) and (c), is given by the expression

$$\theta_B = -\frac{(l-\bar{x})}{lEI}\overline{A} + \frac{l}{3EI}M_{BA} \quad \ldots \ldots \quad (18)$$

Then, for $\theta_B = 0$, the fixed-end moment at B equals

$$HM_{BA} = +\frac{3(l-\bar{x})}{l^2}\overline{A} \quad \ldots \ldots \ldots \quad (19)$$

Eq. (19) is the general expression for fixed-end moment at the restrained end of a member, with constant moment of inertia, the other end of which is free to rotate. Compared with eqs. (16) and (16a), corresponding expressions for the case where both ends of the member were restrained, it is seen that

$$HM_{BA} = FM_{BA} - \frac{1}{2}FM_{AB} \quad \ldots \ldots \quad (20)$$

(Note that FM_{AB} is a negative quantity, and therefore the two terms in the right hand side of eq. (20) are numerically added.)

ILLUSTRATIVE EXAMPLES

1. Determine the fixed-end moments of the beam shown in Fig. 21(a), subjected to a triangular loading W, and restrained at both ends. The moment of inertia of the beam is assumed to be constant.

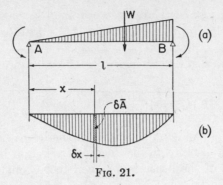

Fig. 21.

Solution: In Fig. 21(b), representing the simple beam bending moment diagram, the area of a strip δx, located at a distance x from the left support is given by the expression

$$\delta\overline{A}=M\delta x=\left(\frac{W}{3}x - \frac{W}{l^2}\cdot\frac{x^3}{3}\right)\delta x$$

$$=\frac{W}{3}\left(x - \frac{x^3}{l^2}\right)\delta x \quad \ldots \ldots \ldots \ldots (a)$$

and the moment of the same strip about the support A equals

$$x\delta\overline{A}=\frac{W}{3}\left(x^2 - \frac{x^4}{l^2}\right)\delta x \quad \ldots \ldots \ldots \ldots (b)$$

Integrating expressions (a) and (b) between the limits 0 and l, we will obtain the area of the moment diagram in Fig. 21(b) and the moment of this area about the left support, respectively; thus,

$$\overline{A}=\frac{W}{3}\left[\frac{x^2}{2} - \frac{x^4}{4l^2}\right]_0^l=\frac{Wl^2}{12}, \quad \ldots \ldots \ldots \ldots (c)$$

$$\overline{A}x=\frac{W}{3}\left[\frac{x^3}{3} - \frac{x^5}{5l^2}\right]_0^l=\frac{2Wl^3}{45} \quad \ldots \ldots \ldots \ldots (d)$$

The distance of the centroid of area $\overline{A}$ from the left support equals

$$x=\frac{\overline{A}x}{\overline{A}}=\frac{8}{15}l, \quad \ldots \ldots \ldots \ldots \ldots (e)$$

or, if measured from the right support,

$$\overline{x}=l-x=\frac{7}{15}l \quad \ldots \ldots \ldots \ldots \ldots (f)$$

The two fixed-end moments are then obtained by substituting values of $\bar{A}$ and $\bar{x}$ from eqs. (c) and (f) in eqs. (16) and (16a):

$$FM_{AB} = -\frac{2Wl^2}{12l^2}\left(\frac{7}{5}l - l\right) = -\frac{Wl}{15}, \quad \ldots \ldots \quad (21)$$

$$FM_{BA} = +\frac{2Wl^2}{12l^2}\left(2l - \frac{7}{5}l\right) = +\frac{Wl}{10} \quad \ldots \ldots \quad (21a)$$

2. Determine the fixed-end moments of the beam shown in Fig. 22, subjected to a partial uniform load and restrained at both ends. The moment of inertia of the beam is assumed to be constant.

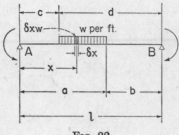

FIG. 22.

Solution: The fixed-end moment at the support B, due to the load $w\delta x$ (load covering a small length δx of the loaded portion of the span), located at a distance x from the left support, equals, in accordance with eq. (17a),

$$\delta FM_{BA} = +\frac{wx^2}{l^2}(l-x)\delta x \quad \ldots \ldots \ldots \quad (g)$$

The total fixed-end moment at B is then obtained by integrating eq. (g) between the limits c and a:

$$FM_{BA} = \frac{w}{l^2}\left[\frac{lx^3}{3} - \frac{x^4}{4}\right]_c^a = \frac{w}{12l^2}[4l(a^3 - c^3) - 3(a^4 - c^4)]$$

$$= \frac{w}{12l^2}[a^3(4l - 3a) - c^3(4l - 3c)] \quad \ldots \ldots \ldots \quad (22)$$

Likewise, measuring x from the right support and integrating the partial fixed-end moment expression at support A between the limits b and d,

$$FM_{AB} = -\frac{w}{12l^2}[d^3(4l - 3d) - b^3(4l - 3b)] \quad \ldots \ldots \quad (22a)$$

3. A continuous beam of two equal spans and constant moment of inertia (Fig. 23) is loaded with a concentrated load P in each span, placed at a distance a from the middle support. Assuming the beam hinged at the end supports, determine the moment at the middle support.

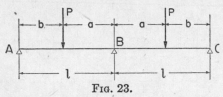

FIG. 23.

Solution: Since the loading is symmetrical about the center support, the value of the deflection angle at this support equals zero. But the moment which will restrain the tangent to the elastic curve at B against rotation is, by definition, the fixed-end moment at the support. Therefore,

$$M_{BC} = -M_{BA} = HM_{BC} = +\frac{Pab^2}{l^2} + \frac{Pa^2b}{2l^2} = \frac{Pab}{2l^2}(l+b) \quad . \quad . \quad (23)$$

(The moment may also be determined by writing the expressions for deflection angle at the middle support, obtained from the conjugate beam loading in each span, and solving for the unknown moment.)

PROBLEMS

7. Assume the beam in example 3, Fig. 23, fixed at the end supports and compute the following:

    (a) Moment at the middle support;
    (b) Moment under the load P;
    (c) Moment at the end supports.

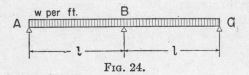

FIG. 24.

8. A two-span continuous beam of constant cross section and equal spans (Fig. 24) is subjected to a uniform load of w per linear foot. Determine the moments at the middle and end supports for the following end conditions:

    (a) Ends hinged;
    (b) Ends restrained;
    (c) Ends 50 percent restrained.

16. Constant Moment of Inertia, Member Loaded With a Moment Couple, Both Ends Restrained.—In certain cases, such as columns with brackets, the loading of the member may consist of a moment couple, produced by an eccentric force. Fig. 25 (*a*) represents this

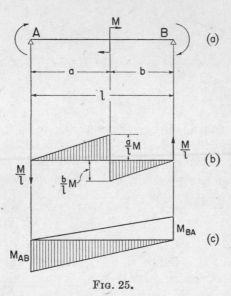

F<small>IG</small>. 25.

condition of loading. Here the clockwise moment couple, denoted by M, is applied at a distance a from the left support. If the two ends of the member were hinged, the resulting moment diagram along the span would assume the form shown in Fig. 25 (*b*). Obviously, this is the simple beam bending moment diagram, and, when divided by EI, will constitute the loading of the conjugate beam. The deflection angles at supports A and B, corresponding to the reactions of the conjugate beam, are given by the expressions

$$EI\theta_{A1} = +\frac{b^2}{2l}M\frac{2b}{3l} - \frac{a^2}{2l}M\left(\frac{a}{3}+b\right)\frac{1}{l}$$

$$= \frac{M}{6l^2}(2b^3 - a^3 - 3a^2b), \quad \ldots \ldots \ldots \quad (24)$$

and

$$EI\theta_{B1} = +\frac{a^2}{2l}M\frac{2a}{3l} - \frac{b^2}{2l}M\left(a+\frac{b}{3}\right)\frac{1}{l}$$

$$= \frac{M}{6l^2}(2a^3 - b^3 - 3ab^2) \quad \ldots \ldots \ldots \quad (24a)$$

Since the member is not hinged to the supports, but restrained with the end moments M_{AB} and M_{BA}, the corresponding conjugate beam loading, indicated in Fig. 25 (c), will produce additional deflection angles at the two supports. Thus,

$$EI\theta_{A2} = +\frac{l}{3}M_{AB} - \frac{l}{6}M_{BA}, \quad \ldots \ldots \ldots \quad (25)$$

$$EI\theta_{B2} = -\frac{l}{6}M_{AB} + \frac{l}{3}M_{BA} \quad \ldots \ldots \ldots \quad (25a)$$

And the total or resultant deflection angles, given by eqs. (24) and (25) become:

$$EI\theta_A = EI(\theta_{A1} + \theta_{A2}) = \frac{M}{6l^2}(2b^3 - a^3 - 3a^2b) + \frac{l}{3}M_{AB} - \frac{l}{6}M_{BA}, \quad (26)$$

$$EI\theta_B = EI(\theta_{B1} + \theta_{B2}) = \frac{M}{6l^2}(2a^3 - b^3 - 3ab^2) - \frac{l}{6}M_{AB} + \frac{l}{3}M_{BA} \quad (26a)$$

The two fixed-end moments are then obtained by equating eqs. (26) and (26a) to zero and solving simultaneously for the end moments:

$$FM_{AB} = +\frac{Mb}{l^2}(2a - b), \quad \ldots \ldots \ldots \quad (27)$$

$$FM_{BA} = +\frac{Ma}{l^2}(2b - a) \quad \ldots \ldots \ldots \quad (27a)$$

17. Constant Moment of Inertia, Member Loaded with a Moment Couple, One End Restrained and the Other Hinged.—The beam shown in Fig. 26 (a) is restrained at A and hinged at B. The resultant deflec-

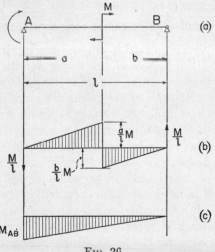

FIG. 26.

tion angle at the left support, corresponding to the moment diagrams shown in Fig. 26 (b) and (c), may be obtained directly from eq. 26, by omitting the last term of the expression. Thus,

$$EI\theta_A = \frac{M}{6l^2}(2b^3 - a^3 - 3a^2b) + \frac{l}{3}M_{AB} \quad \cdots \cdots \quad (28)$$

Then, equating the deflection angle to zero, and solving for the end moment M_{AB},

$$HM_{AB} = \frac{M}{2l^3}(a^3 + 3a^2b - 2b^3)$$

$$= \frac{M}{2}\left(1 - \frac{3b^2}{l^2}\right) \cdots \cdots \cdots \quad (29)$$

Similarly, if the member is restrained at B and hinged at A, the fixed-end moment at B, resulting from a clockwise moment couple M, is given by the expression

$$HM_{BA} = \frac{M}{2l^3}(b^3 + 3ab^2 - 2a^3)$$

$$= \frac{M}{2}\left(1 - \frac{3a^2}{l^2}\right) \cdots \cdots \cdots \quad (29a)$$

18. Fixed-end Moments in Members with Variable Moment of Inertia.—In the preceding derivations of fixed-end moments, the term EI, appearing in the expressions of conjugate beam loading and deflection angles, was carried through the operations as a constant factor. When the cross section of the member varies along the span, then it becomes necessary—as an additional step in the calculations— to modify the areas of $\frac{M}{EI}$ diagrams, corresponding to bending of the member as a simply supported beam and restraining moments at the two supports, and the values of the respective distances of the centroids from the supports—in accordance with the variation of moment of inertia through the length of the span. The modification of moment diagrams is easily accomplished by first expressing moments of inertia at various points of the span in terms of a common I (usually taken as the smallest moment of inertia of the span) and then changing moment ordinates by the respective ratios of the common moment of inertia to the moment of inertia at the location considered. Once these modified values of moment areas and centroids thereof are obtained, the work involved in computing fixed-end moments becomes identical with that for members of constant moment of inertia.

As an example, consider the beam shown in Fig. 27 (a), subjected to a system of loading P. The width of the beam is constant, but the depth varies as shown in Fig. 27 (b). Denoting the moment of inertia

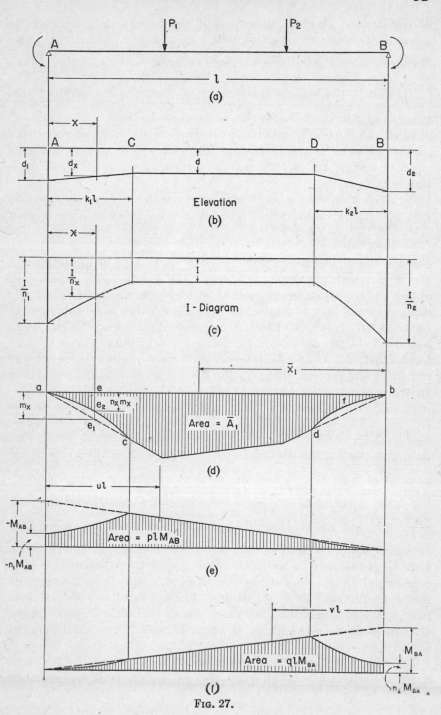

Fig. 27.

of the straight or shallow portion of the beam by I, then for the moment of inertia of a section within the haunch, located, say, at a distance x from the left support, we can write $\dfrac{I}{n_x}$; in which n_x equals $\left(\dfrac{d}{d_x}\right)^3$, that is, the ratio of the moment of inertia at the middle to the moment of inertia at the section under consideration. The moments of inertia at the other sections of the span are similarly expressed and plotted to some convenient scale (the common I may be assumed equal to unity), and the moment of inertia diagram of Fig. 27 (*c*) is thus obtained.

Now consider the simple beam bending moment diagram shown in Fig. 27 (*d*). If the depth of the beam were constant, the moment diagram and the $\dfrac{M}{EI}$ diagram would have similar outlines; the ordinates in the former representing certain percentage of the latter and the ratio remaining constant through the length of the span. To obtain the conjugate beam loading for that case, one would need only compute small strips of moment areas and divide each value by the constant EI. Addition of end haunches would cause no changes in the outline of the moment diagram for the straight portion of the beam, located between C and D, intensities of the conjugate beam loading remaining the same as those for the beam with constant cross-section. In the regions of the haunches, however, the moment of inertia becomes a variable quantity and the similarity of outline between the simple beam bending and conjugate loading $\left(\dfrac{M}{EI}\right)$ diagrams vanishes. At a distance x from the left support, for instance, the value of the moment of inertia is $\dfrac{I}{n_x}$, and the moment ordinate $m_x = ee_1$. Accordingly, the intensity of conjugate beam loading at that location equals $\dfrac{m_x.n_x}{I}$. If now the constant I, appearing as common denominator in each expression, be factored out, then the numerator of the expression may be considered as the modified value of the moment ordinate, represented by the line ee_2 in the diagram. Similar changes in the moment ordinates at other points of the haunches will result in moving the original boundary lines (shown dotted in Fig. 27 (*d*)) to the new positions ae_2c and bfd, the net effect being a reduced moment area.

Likewise, the diagrams of the restraint moments at the two supports are affected by similar changes in the moment ordinates for portions corresponding to the haunches. These changes, indicated by the shaded areas in Fig. 27 (e) and (f), are self-explanatory.

To obtain expressions of fixed-end moments from these modified areas, let

$\overline{A}_1$=modified moment area of bending of the member as a simply supported beam (shaded area in Fig. 27 (d));

$\overline{x}_1$=centroid distance of $\overline{A}_1$, measured from the right support;

plM_{AB}=modified moment area of restraint moment at the left support (shaded area in Fig. 27 (e));

ul=centroid distance of plM_{AB} from the left support;

qlM_{BA}=modified moment area of restraint moment at the right support (shaded area in Fig. 27 (f));

vl=centroid distance of qlM_{BA} from the right support;

I=moment of inertia of the straight portion of the beam.

Then for the deflection angles at the two supports, resulting from the three moment areas listed above, we have:

$$EI\theta_A = +\frac{\overline{x}_1}{l}\overline{A}_1 - pM_{AB}(l-ul) - qM_{BA}vl, \quad \ldots \ldots \quad (30)$$

$$EI\theta_B = -\frac{(l-\overline{x}_1)}{l}\overline{A}_1 + pM_{AB}ul + qM_{BA}(l-vl) \quad \ldots \quad (30a)$$

Equating the values of the deflection angles to zero, and solving simultaneously for the end moments,

$$FM_{AB} = -\frac{\overline{A}_1}{pl^2}\cdot\frac{(\overline{x}_1-vl)}{(1-u-v)}, \quad \ldots \ldots \ldots \quad (31)$$

$$FM_{BA} = +\frac{\overline{A}_1}{ql^2}\cdot\frac{(l-ul-\overline{x}_1)}{(1-u-v)} \quad \ldots \ldots \ldots \quad (31a)$$

The term p in the above expressions may be defined as the area of the modified moment diagram for a span length of unity and a restraint moment at the left support equal to unity; and u, the distance of the centroid of p from the left support. Likewise, the terms q and v represent similar values corresponding to a unit moment applied at the right support. These values, as well as the values of $\overline{A}_1$ and $\overline{x}_1$, may be computed by integration, determined graphically or taken from tables.[1] It is to be noted that for a beam of constant cross section,

$$p=q=\frac{1}{2}; \ u=v=\frac{1}{3}; \ \overline{A}=\overline{A}_1 \text{ and } \overline{x}=\overline{x}_1.$$

With these substitutions, expressions (31) and (31a) are reduced to the respective forms of eqs. (16) and (16a) previously derived in Art. 14.

---

[1] See, for example, the excellent tables by Walter Ruppel, Transactions Am. Soc. C. E., 1927, Vol. 90, pp. 167-187, part of which are reproduced in Tables 12 and 13 in the Appendix. Tables 14 to 17 inclusive, giving coefficients for the determination of $\overline{A}_1$ and $\overline{x}_1$, were also prepared from data furnished by the same author.

If the member shown in Fig. 27 (a) is assumed to be fixed at A and hinged at B, then the corresponding fixed-end moment at the left support may be obtained directly from eq. (31), by substituting zero for v; thus,

$$HM_{AB} = -\frac{\overline{A}_1}{pl^2} \cdot \frac{\overline{x}_1}{(1-u)} \quad \cdots \cdots \cdots \cdots \quad (32)$$

Similarly, for the expression of fixed-end moment at the right support, when the member is hinged to the left support and restrained at the right support, we have:

$$HM_{BA} = +\frac{\overline{A}_1}{ql^2} \cdot \frac{(l-\overline{x}_1)}{(1-v)} \quad \cdots \cdots \cdots \cdots \quad (32a)$$

PROBLEMS

9. A column of height h is subjected to an eccentric force P (Fig. 28), producing a counterclockwise moment. The eccentricity of the force is e, and the bracket is

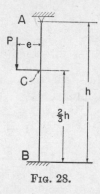

Fig. 28.

located at $\frac{2}{3}h$ from the bottom. Assuming the column fixed at the base and hinged at the top, compute moments at following locations:

    (a) Top;

    (b) Just above bracket;

    (c) Just below bracket;

    (d) Base.

10. Compute the fixed-end moments for the beam in problem No. 4, Fig. 10, assuming:

    (a) Both ends of member fixed;

    (b) Restrained at the left support and hinged to the right.

THREE MOMENT RELATION

19. Moment Relation in Continuous Beams.—In the solution of moments in continuous beams, use is often made of a relation existing between the moments at three adjoining supports and known as "the three moment equation," which can be readily derived by simple application of moment area properties. The derivation is similar to that of fixed-end moments, and is obtained from the expressions of deflection angle at a support.

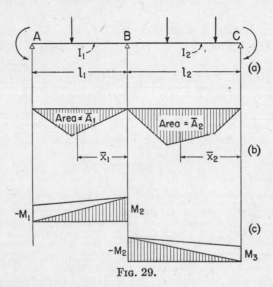

FIG. 29.

20. Case I, Constant Moment of Inertia.—The beam shown in Fig. 29 (a) represents a portion of a continuous beam. The moment of inertia is constant in each span but different for the two spans, and the loading is unsymmetrical. Let

I_1=moment of inertia, first span;

$\overline{A}_1$=area of the simple moment diagram, first span;

$\overline{x}_1$=centroid distance of $\overline{A}_1$, measured from right (second) support;

I_2=moment of inertia, second span;

$\overline{A}_2$=area of the simple moment diagram, second span;

$\overline{x}_2$=centroid distance of $\overline{A}_2$, measured from right (third) support;

M_1, M_2, M_3=moments at first, second and third supports, respectively. The deflection angle at the second support, obtained from the conjugate beam loading of the first span, Fig. 29 (b) and (c), may then be expressed by,

$$EI_1\theta_B = -\frac{\overline{A}_1}{l_1}(l_1-\overline{x}_1) + M_1\frac{l_1}{6} + M_2\frac{l_1}{3} \quad . \quad . \quad . \quad . \quad . \quad (33)$$

The value of the deflection angle at the same support, obtained from the conjugate beam loading of the second span, is also given by the expression

$$EI_2\theta_B = \overline{A}_2\frac{\overline{x}_2}{l_2} - M_2\frac{l_2}{3} - M_3\frac{l_2}{6} \quad . \quad . \quad . \quad . \quad . \quad . \quad (33a)$$

The relation between moments M_1, M_2 and M_3 is then obtained by equating the value of θ_B in expression (33) to that in eq. (33a). Thus,

$$M_1\frac{l_1}{I_1} + 2M_2\left(\frac{l_1}{I_1} + \frac{l_2}{I_2}\right) + M_3\frac{l_2}{I_2} = \frac{6\overline{A}_1}{l_1 I_1}(l_1-x_1) + \frac{6\overline{A}_2}{l_2 I_2}x_2 \quad . \quad . \quad . \quad (34)$$

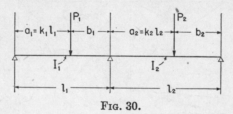

FIG. 30.

For loading as shown in Fig. (30),

$$\overline{A}_1 = P_1\frac{a_1 b_1}{2}, \quad l_1 - \overline{x}_1 = \frac{l_1+a_1}{3},$$

$$\overline{A}_2 = P_2\frac{a_2 b_2}{2}, \quad \overline{x}_2 = \frac{l_2+b_2}{3};$$

and

$$\frac{6\overline{A}_1}{l_1 I_1}(l_1-\overline{x}_1) = \frac{P_1 a_1 b_1}{l_1 I_1}(l_1+a_1) = \frac{P_1 a_1}{l_1 I_1}(l_1^2-a_1^2)$$

$$= \frac{P_1 l_1^2}{I_1}(k_1-k_1^3) , \quad . \quad . \quad . \quad . \quad . \quad . \quad (35)$$

$$\frac{6x_2}{l_2 I_2}\overline{A}_2 = \frac{P_2 a_2 b_2}{l_2 I_2}(l_2+b_2) = \frac{P_2 a_2}{l_2 I_2}(2l_2^2-3a_2 l_2+a_2^2)$$

$$= \frac{P_2 l_2^2}{I_2}(2k_2-3k_2^2+k_2^3) \quad . \quad . \quad . \quad . \quad . \quad . \quad . \quad (35a)$$

With these substitutions, eq. (34) takes the more familiar form

$$M_1\frac{l_1}{I_1}+2M_2\Big(\frac{l_1}{I_1}+\frac{l_2}{I_2}\Big)+M_3\frac{l_2}{I_2}=\frac{P_1l_1^2}{I_1}(k_1-k_1^3)$$

$$+\frac{P_2l_2^2}{I_2}(2k_2-3k_2^2+k_2^3) \;\; . \;\; . \;\; . \;\; . \;\; (36)$$

For a uniform load of w_1 per linear foot in the first span, and of w_2 in the second span,

$$\overline{A}_1=\frac{w_1l_1^3}{12}, \qquad \overline{A}_2=\frac{w_2l_2^3}{12}, \qquad \overline{x}_1=\frac{l_1}{2}, \qquad \overline{x}_2=\frac{l_2}{2}.$$

With these substitutions in expression (34), the three moment equation becomes

$$M_1\frac{l_1}{I_1}+2M_2\Big(\frac{l_1}{I_1}+\frac{l_2}{I_2}\Big)+M_3\frac{l_2}{I_2}=\frac{w_1l_1^3}{4I_1}+\frac{w_2l_2^3}{4I_2} \;\; . \;\; . \;\; . \;\; . \;\; (37)$$

It is to be noted that when drawing the moment diagram in Fig. 29 (c), it was assumed that moments at all three supports were negative; and, in accordance with our sign convention, so indicated on the diagram. If the solution of equations should provide positive values for the moments, the assumption is justified. On the other hand, a negative value for any one moment will indicate that the moment at that support is positive, i. e., bottom fibers of the beam are in tension for a downward loading as shown in Fig. (29).

21. Case II, Variable Moment of Inertia.—In the case of a continuous beam with haunches, it becomes necessary to replace the moment areas of Fig. 29 with their modified values corresponding to change in moment of inertia for each span, in order to derive the three moment equation as in the preceding case.

The modified moment diagrams of such a haunched beam are shown in Fig. 31 (shaded areas). With the notations of areas and centroids as indicated on the diagrams, the two expressions of the deflection angle at the middle support, corresponding to the conjugate beam loadings of the two spans, are written:

$$EI_1\theta_B=\overline{A}_1'\frac{(l_1-\overline{x}_1')}{l_1}+M_{1p_1}u_1l_1+M_{2q_1}(l_1-v_1l_1), \;\; . \;\; . \;\; . \;\; (38)$$

and

$$EI_2\theta_B=\overline{A}_2'\frac{x_2}{l_2}-M_{2p_2}(l_2-u_2l_2)-M_{3q_2}v_2l_2 \;\; . \;\; . \;\; . \;\; . \;\; (38a)$$

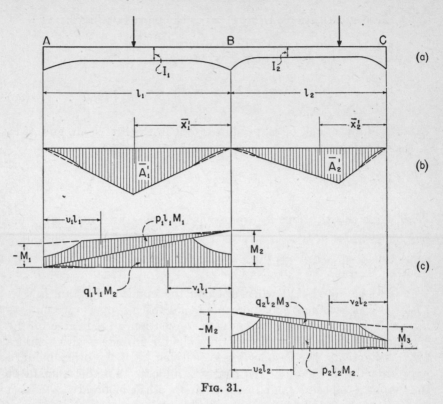

FIG. 31.

The relation between the moments at the three supports is then found by equating the values of θ_B in eqs. (38) and (38a). Thus,

$$M_1 p_1 \frac{u_1 l_1}{I_1} + M_2 \left[q_1 \frac{(l_1 - v_1 l_1)}{I_1} + p_2 \frac{(l_2 - u_2 l_2)}{I_2} \right]$$

$$+ M_3 q_2 \frac{v_2 l_2}{I_2} = \overline{A_1'} \frac{(l_1 - \overline{x_1'})}{l_1 I_1} + A_2' \frac{\overline{x_2'}}{l_2 I_2} \quad \cdots \cdots \quad (39)$$

22. Case III, Supports at Different Levels.—The three moment equations derived in Arts. 20 and 21 apply only when the supports of the continuous beam remain on the same level during bending. If, because of uneven settlement, one of the supports deviates from a straight line drawn through the other two supports, then eqs. (34) and (39) will need a modification to include an additional term, corresponding to the differing levels.

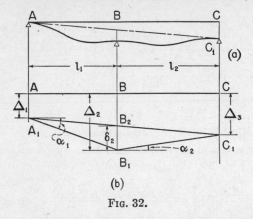

FIG. 32.

Consider, for example, the beam shown in Fig. 32 (a). Here the middle support B falls below the straight line AC_1 joining the end supports. Let the displacements of supports A, B, and C, measured from the horizontal reference line AC, Fig. 32 (b), be denoted by Δ_1, Δ_2 and Δ_3, respectively. Because of the rotation of the line A_1B_1 from its original position by an angle $\alpha_1 = \dfrac{\Delta_2 - \Delta_1}{l_1}$ (since the angle is small and unlike the exaggerated representation in the diagram), the angle θ_B of the first span will now become $\theta'_B = \theta_B - \alpha_1$. Likewise, due to the rotation of the line BC to its new position B_1C_1, the angle θ_B in the second span will be augmented by an angle $\alpha_2 = \dfrac{\Delta_3 - \Delta_2}{l_2}$.

Then, for a beam of constant cross section, with moment areas as shown in Fig. 29, we have:

$$EI_1\theta'_B = -\frac{\overline{A_1}}{l_1}(l_1 - \bar{x}_1) + M_1\frac{l_1}{6} + M_2\frac{l_1}{3} + \frac{(\Delta_2 - \Delta_1)}{l_1}EI_1, \quad . \quad . \quad (40)$$

and

$$EI_2\theta'_B = \overline{A_2}\frac{\bar{x}_2}{l_2} - M_2\frac{l_2}{3} - M_3\frac{l_2}{6} + \frac{(\Delta_3 - \Delta_2)}{l_2}EI_2 \quad . \quad . \quad (40a)$$

The relation between the three moments is obtained by equating the value of θ'_B in eq. (40) to that in eq. (40a). Thus,

$$M_1\frac{l_1}{I_1} + 2M_2\left(\frac{l_1}{I_1} + \frac{l_2}{I_2}\right) + M_3\frac{l_2}{I_2} = \frac{6\overline{A_1}}{l_1I_1}(l_1 - \overline{x}_1)$$

$$+ \frac{6x_2}{l_2I_2}\overline{A_2} - 6E\left(\frac{\Delta_2 - \Delta_1}{l_1} + \frac{\Delta_2 - \Delta_3}{l_2}\right); \quad . \quad . \quad . \quad . \quad . \quad (41)$$

or,

$$M_1\frac{l_1}{I_1}+2M_2\left(\frac{l_1}{I_1}+\frac{l_2}{I_2}\right)+M_3\frac{l_2}{I_2}=\frac{6\overline{A}_1}{l_1I_1}(l_1-\overline{x}_1)$$

$$+\frac{6\overline{A}_2}{l_2I_2}\overline{x}_2-6E\delta_2\left(\frac{1}{l_1}+\frac{1}{l_2}\right)\quad\ldots\ldots\ldots\ldots\quad(42)$$

in which, $\delta_2=$ distance $\overline{B_1B_2}$ (Fig. 32 (b)), the deflection of B, measured from a straight line joining the end supports.

Similarly, for a beam of variable cross section, with moment areas as indicated in Fig. 31, the three moment equation becomes,

$$M_1p_1\frac{u_1l_1}{I_1}+M_2\left[q_1\frac{(l_1-v_1l_1)}{I_1}+p_2\frac{(l_2-u_2l_2)}{I_2}\right]+M_3q_2\frac{v_2l_2}{I_2}$$

$$=\frac{\overline{A}'_1}{l_1I_1}(l_1-\overline{x}'_1)+\frac{\overline{x}'_2}{l_2I_2}\overline{A}'_2-E\left(\frac{\Delta_2-\Delta_1}{l_1}+\frac{\Delta_2-\Delta_3}{l_2}\right);\quad\ldots\quad(43)$$

or,

$$M_1p_1\frac{u_1l_1}{I_1}+M_2\left[q_1\frac{(l_1-v_1l_1)}{I_1}+p_2\frac{(l_2-u_2l_2)}{I_2}\right]+M_3q_2\frac{v_2l_2}{I_2}$$

$$=\frac{\overline{A}'_1}{l_1I_1}(l_1-\overline{x}'_1)+\frac{x'_2}{l_2I_2}\overline{A}'_2-E\delta_2\left(\frac{1}{l_1}+\frac{1}{l_2}\right).\quad\ldots\ldots\quad(44)$$

NOTE.—If the displacement of the middle support is upward with respect to the end supports, i. e., point B_1 in Fig. 32 (b) located above the line A_1C_1, the negative sign of the last term in eqs. (42) and (44) becomes positive.

ILLUSTRATIVE EXAMPLE

1. A two-span continuous beam of constant width has a tapering depth (Fig. 33), varying from d at the end supports to $2d$ at the middle support. The beam is symmetrical about the middle support and each span is loaded with a force P, applied at midspan. Assuming the beam hinged to the end supports, determine the moment at the middle support, by use of the three moment equation.

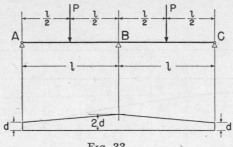

FIG. 33.

Solution: Before computing the desired moment, it is necessary first to determine the values of $\overline{A}'$, $\overline{x}'$, p, q, u and v, as defined in Art. 18. The graphical method will be used; and since the beam is symmetrical about the middle support, the computations of these values will be confined to one span only.

In Fig. 34 (a) the moment of inertia curve for the span AB is drawn to scale, in units of the smallest moment of inertia (I) corresponding to the depth d at A. With this diagram as basis, the ordinates of the simple beam moment diagram of the load P in Fig. 34 (b), and p and q diagrams in Fig. 34 (c) and (d) have been modified, and areas and centroids determined. These values, noted on the respective diagrams, are listed below for the two spans:

Item	First span (AB)	Second span (BC)
$\overline{A}'$	0. 042 Pl^2	0. 042 Pl^2
$\overline{x}'$	0. 582 l	0. 418 l
p	0. 250	0. 125
q	0. 125	0. 250
u	0. 232	0. 457
v	0. 457	0. 232

Applying eq. (39), and noting that M_1 and $M_3 = 0$, $q_1 = p_2$, $v_1 = u_2$, $\overline{x}_2' = l - \overline{x}_1'$ the moment expression becomes

$$M_2 = \frac{\overline{A}'\overline{x}_2'}{p_2 l^2 (1 - u_2)} = \frac{0.042 \times 0.418}{0.125 \times 0.543} Pl = 0.259 \, Pl. \quad . \quad . \quad (45)$$

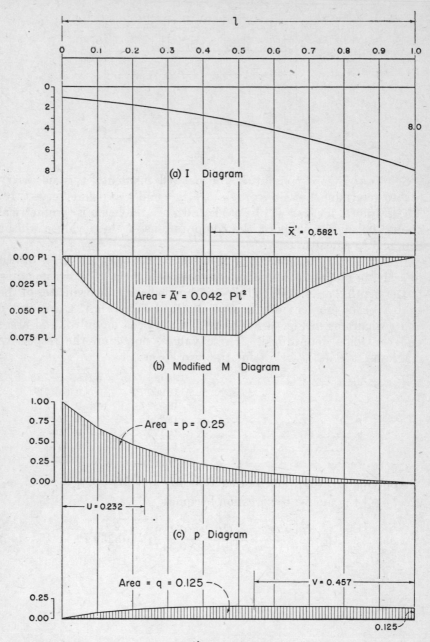

(a) I Diagram

(b) Modified M Diagram

(c) p Diagram

(d) q Diagram

Fig. 34.

PROBLEMS

11. Determine the fixed-end moment at the middle support for the beam in the above example, assuming:

    (*a*) Hinged at the end supports;
    (*b*) Fixed at the end supports.

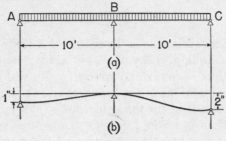

FIG. 35.

12. A two-span continuous beam of constant cross section is loaded with a uniform load of 1,000 pounds per linear foot. Assuming $I=10$ in.^{4}, $l=10$ feet, $E=3\times10^7$ lb.in.$^{-2}$ and the ends hinged, determine:

    (*a*) Moment at the middle support;
    (*b*) Additional moment at the middle support, resulting from displacement of the supports, as shown in Fig. 35 (*b*).

CHAPTER II

SLOPE DEFLECTION

23. Moment Expression as a Function of Rotations and Relative Displacements of Ends of a Member.—When a beam is supported in such a manner that its ends can rotate freely, while subjected to a given loading, the reactions at the supports and the moments along the span are readily obtained by the equations of static equilibrium. In a frame or a continuous beam, however, the two ends of a member are restrained against free rotation—because of the rigidity of the joints or the continuity at the supports, resulting in restraining end moments. These latter moments are statically indeterminate, their magnitude depending on the degree of restraint at the joints.

Consider, for example, the beam shown in Fig. 36 (a). If it be

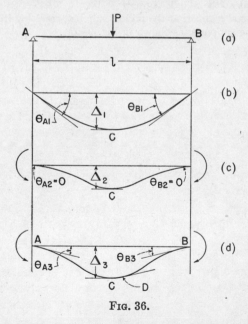

Fig. 36.

assumed hinged to the supports, the elastic curve of the member will assume the position (greatly exaggerated) shown in Fig. 36 (b), with end rotations measured by the deflection angles θ_{A1} and θ_{B1}. By assumption, there is no restraint at the supports, the end tangents rotate freely and the corresponding moments become zero. Fig. 36 (c) shows the elastic curve of the beam for a condition where the end tangents are completely prevented against rotation by application of restraining moments at the two supports. The deflection angles being zero, this is the condition of full restraint or fixity, and, consequently, the intensities of the restraining moments are those of the two fixed-end moments of the beam. If the magnitude of the restraining moments are such that they partially prevent the rotations of the end tangents, we will have the position indicated in Fig. 36 (d), in which the end deflection angles θ_{A3} and θ_{B3} are smaller than the corresponding angles θ_{A1} and θ_{B1} of the free or hinged condition in Fig. 36 (b). Conversely, it is seen that if the magnitudes of the deflection angles are known, then the intensities of the restraining end moments can be determined from the properties of the conjugate beam.

Now let us consider the portion AC of the beam (Fig. 36) as a separate member. Here the displacement of the point C is given by the deflections Δ_1, Δ_2 and Δ_3, corresponding to the three conditions of end restraint, and measured from the original or unstrained position of the member. Obviously, to obtain the end moments at A and C, we need not only the magnitudes of the deflection angles at the two points, but also the relative displacement of one end with respect to the other—as indicated by the deflections Δ_1, Δ_2 and Δ_3.

The method of expressing the end moments of a restrained member in terms of the rotations or slopes of the tangents and the displacements of its ends is called *slope deflection*.[1] The derivation of the fundamental relation for each case, corresponding to a member with constant and variable moment of inertia, and with and without intermediate loading, will be given in the following articles.

84. Constant Moment of Inertia, No Intermediate Loading between Ends of Member.—The member shown in Fig. 37 (a), originally in the position A_1B, is bent to the form AB, similar to that of the portion DB of the beam in Fig. 36 (d). Both end moments at A and B are positive (resisting moments rotating in a clockwise direction). The deflection Δ, representing the displacement of the point A from its original position at A_1, may be considered as the sum of two displacements: (1) the deflection $A_1T_1(=l\theta_B)$ corresponding to the deflection angle at B, and (2) the displacement T_1A or the deviation of A from the tangent T_1B to the elastic curve at B. Or, assuming AB_1

---

[1] The introduction of the Slope-deflection method in this country, as well as its application to the general case of a member with intermediate loading between the ends, is due to Prof. G. A. Maney; see Bull. No. 1, Studies in Engineering, University of Minnesota.

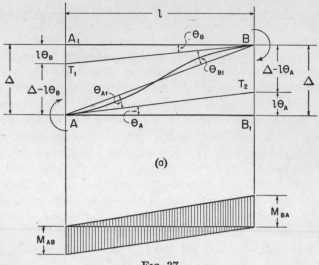

FIG. 37.

to be the original position of the member, for Δ at the right end we can write $BT_2+T_2B_1$; the first term being the displacement of B from the tangent AT_2, and the second term being the tangent distance of the deflection angle θ_A and the span $l(=l\theta_A)$. The conjugate beam loading of the member, producing the deflection angles and the displacements shown in Fig. 37 (a), consists of the moment areas of the end moments M_{AB} and M_{BA} shown in Fig. 37 (b). Accordingly, for the values of the two end deflection angles, given by the reactions of the conjugate beam with reference to line AB, we have:

$$R_A=\theta_{A1}=+\frac{l}{3EI}M_{AB}-\frac{l}{6EI}M_{BA},$$

$$R_B=\theta_{B1}=-\frac{l}{6EI}M_{AB}+\frac{l}{3EI}M_{BA};$$

and noting that the change in deflection angle from B to A with reference to line AB is the same as with reference to a horizontal or unstrained position of the member, that is, $\theta_{A1}-\theta_{B1}=\theta_A-\theta_B$, we have:

$$\theta_A-\theta_B=+\frac{l}{2EI}M_{AB}-\frac{l}{2EI}M_{BA} \quad . \quad . \quad . \quad . \quad . \quad (46)$$

Likewise, from the second principle of the moment area theory, the displacement BT_2 of the point B, from the tangent AT_2, equals the moment of the conjugate beam loading, consisting of the downward-acting M_{AB} and the upward-acting M_{BA} moment area loads, taken about B:

$$\overline{BT_2} = -\frac{l^2}{3EI}M_{AB} + \frac{l^2}{6EI}M_{BA} \quad \cdots \cdots \quad (47)$$

But the deflection BT_2 in Fig. 37 (a) also equals $\Delta - l\theta_A$, therefore,

$$BT_2 = \Delta - l\theta_A = -\frac{l^2}{3EI}M_{AB} + \frac{l^2}{6EI}M_{BA} \quad \cdots \cdots \quad (48)$$

or, multiplying each term by $\frac{3}{l}$ and changing the signs,

$$3\theta_A - 3\frac{\Delta}{l} = \frac{l}{EI}M_{AB} - \frac{l}{2EI}M_{BA}; \quad \cdots \cdots \quad (49)$$

and subtracting eq. (46) from eq. (49),

$$2\theta_A + \theta_B - 3\frac{\Delta}{l} = \frac{l}{2EI}M_{AB};$$

from which the moment expression at A is obtained in the form

$$M_{AB} = 2E\frac{I}{l}\left(2\theta_A + \theta_B - 3\frac{\Delta}{l}\right) \quad \cdots \cdots \quad (50)$$

Similarly, multiplying both sides of eq. (48) by $\frac{3}{2l}$,

$$\frac{3}{2}\theta_A - \frac{3}{2}\frac{\Delta}{l} = \frac{l}{2EI}M_{AB} - \frac{l}{4EI}M_{BA}; \quad \cdots \cdots \quad (51)$$

and subtracting eq. (46) from eq. (51),

$$\frac{1}{2}\theta_A + \theta_B - \frac{3\Delta}{2l} = +\frac{l}{4EI}M_{BA};$$

or,

$$M_{BA} = 2E\frac{I}{l}\left(2\theta_B + \theta_A - 3\frac{\Delta}{l}\right). \quad \cdots \cdots \quad (50a)$$

Eqs. (50) and (50a) are the fundamental slope-deflection expressions for end moments of a member with constant cross section and no loading between the ends.

25. Constant Moment of Inertia, Intermediate Loading between Ends of Member.—Fig. 38(a) represents the more general case, in which the member AB is not only acted upon by end moments and forces but also a system of loading P in the span. The direction of the end moments and the bent position of the member, shown in Fig. 38 (b), are assumed to be similar to those in the preceding case.

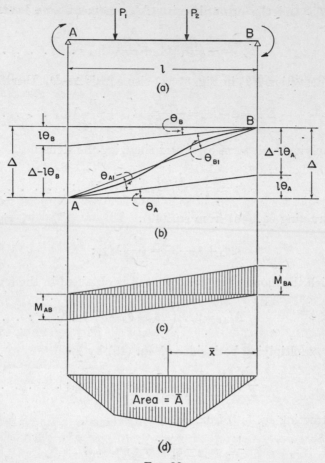

As a result of the added loads P_1 and P_2, the conjugate beam loading is augmented by the corresponding simple beam bending moment area $\overline{A}$ indicated in Fig. 38 (d). Then, the deflection angles at the two ends become:

$$R_A = \theta_{A1} = +\frac{l}{3EI}M_{AB} - \frac{l}{6EI}M_{BA} + \frac{\overline{x}}{lEI}\overline{A},$$

$$R_B = \theta_{B1} = -\frac{l}{6EI}M_{AB} + \frac{l}{3EI}M_{BA} - \frac{(l-\overline{x})}{lEI}\overline{A};$$

and the change in deflection angle from B to A,

$$\theta_A - \theta_B = \frac{l}{2EI}M_{AB} - \frac{l}{2EI}M_{BA} + \frac{\overline{A}}{EI} \quad . \quad . \quad . \quad . \quad . \quad (52)$$

For the deflection of B, from the tangent drawn at A, we have:

$$\Delta - l\theta_A = -\frac{l^2}{3EI}M_{AB} + \frac{l^2}{6EI}M_{BA} - \frac{\bar{x}}{EI}\bar{A} \quad \ldots \quad (53)$$

The end moment expressions M_{AB} and M_{BA}, obtained by simultaneous solution of eqs. (52) and (53)—as in the preceding case—take the forms

$$M_{AB} = 2E\frac{I}{l}\left(2\theta_A + \theta_B - 3\frac{\Delta}{l}\right) - \frac{2\bar{A}}{l^2}(3\bar{x} - l), \quad \ldots \quad (54)$$

$$M_{BA} = 2E\frac{I}{l}\left(2\theta_B + \theta_A - 3\frac{\Delta}{l}\right) + \frac{2\bar{A}}{l^2}(2l - 3\bar{x}) \quad \ldots \quad (54a)$$

or, noting that the last term of each equation represents the fixed-end moment for that end, as derived in Art. 14 and given by eqs. (16) and (16a),

$$M_{AB} = 2E\frac{I}{l}\left(2\theta_A + \theta_B - 3\frac{\Delta}{l}\right) + FM_{AB}, \quad \ldots \quad (55)$$

$$M_{BA} = 2E\frac{I}{l}\left(2\theta_B + \theta_A - 3\frac{\Delta}{l}\right) + FM_{BA} \quad \ldots \quad (55a)$$

Comparison of eqs. (55) and (55a) with the corresponding eqs. (50) and (50a) of the preceding case, discloses the fact that the former expressions differ from the latter by only the fixed-end moment term, resulting from the loading between the ends of the member. This is evident from the principle of superposition.

26. Variable moment of Inertia, Intermediate Loading between Ends of Member.—The cross section of the member AB shown in Fig. 39 (a) varies along the span. The assumed position of the elastic curve in bending is indicated in Fig. 39 (b); and the modified moment diagrams or conjugate beam loading—corresponding to the end moments M_{AB} and M_{BA}, and the simple beam moment due to the loading in the span—are shown by the shaded areas in Fig. 39 (c) and (d). The notations used in the latter diagrams are in accordance with Art. 18.

Similar to the preceding two cases,

$$EI\theta_{A1} = pl(1-u)M_{AB} - qvlM_{BA} + \frac{\bar{x}_1}{l}\bar{A}_1,$$

$$EI\theta_{B1} = -pulM_{AB} + ql(1-v)M_{BA} - \frac{(l-\bar{x}_1)}{l}\bar{A}_1,$$

$$EI(\theta_A - \theta_B) = +plM_{AB} - qlM_{BA} + \bar{A}_1; \quad \ldots \quad \ldots \quad (56)$$

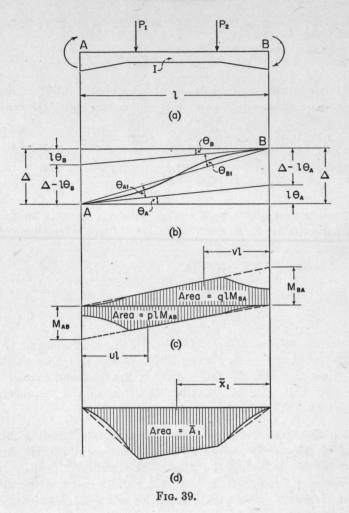

Fig. 39.

and

$$EI(\Delta - l\theta_A) = -pl^2(1-u)M_{AB} + qvl^2 M_{BA} - \overline{x}_1 \overline{A}_1 \quad . \quad . \quad . \quad (57)$$

Solving eqs. (56) and (57) simultaneously for the values of the two end moments,

$$M_{AB} = \frac{E}{p(1-u-v)} \cdot \frac{I}{l}\left[(1-v)\theta_A + v\theta_B - \frac{\Delta}{l}\right] - \frac{(\overline{x}_1 - vl)}{pl^2(1-u-v)}\overline{A}_1, \quad . \quad (58)$$

$$M_{BA} = \frac{E}{q(1-u-v)} \cdot \frac{I}{l}\left[(1-u)\theta_B + u\theta_A - \frac{\Delta}{l}\right] + \frac{(l-ul-\overline{x}_1)}{ql^2(1-u-v)}\overline{A}_1 . \quad (59)$$

Noting that the last term of each of eqs. (58) and (59) represents the fixed-end moment for the respective end, as derived in Art. 18 and given by eqs. (31) and (31a), we have:

$$M_{AB} = \frac{E}{p(1-u-v)} \cdot \frac{I}{l}\left[(1-v)\theta_A + v\theta_B - \frac{\Delta}{l}\right] + FM_{AB}, \quad . \quad . \quad (60)$$

$$M_{BA} = \frac{E}{q(1-u-v)} \cdot \frac{I}{l}\left[(1-u)\theta_B + u\theta_A - \frac{\Delta}{l}\right] + FM_{BA} \quad . \quad . \quad (60a)$$

Eqs. (60) and (60a) are the general slope-deflection expressions for end moments of a member with variable cross section and subjected to intermediate loading. By substitution of ½ for p and q, and ⅛ for u and v, they reduce to the respective forms of eqs. (55) and (55a) of the preceding case, in which the moment of inertia of the member was assumed to be constant.

If the member is assumed to be hinged at D, then q and v are zero, and eq. (58) becomes

$$M_{AB} = \frac{E}{p(1-u)} \cdot \frac{I}{l}\left(\theta_A - \frac{\Delta}{l}\right) - \frac{\overline{x}_1}{pl^2(1-u)}\overline{A}_1, \quad . \quad . \quad . \quad (61)$$

or

$$M_{AB} = \frac{E}{p(1-u)} \cdot \frac{I}{l}\left(\theta_A - \frac{\Delta}{l}\right) + HM_{AB} . \quad . \quad . \quad . \quad . \quad (62)$$

ILLUSTRATIVE EXAMPLES

1. A beam of a constant cross section is loaded with a force P (Fig. 40), placed at midspan. Determine the magnitude of the end moments which will produce deflection angles at the two ends equal to one half those for the simply supported case.

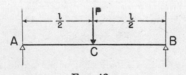

FIG. 40.

Solution: The end deflection angles for the simply supported beam are:

$$\theta_A = +\frac{Pl^2}{16EI}; \quad \theta_B = -\frac{Pl^2}{16EI}.$$

Substituting half these values in the fundamental slope-deflection expression (eq. 55 in this case) and noting that Δ equals zero, we have:

$$M_{AB} = 2E\frac{I}{l}\left(\frac{Pl^2}{16EI} - \frac{Pl^2}{32EI}\right) - \frac{Pl}{8} = -\frac{Pl}{16}.$$

Likewise,

$$M_{BA} = +\frac{Pl}{16}.$$

2. Assuming the beam in the above example fixed at the two supports and using the slope-deflection expression, determine the deflection under the load.

Solution: Since the beam is fixed at the ends and the load symmetrical, the deflection angles at the supports and at midspan are zero. Considering the portion AC (Fig. 41) of the beam as a separate

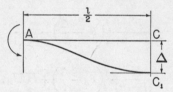

Fig. 41.

member and writing the end moment expression at A,

$$M_{AC} = 2E\frac{I}{l/2}\left(0 + 0 - 3\frac{\Delta}{l/2}\right) = -\frac{Pl}{8};$$

from which,

$$\Delta = \frac{Pl^3}{192EI}.$$

PROBLEMS

13. By the method used in the solution of Example 2, determine the maximum deflection of a beam of constant cross section and under a uniform load, assuming:

    (*a*) Ends simply supported;
    (*b*) Ends fixed.

14. Compute the deflection angle at the first support (A) of the two-span tapering beam shown in Fig. 33.

27. Abbreviated Moment Expression.—In the case of members with constant moment of inertia (and constant modulus of elasticity, E), the fundamental moment equation

$$M_{AB}=2E\frac{I}{l}\left(2\theta_A+\theta_B-3\frac{\Delta}{l}\right)+FM_{AB},$$

can be written in the abbreviated form

$$M_{AB}=K\left(A+\frac{B}{2}-R\right)+FM_{AB}, \quad \ldots \ldots \ldots (63)$$

in which

$$K=\frac{I}{l}, \; A=4E\theta_A, \; B=4E\theta_B \text{ and } R=6E\frac{\Delta}{l}.$$

According to this notation the letters A and B in eq. (63) indicate the ends of the member (Fig. 42) and also $4E$ times the true values of the

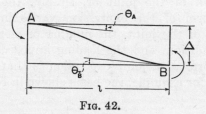

FIG. 42.

deflection angles of the respective ends. For further simplicity, the terms A and B will be referred to hereafter as the deflection angles of the member AB; R, the deflection; and K, its stiffness ratio.

If the member is assumed to be hinged at the end B, eq. (63) becomes

$$M_{AB}=K\left(\frac{3}{4}A-\frac{R}{2}\right)+HM_{AB} \quad \ldots \ldots \ldots (64)$$

Likewise, by assuming the member fixed at the end B,

$$M_{AB}=K(A-R)+FM_{AB}. \quad \ldots \ldots \ldots (65)$$

With similar substitutions, the moment equation for a member with a variable cross section, corresponding to eqs. (63), (64) and (65), is obtained from the general slope-deflection expression

$$M_{AB}=\frac{I}{l}\cdot\frac{E}{p(1-u-v)}\left[(1-v)\theta_A+v\theta_B-\frac{\Delta}{l}\right]+FM_{AB} \quad \ldots (60)$$

Thus, when both ends of the member are restrained, the equation becomes

$$M_{AB} = \frac{K}{4p(1-u-v)}\left[(1-v)A + vB - \frac{2}{3}R\right] + FM_{AB} \quad . \quad . \quad . \ (66)$$

Restrained at A and hinged at B,

$$M_{AB} = \frac{K}{4p(1-u)}\left[A - \frac{2}{3}R\right] + HM_{AB} \quad . \quad . \quad . \quad . \quad . \ (67)$$

Restrained at A and fixed at B,

$$M_{AB} = \frac{K}{4p(1-u-v)}\left[(1-v)A - \frac{2}{3}R\right] + FM_{AB} \quad . \quad . \quad . \ (68)$$

28. Joint Expression.—The expression obtained by summing up the end moments of all members meeting at a joint is called the moment expression of the joint or, simply, the joint expression. Obviously, the form of the expression varies in accordance with support condition of the joint, the number of members at the joint and their end condition, and the loading imposed on the members.

The simplest form of a joint expression is that for a continuous beam. Consider, for example, the beam shown in Fig. 43. Assuming

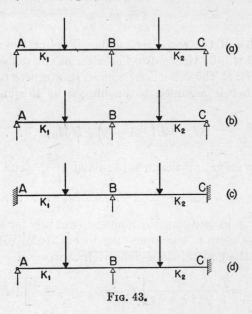

Fig. 43.

the supports to be at the same level (the deflection term $R=0$), and the ends A and C restrained, as is shown in (a), the joint expression at B is then obtained from the two end moments at that support. Thus, by eq. (63),

$$M_{BA}=K_1\left(B+\frac{A}{2}\right)+FM_{BA}$$

$$M_{BC}=K_2\left(B+\frac{C}{2}\right)+FM_{BC}$$

$$M_{BA}+M_{BC}=(K_1+K_2)B+K_1\frac{A}{2}+K_2\frac{C}{2}+FM_{BA}+FM_{BC}=0. \quad (69a)$$

If the ends A and C are hinged, Fig. 43 (b), by application of eq. 64 we will have:

$$M_{BA}=K_1\left(\frac{3}{4}B\right)+HM_{BA}$$

$$M_{BC}=K_2\left(\frac{3}{4}B\right)+HM_{BC}$$

$$M_{BA}+M_{BC}=\frac{3}{4}(K_1+K_2)B+HM_{BA}+HM_{BC}=0 \quad . \quad . \quad (69b)$$

Similarly, assuming the ends A and C fixed, as in Fig. 43 (c), and applying eq. (65), the joint expression at B becomes.

$$M_{BA}=K_1B+FM_{BA}$$
$$M_{BC}=K_2B+FM_{BC}$$
$$M_{BA}+M_{BC}=(K_1+K_2)B+FM_{BA}+FM_{BC}=0 \quad . \quad . \quad (69c)$$

If the beam is hinged at A and fixed at C, Fig. 43 (d), the joint expression at B is in the form

$$M_{BA}+M_{BC}=\left(\frac{3}{4}K_1+K_2\right)B+HM_{BA}+FM_{BC}=0 \quad . \quad . \quad (69d)$$

The joint expression of the two-legged bent, shown in Fig. 44, is equally simple. Assuming the bent fixed at C and D, as in Fig. 44 (a),

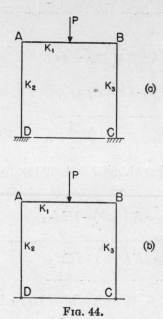

Fig. 44.

and noting that the deflection R of the horizontal member AB is zero, the joint expression at A, for example, is obtained thus:

$$M_{AB}=K_1\left(A+\frac{B}{2}\right)+FM_{AB}$$

$$\underline{M_{AD}=K_2(A+0-R)}$$

$$M_{AB}+M_{AD}=(K_1+K_2)A+K_1\frac{B}{2}-K_2R+FM_{AB}=0 \quad . \quad (70a)$$

Likewise, if the legs are hinged at C and D, Fig. 44 (b),

$$M_{AB}=K_1\left(A+\frac{B}{2}\right)+FM_{AB}$$

$$\underline{M_{AD}=K_2\left(\frac{3}{4}A-\frac{R}{2}\right)}$$

$$M_{AB}+M_{AD}=\left(K_1+\frac{3}{4}K_2\right)A+K_1\frac{B}{2}-K_2\frac{R}{2}+FM_{AB}=0 \quad . \quad (70b)$$

In the special case of symmetrical loading and framing, that is, when $FM_{AB}=-FM_{BA}$ and $K_2=K_3$, A equals $-B$ and the deflection R of the legs reduces to zero. Accordingly, for fixed bases, the joint expression at A becomes

$$M_{AB}+M_{AD}=\left(\frac{1}{2}K_1+K_2\right)A+FM_{AB}=0; \ . \ . \ . \ . \ (71a)$$

and that corresponding to the hinged bases is in the form

$$M_{AB}+M_{AD}=\left(\frac{1}{2}K_1+\frac{3}{4}K_2\right)A+FM_{AB}=0 \ . \ . \ . \ . \ (71b)$$

The derivation of the joint expression in frames with more than one story and bay presents no additional difficulty. The bent shown in Fig. 45 will serve for illustration. At joint A, for example, from

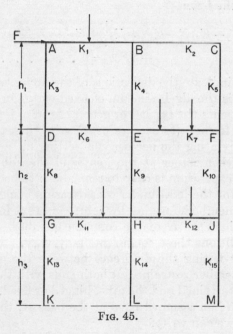

FIG. 45.

the end moments of the members AB and AD we have:

$$M_{AB}=K_1\left(A+\frac{B}{2}\right)+FM_{AB}$$

$$M_{AD}=K_3\left(A+\frac{D}{2}-R_1\right)$$

$$\overline{M_{AB}+M_{AD}=(K_1+K_3)A+K_1\frac{B}{2}+K_3\frac{D}{2}-K_3R_1+FM_{AB}=0.}$$

At B, moments of three members are to be considered. Thus,

$$M_{BA} = K_1\left(B + \frac{A}{2}\right) + FM_{BA}$$

$$M_{BC} = K_2\left(B + \frac{C}{2}\right)$$

$$M_{BE} = K_4\left(B + \frac{E}{2} - R_1\right)$$

$$M_{BA} + M_{BC} + M_{BE} = (K_1 + K_2 + K_4)B + K_1\frac{A}{2} + K_2\frac{C}{2}$$
$$+ K_4\frac{E}{2} - K_4 R_1 + FM_{BA} = 0.$$

Likewise, joint E is formed by the ends of four members, and the expression is in the form

$$(K_4 + K_6 + K_7 + K_9)E + K_4\frac{B}{2} + K_6\frac{D}{2} + K_7\frac{F}{2} + K_9\frac{H}{2} - K_4 R_1 - K_9 R_2$$
$$+ \Sigma FM_E = 0 \ldots \ldots \ldots \ldots \quad (72)$$

where R_1 and R_2 indicate the deflections of the upper two stories of the bent and ΣFM_E is the algebraic sum of fixed-end moments at E.

Eq. (72) represents the typical or general form of a joint expression in a rectangular frame. It enables us to write the expression at any joint directly, obviating the necessity of setting up separate moment equations for each member at the joint and then obtain their sum. The form of the expression is easy to remember: the coefficient of the deflection angle for the joint under consideration being the sum of the K values of the members forming the joint, and that for each adjacent joint being one-half the K of the common member. Obviously, for certain end conditions these coefficients may vary. The changes are readily made by noting the difference between the general moment equation for a member restrained at both ends with that of a member having one end restrained and the other hinged or fixed. For instance, if the member GK be assumed fixed at the base K, then for the joint expression at G we can write:

$$(K_8 + K_{11} + K_{13})G + K_8\frac{D}{2} + K_{11}\frac{H}{2} - K_8 R_2 - K_{13}R_3 + FM_{GH} = 0.$$

Similarly, if the member HL is hinged at L, the joint expression at H becomes

$$\left(K_9 + K_{11} + K_{12} + \frac{3}{4}K_{14}\right)H + K_9\frac{E}{2} + K_{11}\frac{G}{2} + K_{12}\frac{J}{2} - K_9 R_2 - \frac{1}{2}K_{14}R_3$$
$$+ \Sigma FM_H = 0.$$

29. Shear Expression.—The relation between the end moments and the end reactions of a member is called the shear expression of the member. This relation is obtained from the fundamental principle which, by reference to Fig. 46, may be stated thus: if M_{AB} and M_{BA}

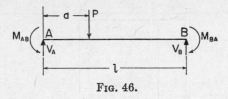

FIG. 46.

indicate the moments at the two ends of a member AB, and V_A and V_B the shears or reactions at the respective ends, then the change in moment from A to B is equal to the moment produced by the reaction V_A and the loads contained between the two ends, taken about B. In accordance with our sign convention—as determined by the direction of the resisting moment couple acting upon the section limiting the portion of the member under consideration—the moments at the two sides of a section have opposite signs, and, therefore, the change or difference in moments between A and B will be given by the algebraic sum of the two end moments. Thus,

$$M_{AB}+M_{BA}=-V_Al+P(l-a)=+V_Bl-Pa \ . \ . \ . \ . \ (73)$$

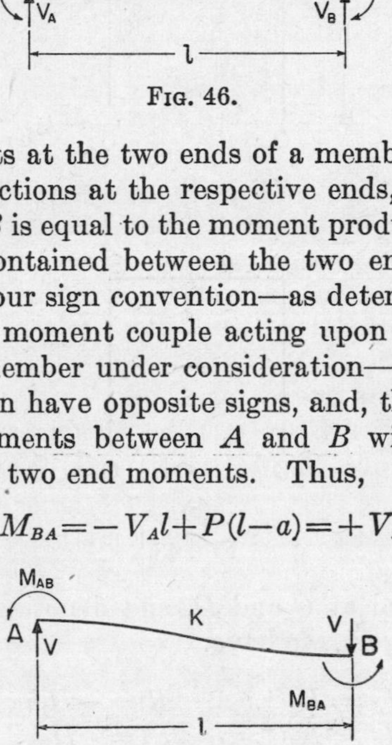

FIG. 47.

If there is no external force between the two ends of the member, as in Fig. 47, the relation reduces to the simple form

$$M_{AB}+M_{BA}=-Vl \ . \ . \ . \ . \ . \ . \ . \ . \ (74)$$

or, since

$$M_{AB}=K\Big(A+\frac{B}{2}-R\Big),$$

and

$$M_{BA}=K\Big(B+\frac{A}{2}-R\Big);$$

$$\overline{M_{AB}+M_{BA}}=\overline{K(1.5A+1.5B-2R)}=-Vl \ ; \ . \ . \ . \ (75)$$

which is the important shear expression, supplementing the joint expression in frames involving side-sway. Some examples of application of eq. (75) will now be given.

As a first example, refer to the two-legged bent shown in Fig. 48 (a).

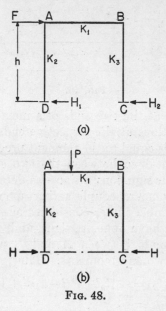

FIG. 48.

Assuming bases fixed at C and D, and denoting the two horizontal reactions by H_1 and H_2, we have:

$$M_{AD}+M_{DA}=K_2(1.5A-2R)=-H_1h$$
$$M_{BC}+M_{CB}=K_3(1.5B-2R)=-H_2h$$

$$1.5K_2A+1.5K_3B-2(K_2+K_3)R=-(H_1+H_2)h=-Fh \ . \ . \ (76)$$

If the two legs are equally stiff, that is, $K_2=K_3$, then A equals B, and eq. (76) becomes

$$3K_2A-4K_2R=-Fh.$$

As a second example, the lateral force F in Fig. 48 (a) is replaced with a vertical load, shown in Fig. 48 (b). It is evident that the two horizontal reactions at the base are of the same magnitude and acting in opposite directions. Then,

$$M_{AD}+M_{DA}=K_2(1.5A-2R)=+Hh$$
$$M_{BC}+M_{CB}=K_3(1.5B-2R)=-Hh$$

$$1.5K_2A+1.5K_3B-2(K_2+K_3)R=0 \ . \ . \ . \ . \ . \ (77)$$

As a third example, the derivation of the shear expression for the top story of the bent in Fig. 45 is given below:

$$M_{AD}+M_{DA}=1.5K_3(A+D)-2K_3R_1=-H_1h_1$$
$$M_{BE}+M_{EB}=1.5K_4(B+E)-2K_4R_1=-H_2h_1$$
$$M_{CF}+M_{FC}=1.5K_5(C+F)-2K_5R_1=-H_3h_1$$

$$1.5K_3(A+D)+1.5K_4(B+E)$$
$$+1.5K_5(C+F)-2(K_3+K_4+K_5)R_1=-(H_1+H_2+H_3)h_1=-Fh_1 \quad (78)$$

PROBLEMS

15. The exterior legs of the bent shown in Fig. 49 are tapered. All members have the same breadth and their depths are as indicated. Assuming the bases fixed, write the joint expressions at A and B. Express all Ks in terms of the K for the member BE.

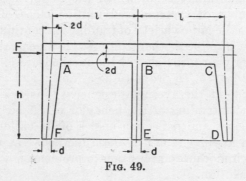

Fig. 49.

16. Derive the shear expression for the bent in Fig. 50, assuming:

    (a) Legs fixed at the bases;

    (b) Legs hinged at the bases.

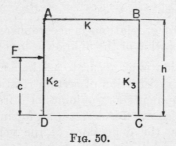

Fig. 50.

PART II. FRAMES WITHOUT SIDE SWAY

Chapter I

DIRECT METHOD OF SOLUTION

30. Slope Deflection as a Basis of a General Method of Solution.— For its simple principles and their easy application, *slope deflection* constitutes an ideal method of attack for the solution of problems involving statically indeterminate structures. In addition to its direct application, it also serves as a basis of the many so-called methods of rigid frame analysis, in which the required work is carried through a number of systematized routine steps of computation. However, due to the large variety of framings in continuous structures, obviously, no such single method can provide a general solution, and, unless the underlying principles of the method are clearly known, a mere procedure may often prove to be a faulty, and even dangerous tool in the hands of the average designer. It is evident, therefore, that a good understanding of the behavior of the structure, as indicated by the slopes and deflection angles of its various members, is essential for an intelligent use of these methods—as well as for the extension or their modified application to problems not directly within their range of solution.

31. General Procedure of Solution.—There are two distinct phases in the analysis of rigid frames:

- (*a*) Initial assumptions or conceived probable behavior of the structure; and
- (*b*) The setting up of relations in accordance with this conception and the solution of the unknowns involved.

Obviously, a solution is as accurate as the conception upon which it is based. A mere satisfaction of certain relations, such as the balanced condition of moments at the joints of a frame, does not necessarily mean that the solution is correct; as, for instance, when writing the joint expressions, the deflections of the vertical members were assumed to be zero, while in actuality the frame had a side-sway. The error due to faulty conception may or may not be detected, according to the type of the framing and the nature of the omission or assumption. In the case of the rectangular frame, the error due to omission of sidesway is readily discovered from the shear expression of each story. On the other hand, in a trapezoidal bent, we may neglect the deflections of the horizontal members and obtain erroneous results which will, however, satisfy the equilibrium conditions of both the moments and the reactions.

In proceeding with the solution, we must first consider the physical characteristics of the frame, namely:

(a) Position of the external loading;

(b) Symmetry of framing; and

(c) Support condition of the ends.

If there is symmetry of both loading and framing, then the computations will naturally be confined to only one-half of the frame. However, when writing the joint expression for the bays containing the vertical axis of symmetry, care must be taken in assigning signs to the deflection angles at the ends of the members cut by the axis. To illustrate, refer to the bents shown in Fig. 51.

The loading of the bent shown in Fig. 51 (a) consists of a vertical force P, applied between the joints A and B. When the distance a equals b, the load becomes symmetrical with respect to the vertical center line of the bent, producing fixed-end moments at the joints A and B of the same magnitude but of opposite sign. If, in addition to this load condition, the legs AD and BC are of equal stiffness, that is, $K_2=K_3$, then symmetry of both loading and framing is obtained, in which case side-sway vanishes, and in accordance with the exaggerated deformation diagram shown in Fig. 51 (b), $\theta_A=-\theta_B$ and $\theta_D=-\theta_C$.

In Fig. 51 (c) the bent is subjected to a lateral load load F, applied between the joints A and D. If the distance d is made equal to the height h of the bent, that is, the load applied at the joint A, and K_2 equals K_3, the bent will deform as in Fig. 51 (d), the two legs assuming curvatures in the same direction and magnitude. Accordingly, the deflection angles at A and D equal respectively those at B and C. (It is also to be noted that the deformation diagram shown in Fig. 51 (d) does not show the effect of axial stresses—which are only of secondary importance and will be considered separately.)

The values of the deflection angles at the bases C and D, and hence the form of the joint expressions at A and B and the shear equation of the panel, are subject to our initial assumption for the end support condition. If the legs are assumed to be fixed at the bases, the corresponding deflection angles become zero. When assumed as hinged at the bases (end tangents at C and D free to rotate), the moment equations at the upper ends of the legs—and consequently the joint and shear expressions—are adjusted accordingly. For an end fixity intermediate between the fixed and hinged conditions, evaluation of moments are made from the results of the two cases in accordance with the degree of restraint considered.

The solution of the moments for the bent shown in Fig. 51 (a), with identical legs and symmetrical loading, is dependent upon a single unknown—the deflection angle θ_A, which is obtained from the joint expression at A. That of the bent in Fig. 51 (c), for the same special

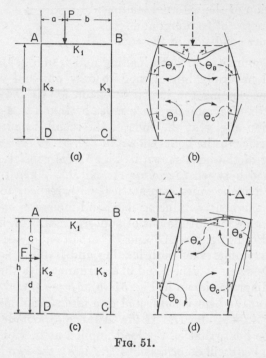

Fig. 51.

case of symmetry, contains an additional unknown, the common deflection Δ of the two legs, necessitating the simultaneous solution of two equations, namely, the joint expression at A and the shear equation of the bay. In the more general case of unsymmetrical loading or framing, each bent has two unknown deflection angles and one unknown deflection term R, requiring the solution of three simultaneous equations. For these bents, as well as for other frames of equal simplicity, containing three or less unknowns, the direct solution of the corresponding equations by the conventional method of substitution or successive elimination of the unknowns provides the shortest and best solution. This direct method of solution will be illustrated by the following examples.

1. The loading and stiffness ratios of a two-span continuous beam, with supports on the same level, are shown in Fig. 52. Compute the moments at the supports, assuming:

(a) Ends A and C fixed;

(b) Ends A and C hinged.

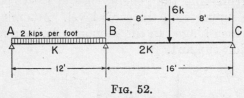

FIG. 52.

Solution: (a)

$$FM_{AB} = \frac{2 \times 12^2}{12} = 24 \text{ ft.-kips,}$$

$$FM_{CB} = +\frac{6 \times 16}{8} = +12 \text{ ft.-kips.}$$

The value of the deflection angle at B is obtained from the joint expression at the same support. Thus, from eq. 69 (c),

$$(K+2K)B+24-12=0;$$

$$B=-\frac{12}{3K}=-\frac{4}{K}.$$

(The true value of the deflection angle θ_B equals $\frac{4 \times 12}{4EI_{AB}}$, since $K=\frac{1}{12}I_{AB}$ and $B=4E\theta_B$.)

Then, substituting this value for B in the fundamental moment expression,

$$M_{AB}=K\left(-\frac{2}{K}\right)-24=-26 \text{ ft.-kips,}$$

$$M_{BA}=K\left(-\frac{4}{K}\right)+24=+20 \text{ ft.-kips,}$$

$$M_{BC}=2K\left(-\frac{4}{K}\right)-12=-20 \text{ ft.-kips.}$$

(b) By assumption,

$$M_{AB}=0, \quad M_{CB}=0.$$

From the joint expression at B, as given by eq. 69 (b),

$$\frac{3}{4}(K+2K)B+36-18=0;$$

$$B=-\frac{8}{K}.$$

Then,

$$M_{BA} = \frac{3}{4}K\left(-\frac{8}{K}\right) + 36 = +30 \text{ ft.-kips,}$$

$$M_{BC} = \frac{3}{4} \cdot 2K\left(-\frac{8}{K}\right) - 18 = -30 \text{ ft.-kips.}$$

2. Fig. 52a represents the general case of a two-span continuous beam, with the supports on the same level. Assuming first the two ends fixed, and then hinged to the supports, derive a moment expression for the middle support.

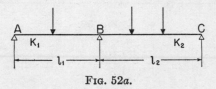

FIG. 52a.

Solution: (a) As in the preceding example,

$$(K_1 + K_2)B + FM_{BA} + FM_{BC} = 0;$$

$$B = -\frac{FM_{BA} + FM_{BC}}{K_1 + K_2}.$$

Then,

$$M_{BA} = -\frac{K_1}{K_1 + K_2}(FM_{BA} + FM_{BC}) + FM_{BA},$$

$$M_{BC} = -\frac{K_2}{K_1 + K_2}(FM_{BA} + FM_{BC}) + FM_{BC}.$$

(b) Similarly,

$$\frac{3}{4}(K_1 + K_2)B + HM_{BA} + HM_{BC} = 0;$$

$$B = -\frac{4(HM_{BA} + HM_{BC})}{3(K_1 + K_2)}.$$

$$M_{BA} = -\frac{K_1}{K_1 + K_2}(HM_{BA} + HM_{BC}) + IIM_{BA},$$

$$M_{BC} = -\frac{K_2}{K_1 + K_2}(HM_{BA} + HM_{BC}) + HM_{BC}.$$

Since $M_{BA}=-M_{BC}$, agreement of the two moment values at the joint constitutes a check upon the accuracy of the computation.

3. The three-span continuous beam shown in Fig. 53 is subjected to a uniform load of 1 kip per linear foot. The supports are on the same level, and the stiffness ratios of the members indicated on the sketch. Assuming the beam fixed at the ends, compute the moments at the supports.

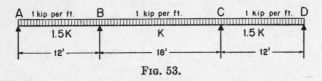

FIG. 53.

Solution: By the symmetry of the loading and beam,

$$B=-C;$$

$$M_{BC}=-M_{CD};$$

$$FM_{AB}=-12 \text{ ft.-kips.}$$

From the joint expression at B,

$$(1.5K+K-0.5K)B+12-27=0;$$

$$B=+\frac{7.5}{K}.$$

Then,

$$M_{AB}=1.5K\left(\frac{7.5}{2K}\right)-12=-6.375 \text{ ft.-kips,}$$

$$M_{BA}=1.5K\left(\frac{7.5}{K}\right)+12=+23.25 \text{ ft.-kips,}$$

$$M_{BC}=K\left(\frac{7.5}{2K}\right)-27=-23.25 \text{ ft.-kips.}$$

4. The two-legged rectangular bent shown in Fig. 54 is carrying a system of symmetrical vertical loading. The two legs have the same stiffness ratio. Determine the moments at the joints, assuming:

(a) Bases fixed;
(b) Bases hinged.

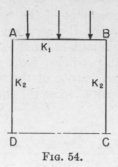

FIG. 54.

Solution: (*a*) Due to the symmetry of loading and bent,

$$A=-B; \quad M_{AB}=-M_{BA}.$$

Noting also that there is no side-sway ($R=0$), from the joint expression at A,

$$\left(\frac{K_1}{2}+K_2\right)A+FM_{AB}=0;$$

$$A=-\frac{2}{K_1+2K_2}FM_{AB}.$$

Then,

$$M_{AB}=-\frac{K_1}{K_1+2K_2}FM_{AB}+FM_{AB},$$

or

$$M_{AD}=-\frac{2K_2}{K_1+2K_2}FM_{AB};$$

and

$$M_{DA}=-\frac{K_2}{K_1+2K_2}FM_{AB}.$$

(*b*)
$$A=-B; M_{AB}=-M_{BA}; M_{DA}=M_{CB}=0$$

$$\left(\frac{K_1}{2}+\frac{3}{4}K_2\right)A+FM_{AB}=0; \quad A=-\frac{4}{2K_1+3K_2}FM_{AB}.$$

$$M_{AB}=-\frac{2K_1}{2K_1+3K_2}FM_{AB}+FM_{AB},$$

or

$$M_{AD}=-\frac{3K_2}{2K_1+3K_2}FM_{AB}.$$

5. A two-legged trapezoidal bent, Fig. 55, is subjected to a vertical loading, placed symmetrically with respect to the vertical center line of the bent. The legs have the same inclination and stiffness ratio. Assuming the legs first as fixed and then hinged to the bases, determine the moments at the joints.

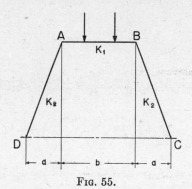

FIG. 55.

Solution: Since the bent and the loading are symmetrical, and there is no side-sway, the solution of the problem becomes identical with that in Example 4.

6. The symmetrical bent shown in Fig. 56 is loaded with a lateral force, applied at the top. Determine the moments at the joints, for

    (*a*) Fixed bases;

    (*b*) Hinged bases.

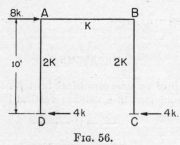

FIG. 56.

Solution: (*a*) Since the two legs are of equal stiffness, A equals B. The joint expression at A is in the form

$$(1.5K+2K)A-2KR=0; \quad \text{......} \quad (a)$$

and the shear expression, written for the leg AD,

$$3KA-4KR=-4\times10 \text{ ......} \quad (b)$$

from which,

$$R=\frac{3}{4}A+\frac{10}{K} \text{ ....} \quad (c)$$

Substituting this value of R in eq. (*a*),

$$2KA-20=0,$$

or

$$A=+\frac{10}{K};$$

and

$$R = +\frac{7.5}{K} + \frac{10}{K} = +\frac{17.5}{K}.$$

Then,

$$M_{AB} = M_{BA} = 1.5K\frac{10}{K} = +15 \text{ ft.-kips,}$$

or

$$M_{AD} = M_{BC} = 2K\left(\frac{10}{K} - \frac{17.5}{K}\right) = -15 \text{ ft.-kips;}$$

and

$$M_{DA} = M_{CB} = 2K\left(\frac{5}{K} - \frac{17.5}{K}\right) = -25 \text{ ft.-kips.}$$

(b) By assumption,

$$M_{DA} = M_{CB} = 0.$$

The horizontal reaction at the base of each leg being 4 kips (= one-half the applied load), the moment at A may then be directly obtained from this reaction, without the necessity of computing the deflection angle and the deflection.   Thus,

$$M_{AD} = -M_{AB} = -4 \times 10 = -40 \text{ ft.-kips.}$$

PROBLEMS

17. The top strut AB of an unsymmetrical bent (one leg is twice as stiff as the other), Fig. 57, is subjected to a uniform vertical load of w per linear foot.

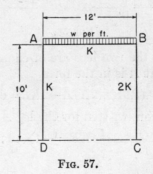

Fig. 57.

Assuming the legs to be fixed at the bases, determine the moments at the joints:

    (a) Neglecting side-sway;
    (b) Considering side-sway.

18. The vertical loading of the three-legged bent, shown in Fig. 58, is sym-

metrical about the center joint B; and the exterior legs are of equal stiffness. Determine the moments at the joints—expressed in terms of the fixed-end moments—assuming:

(a) Fixed bases;

(b) Hinged bases.

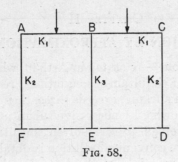

Fig. 58.

$$A = 4E\theta$$
$$R = \frac{6E\Delta}{L}$$
$$K = \frac{I}{L}$$
$$h = L$$

$$3KA - 4KR = -Fh$$

$3\times$

CHAPTER II

SOLUTION BY APPROXIMATIONS

32. Method of Solution.—As stated in Art. 30, when the number of unknowns of a series of simultaneous equations, resulting from joint and shear expressions of a frame, exceeds three, then the direct method of solution of the unknowns, by successive substitutions and eliminations, becomes an involved process, often unsuitable for ordinary slide-rule work. A more convenient solution is obtained by successive approximations. The principle of the latter method of solution is not new—being perhaps as old as algebra; and it has been used in many varying forms in accordance with the type of the simultaneous equations considered. With proper procedure, this method of solution will furnish an invaluable supplement to slope deflection in the analysis of rigid frames. To illustrate the procedure, consider the two simple relations

$$2x+y=16, \quad\ldots\ldots\ldots\ldots \quad (a)$$

$$5y-x=25 \quad\ldots\ldots\ldots\ldots \quad (b)$$

In the first expression, which may be called the equation of x—since it has the larger coefficient, the value of x is dependent upon the numerical constant, 16, and the other unknown, y, of the equation. If we assume, temporarily, the latter value to be equal to zero, then the first approximate value for x is at once obtained from the numerical constant. Denoted by x_1, this value becomes

$$x_1=\frac{16}{2}=8.$$

Similarly, for the first approximate value of y, obtained from eq. (b), we have:

$$y_1=\frac{25}{5}=5.$$

Obviously, we were in error in assuming the value of y in eq. (a) to be zero. To rectify the error, it is necessary to substitute for y in that

72

equation its first approximate value, y_1, and obtain a correction or an additional value for x. Denoted by x_2, this correction becomes

$$x_2 = -\frac{1}{2}y_1 = -\frac{1}{2}(5) = -2.5.$$

Likewise, the correction in eq. (b), for having neglected x in obtaining the first approximate value of y, equals

$$y_2 = \frac{1}{5}x_1 = \frac{1}{5}(8) = 1.6.$$

But the values of x_2 and y_2 will, in their turn, require a second correction, performed as in the preceding step and resulting in values x_3 and y_3. Thus,

$$x_3 = -\frac{1}{2}y_2 = -\frac{1}{2}(1.6) = -0.8,$$

$$y_3 = \frac{1}{5}x_2 = \frac{1}{5}(-2.5) = -0.5.$$

Similarly,

$$x_4 = -\frac{1}{2}y_3 = -\frac{1}{2}(-0.5),$$

$$y_4 = \frac{1}{5}x_3 = \frac{1}{5}(-0.8).$$

It is to be noted, however, that these successive corrections converge rapidly to zero—since the decreasing values are multiplied by fractions ($-\frac{1}{2}$ for y and $\frac{1}{5}$ for x values in the above equations), referred to hereafter as factors or coefficients of correction—in a few cycles of multiplication becoming negligible quantities. Accordingly, the final values of x and y are obtained by adding to the first approximate values the later corrections, the number depending upon the degree of accuracy desired. With a single correction, these values are:

$$x = x_1 + x_2 = 8 - 2.5 = 5.5,$$
$$y = y_1 + y_2 = 5 + 1.6 = 6.6.$$

For two corrections, we have:

$$x = x_1 + x_2 + x_3 = 5.5 - 0.8 = 4.7,$$
$$y = y_1 + y_2 + y_3 = 6.6 - 0.5 = 6.1.$$

Three corrections give:

$$x = x_1 + x_2 + x_3 + x_4 = 4.7 + 0.25 = 4.95,$$
$$y = y_1 + y_2 + y_3 + y_4 = 0.1 - 0.16 = 5.01.$$

These latter values differ from the correct answers by only 1 percent.

As a second example, consider the following three relations:

$$8x+2y-z=24, \quad \cdots \cdots \cdots \quad (c)$$

$$-2x+10y+z=60, \quad \cdots \cdots \cdots \quad (d)$$

$$x-y+5z=16. \quad \cdots \cdots \cdots \quad (e)$$

As in the preceding example, for the first approximate values of x, y and z, obtained from eqs. (c), (d) and (e), respectively, we have:

$$x_1=\frac{24}{8}=3;\ y_1=\frac{60}{10}=6;\ z_1=\frac{16}{5}=3.2.$$

The coefficients of correction of x for y and z, that is the factors with which the value of x is to be multiplied for increments or corrections of y and z in eqs. (d) and (e), respectively are:

$$f_{xy}=\frac{2}{10}=0.2,\ f_{xz}=-\frac{1}{5}=-0.2.$$

Similarly, coefficients of correction for y, to be used in obtaining the corresponding increments of x and z,

$$f_{yx}=-\frac{2}{8}=-0.25,\ f_{yz}=-\frac{(-1)}{5}=0.2.$$

For z,

$$f_{zz}=\frac{1}{8}=0.125,\ f_{zy}=-\frac{1}{10}=-0.1.$$

Then, for the first correction or increment of the value of x, we have:

$$x_2=f_{yx}\cdot y_1+f_{zx}\cdot z_1=-0.25\times6+0.125\times3.2=-1.1.$$

Likewise,

$$y_2=f_{xy}\cdot x_1+f_{zy}\cdot z_1=0.2\times3-0.1\times3.2=0.28,$$

$$z_2=f_{xz}\cdot x_1+f_{yz}\cdot y_1=-0.2\times3+0.2\times6=0.6.$$

In order to simplify the involved work in obtaining successive sets of corrections, the required computations may be advantageously arranged in a tabulated form, as shown in Table 1. First, the unknowns are listed in their order, providing a vertical column for each. The coefficients of correction are computed next, and entered in the space marked f, with an identifying letter to indicate the unknown affected. The first approximate values are shown in the following space marked α_1 The multiplications for obtaining the first corrections are given in space $f\alpha_1$, and their sum indicated in the space directly below, marked α_2.

TABLE 1

	x	y	z
f	y 0. 2 z −0. 2	x −0. 25 z 0. 2	x 0. 125 y −0. 1
α_1	3. 0	6. 0	3. 2
$f\alpha_1$	−1. 5 0. 4	0. 6 −0. 32	−0. 6 1. 2
α_2	−1. 10	0. 28	0. 6
$f\alpha_2$	−0. 07 0. 07	−0. 22 −0. 06	0. 22 0. 056
α_3	0	−0. 28	0. 276
$f\alpha_3$	0. 07 0. 03	−0. 028 0	−0. 056 0
α_4	0. 10	−0. 028	−0. 056
α	2. 0	5. 972	4. 02

The second and third increments similarly obtained, are given in the spaces α_3 and α_4, respectively. The last line, α, contains the final values of the unknowns, representing the sum of the first approximate values and three subsequent corrections or increments, that is,

$$\alpha = \alpha_1 + \alpha_2 + \alpha_3 + \alpha_4.$$

It is to be noted that with only three corrections the true value of x is obtained, and the error in the values of y and z remains less than one-half of 1 percent.

33. Application of the Method to Continuous Beams.—A continuous beam of four spans and varying stiffness and loading is shown in Fig. 59. The beam is assumed to be hinged to the support A and fixed at

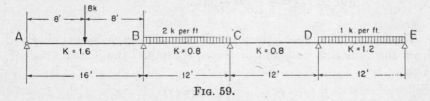

FIG. 59.

the support E. By assumption, the deflection angle at E equals zero, and that at A is a function of the deflection angle and the fixed-end moment at B. From the joint expressions at the supports B, C and

D, the following three relations, corresponding to three unknown deflection angles, are obtained:

$$\left.\begin{array}{l} 2B+0.4C+HM_{BA}+FM_{BC}=0, \\ 1.6C+0.4B+0.4D+FM_{CB}=0, \\ 2D+0.4C+FM_{DE}=0. \end{array}\right\} \quad \ldots \ldots \ldots (f)$$

By substituting the numerical values for the various fixed-end moments in the above equations, the solution of the problem becomes identical with that in the preceding example. Thus,

$$HM_{BA}=\frac{1.5\times8\times16}{8}=24 \text{ ft.-kips;}$$

$$FM_{BC}=-\frac{2\times12^2}{12}=-24 \text{ ft.-kips;}$$

$$FM_{DE}=-\frac{1\times12^2}{12}=-12 \text{ ft.-kips.}$$

Then,

$$\left.\begin{array}{l} 2B+0.4C=0, \\ 1.6C+0.4B+0.4D=-24, \\ 2D+0.4C=12. \end{array}\right\} \quad \ldots \ldots \ldots \ldots (g)$$

The factors of correction are:

$$\text{For } B, f_{BC}=-\frac{0.4}{1.6}=-0.25;$$

$$\text{For } C, f_{CB}=-\frac{0.4}{2}=-0.2, \quad f_{CD}=-\frac{0.4}{2}=-0.2;$$

$$\text{For } D, f_{DC}=-\frac{0.4}{1.6}=-0.25.$$

The first approximate value of each deflection angle is next obtained from the numerical constant of the equation and the joint coefficient. Thus,

$$B_1=0; \quad C_1=-\frac{24}{1.6}=-15; \quad D=\frac{12}{2}=6.$$

The remainder of the necessary computations, involving four corrections, and the final values of the angles are given in Table 2.

TABLE 2

(For Beam shown in Fig. 59)

	B	C	D
f	$C - 0.25$	$B - 0.2$ $D - 0.2$	$C - 0.25$
α_1	0	-15.0	6.0
$f\alpha_1$	3.0	0 -1.5	3.0
α_2	3.0	-1.5	3.0
α_3	0.3	-1.5	0.3
α_4	0.3	-0.15	0.3
α_5	0.03	-0.15	0.03
α	3.63	-18.30	9.63

To check the accuracy of the solution, the final values of the deflection angles are substituted in eqs. (g). However, since these equations were obtained from the moment expressions at each joint, it is more convenient to determine the end moments at each support and note their balance. If the moments are reasonably in balance, the solution may be considered as satisfactory. Thus:

$M_{BA} = 1.2(3.63) + 24 = 28.356$ ft.-kips,
$M_{BC} = 0.8(3.63 - 9.15) - 24 = -28.416$ ft.-kips;
$M_{CB} = 0.8(-18.3 + 1.815) + 24 = 10.812$ ft.-kips,
$M_{CD} = 0.8(-18.3 + 4.815) = -10.788$ ft.-kips;
$M_{DC} = 0.8(9.63 - 9.15) = 0.384$ ft.-kips,
$M_{DE} = 1.2(9.63) - 12 = -0.444$ ft.-kips.

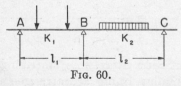

FIG. 60.

Eqs. (f) and (g) were written to obtain certain coefficients of the solution. Due to the typical form of these slope-deflection equations, in the case of members with constant cross section, the desired information may be had from the typical joint expression. Referring to Fig. 60, this expression is in the form

$$(K_1 + K_2)B + K_1\frac{A}{2} + K_2\frac{C}{2} + FM_{BA} + FM_{BC} = 0 \quad \cdots \quad (79)$$

Then the joint coefficient, F, equals $K_1 + K_2$, that is, the sum of the stiffness ratios of the two members meeting at the joint; the factors of correction—to be applied to the angles of the adjacent joints A and C as increments of B—are:

$$f_{AB} = -\frac{K_1}{2(K_1+K_2)}, \quad f_{CB} = -\frac{K_2}{2(K_1+K_2)};$$

that is, the ratio of the K of the common member by twice the joint coefficient; and the numerical constant of the equation is given by the algebraic sum of the fixed-end moments at the joint.

If the member AB is assumed to be fixed at A, f_{AB} becomes zero. If the same end is hinged,

$$F = \frac{3}{4}K_1 + K_2; \quad f_{AB} = 0, \quad f_{CB} = -\frac{2K_2}{3K_1+4K_2}.$$

For members with variable moment of inertia, it is necessary to write the joint expression at each support and determine the various coefficients accordingly.

PROBLEMS

19. Assuming the beam shown in Fig. 59 to be fixed at both end supports, determine:

    (a) Joint coefficients at B, C and D;
    (b) Coefficients of correction for B, C and D;
    (c) Values of B, C and D, after three corrections.

20. The four-span continuous beam shown in Fig. 61 is subjected to a uniform load of 1 kip per linear foot. Assuming the ends A and E fixed, determine the moments at the supports.

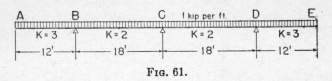

Fig. 61.

34. Frames without Side Sway.—As stated previously, when the members of a rectangular frame are arranged symmetrically with respect to the vertical center line and the loading is vertical and symmetrically placed, then the bent will have no side sway. The procedure used in computing moments in a frame of this type differs but little from that for continuous beams. To obtain the values of the deflection angles, it is necessary to solve a series of simultaneous equations, the number of which corresponds to the number of the joints in the bent. Referring to Fig. 62, which represents a portion of a frame, the typical form of these equations may be had from the joint expression at A:

$$(K_1+K_2+K_3+K_4)A+K_1\frac{B}{2}+K_2\frac{C}{2}+K_3\frac{D}{2}+K_4\frac{E}{2}+FM_A=0,$$

in which FM_A indicates the algebraic sum of fixed-end moments at A.

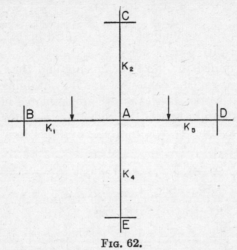

FIG. 62.

The joint coefficient for the deflection angle A equals

$$F_A=K_1+K_2+K_3+K_4 ; \quad \ldots \ldots \ldots \quad (a)$$

that is, the sum of stiffness ratios of all the members meeting at the joint. If the member AE is assumed to be hinged at E, then the corresponding $K(K_4)$ in eq. (a) reduces to $\frac{3}{4}K$, and the joint coefficient takes the form

$$F_A=K_1+K_2+K_3+\frac{3}{4}K_4.$$

If $A=-D$, that is, when the bay AD contains the vertical center line of the frame, then the joint coefficient becomes

$$F_A=K_1+K_2+\frac{1}{2}K_3+K_4.$$

The initial or the first approximate value of the deflection angle A equals,

$$\alpha_1 \text{ of } A=-\frac{FM_A}{F_A}=-\frac{FM_{AB}+FM_{AD}}{K_1+K_2+K_3+K_4};$$

and the correction factors, with which this value is to be multiplied and applied to the adjacent joints B, C, D, and E—as first correction, respectively are:

$$f_{AB}=-\frac{K_1}{2F_B}, \; f_{AC}=-\frac{K_2}{2F_C},$$

$$f_{AD}=-\frac{K_3}{2F_D}, \; f_{AE}=-\frac{K_4}{2F_E};$$

that is, the K of the common member divided by twice the respective joint coefficient, with a minus sign.

Having determined the joint coefficients and the factors of correction, the required routine computations for obtaining the final values of the various deflection angles are then completed in the usual tabulated form. As an illustration, consider the two-story bent shown in Fig. 63. The loading is symmetrical, and the legs are assumed to

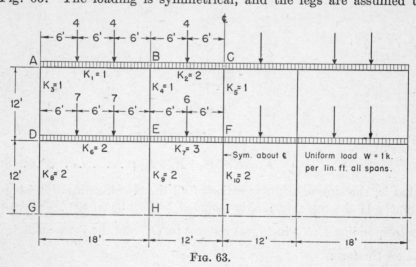

Fig. 63.

be fixed at the bases. Due to symmetry of framing, the deflection angles C and F equal zero and, accordingly, there are only four unknown deflection angles to be determined. The fixed-end moments, joint coefficients and factors of correction at the four joints are listed below:

Joint A:

$$FM_{AB}=-\left(\frac{2}{9}\times4\times18+\frac{18^2}{12}\right)=-43=FM_A;$$

$$F_A=1+1=2; \; f_{AB}=-\frac{1}{2\times4}=-0.125,$$

$$f_{AD}=-\frac{1}{2\times5}=-0.1.$$

Joint B:

$$FM_{BA} = +43, \quad FM_{BC} = -\left(\frac{4 \times 12}{8} + \frac{12^2}{12}\right) = -18,$$

$$FM_B = +43 - 18 = 25;$$

$$F_B = 1 + 2 + 1 = 4; \quad f_{BA} = -\frac{1}{2 \times 2} = -0.25,$$

$$f_{BE} = \frac{1}{2 \times 8} = -0.0625.$$

Joint D:

$$FM_{DE} = -\left(\frac{2}{9} \times 7 \times 18 + 27\right) = -55 = FM_D;$$

$$F_D = 5; \quad f_{DA} = -\frac{1}{2 \times 2} = -0.25,$$

$$f_{DE} = -\frac{2}{2 \times 8} = -0.125.$$

Joint E:

$$FM_{ED} = +55, \quad FM_{EF} = -21,$$

$$FM_E = +55 - 21 = +34;$$

$$F_E = 8; \quad f_{EB} = -\frac{1}{2 \times 4} = -0.125,$$

$$f_{ED} = -\frac{2}{2 \times 5} = -0.2.$$

The remainder of the necessary computations is shown in Table 3.

TABLE 3

(For Bent shown in Fig. 63)

	Joint	A	B	D	E
1	f	$f_B - 0.125$ $f_D - 0.1$	$f_A - 0.25$ $f_E - 0.0625$	$f_A - 0.25$ $f_E - 0.125$	$f_B - 0.125$ $f_D - 0.2$
2	α_1	21.5	-6.25	11.0	-4.25
3	$f\alpha_1$	1.562 -2.75	-2.687 0.531	-2.15 0.85	0.391 -1.375
4	α_2	-1.188	-2.156	-1.30	0.984
5	$f\alpha_2$	0.539 0.325	0.148 0.123	0.119 0.197	0.135 0.162
6	α_3	0.864	0.271	0.316	0.297
7	$f\alpha_3$	-0.068 -0.079	-0.108 -0.037	-0.086 -0.059	-0.017 -0.040
8	α_4	-0.147	-0.145	-0.145	-0.057
9	$f\alpha_4$	0.036 0.036	0.018 0.007	0.015 0.011	0.009 0.018
10	α_5	0.072	0.025	0.026	0.027
11	α	21.101	-8.255	9.897	-4.967

Under the respective joints, the factors of correction are relisted in space 1 of the table. The first approximate values, indicated in space 2, are obtained thus:

$$\alpha_1 \text{ of } A = -\frac{-43}{2} = 21.5;$$

$$\alpha_1 \text{ of } B = -\frac{25}{4} = -6.25;$$

$$\alpha_1 \text{ of } D = -\frac{-55}{5} = 11.0;$$

$$\alpha_1 \text{ of } E = -\frac{34}{8} = -4.25.$$

The first corrections, space 3, are performed by multiplying the α_1 values by the respective factors of correction, and the resulting first ncrements shown in space 4. The second, third and fourth increments, similarly obtained, are given in spaces 6, 8 and 10, respectively. The last space of the table contains the final values of the deflection angles, representing the sums of the first approximate values and subsequent four increments, that is, $\alpha = \alpha_1 + \alpha_2 + \alpha_3 + \alpha_4 + \alpha_5$. By substituting these final values in the general moment equation, we have:

Joint A:

$$M_{AB} = 21.101 - \frac{8.255}{2} - 43 = -26.02,$$

$$M_{AD} = 21.101 + \frac{9.897}{2} = 26.04;$$

Joint B:

$$M_{BA} = -8.255 + \frac{21.101}{2} + 43 = 45.3,$$

$$M_{BC} = 2(-8.255 + 0) - 18 = -34.51,$$

$$M_{BE} = 8.255 - \frac{4.967}{2} = -10.74;$$

Joint C:

$$M_{CB} = 2\left(0 - \frac{8.255}{2}\right) + 18 = 9.74,$$

$$M_{CB'} = 2\left(0 + \frac{8.255}{2}\right) - 18 = -9.74,$$

$$M_{CF} = 0 + 0 = 0;$$

Joint D:

$$M_{DA} = 9.897 + \frac{21.101}{2} = 20.44,$$

$$M_{DE} = 2\left(9.897 - \frac{4.967}{2}\right) - 55 = -40.17,$$

$$M_{DG} = 2(9.897 + 0) = 19.79;$$

Joint E:

$$M_{EB} = -4.967 - \frac{8.255}{2} = -9.09,$$

$$M_{ED} = 2\left(-4.967 + \frac{9.897}{2}\right) + 55 = 54.96,$$

$$M_{EF} = 3(-4.967 + 0) - 21 = -35.90,$$

$$M_{EH} = 2(-4.967 + 0) - -9.93;$$

Joint F:

$$M_{FC} = 0 + 0 = 0,$$

$$M_{FE} = 3\left(0 - \frac{4.967}{2}\right) + 21 = 13.55,$$

$$M_{FE'} = 3\left(0 + \frac{4.967}{2}\right) - 21 = -13.55,$$

$$M_{FI} = 2(0 + 0) = 0;$$

Base G:

$$M_{GD} = 2\left(0 + \frac{9.897}{2}\right) = 9.90;$$

Base H:

$$M_{HE} = 2\left(0 - \frac{4.967}{2}\right) = -4.97;$$

Base I:

$$M_{IF} = 2(0 + 0) = 0.$$

35. Moment Distribution Method.—In the preceding solution, the moments at the ends of the members were determined only after obtaining the final values of the deflection angles at the joints. Obviously this is the shortest way for arriving at the final results. However, the moments may be computed at the end of each cycle of operation. Thus, using the initial values of the deflection angles, we can compute the first approximate values of the moments; and from each set of angle increments, the corresponding increments or corrections of the moments. This constitutes the basis of the well-known method of "Moment Distribution." [1] To illustrate, consider again the bent

---

[1] "Analysis of Continuous Frames by Distributing Fixed End Moments" by Prof. Hardy Cross. Trans. A. S. C. E., Vol. 96, 1932.

shown in Fig. 63. For the initial values at the joint B, for example, we have:

$$M_{BA1} = FM_{BA} + K_1\left(\alpha_1 \text{ of } B + \frac{1}{2}\alpha_1 \text{ of } A\right)$$

$$= FM_{BA} - \frac{K_1}{K_1+K_2+K_4}(FM_{BA}+FM_{BC}) - \frac{K_1 FM_{AB}}{2(K_1+K_3)};$$

$$M_{BC1} = FM_{BC} - \frac{K_2}{K_1+K_2+K_4}(FM_{BA}+FM_{BC}) + 0;$$

$$M_{BE1} = 0 - \frac{K_4}{K_1+K_2+K_4}(FM_{BA}+FM_{BC}) - \frac{K_4(FM_{ED}+FM_{EF})}{2(K_4+K_6+K_7+K_9)}.$$

$$\left.\phantom{\rule{0pt}{10em}}\right\}\ .\ .\ (80)$$

These first moment values in eqs. (80) may be considered as the algebraic sum of three quantities:

(1) The fixed-end moment of the member;
(2) A portion of the unbalanced moment, or the algebraic sum of fixed-end moments at the joint, with the sign reversed, obtained by distributing the unbalanced moment among the members of the joint—in direct ratio of their stiffness; and
(3) One-half the value at the opposite end of the member, obtained as in (2).

The foregoing constitutes the first step of the method. The next step consists in computing moment increments, or corrections, from the increments of the deflection angles. The angle B, for instance, receives first increments from the two adjacent joints A and E. (The joint C does not contribute an increment, since the value of the deflection angle remains zero.) Accordingly, the first moment increments at the joint B are:

$$M_{BA2} = K_1\left(\alpha_2 \text{ of } B + \frac{1}{2}\alpha_2 \text{ of } A\right),$$

$$= -\frac{K_1^2 . \alpha_1 \text{ of } A}{2(K_1+K_2+K_4)} - \frac{K_1 K_4 . \alpha_1 \text{ of } E}{2(K_1+K_2+K_4)} - \frac{K_1 K_3 . \alpha_1 \text{of } D}{4(K_1+K_3)} - \frac{K_1^2 . \alpha_1 \text{ of } B}{4(K_1+K_3)}$$

$$= -\frac{K_1}{K_1+K_2+K_4}(M_{AB1-3}+M_{EB1-3}) - \frac{K_1}{2(K_1+K_3)}(M_{DA1-3}+M_{BA1-3})$$

$$= -\frac{K_1}{K_1+K_2+K_4}(M_{AB1-3}+M_{EB1-3}) - \frac{1}{2}M_{AB2-1},$$

$$M_{BC2} = -\frac{K_2}{K_1+K_2+K_4}(M_{AB1-3}+M_{EB1-3}) + 0,$$

$$M_{BE2} = -\frac{K_4}{K_1+K_2+K_4}(M_{AB1-3}+M_{EB1-3}) - \frac{1}{2}M_{EB2-1}.$$

$$\left.\phantom{\rule{0pt}{8em}}\right\}\ .\ .\ .\ .\ .\ .\ (81)$$

where M_{AB1-3} indicates the third component of the first moment value at end A of member AB, and M_{AB2-1}, the first component of the first increment of M_{AB}. As in the first step, the two terms in each of eqs. (81) may simply be defined thus:

(1) An increment obtained by balancing the third components of the first moments at the adjacent joints, and

(2) An increment equal to one-half the value at the opposite end of the member, computed as in (1).

Other increments or corrections are obtained merely by repeating this second step. Since all values in their final form are functions of the end moments, the routine computations are usually indicated on a sketch of the frame—drawn to some convenient scale and providing sufficient space for the number of corrections contemplated. For illustration, the solution of the end moments of the bent shown in Fig. 63, in accordance with this arrangement, is shown in Fig. 64.

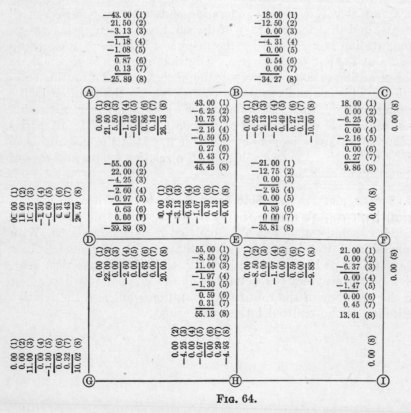

FIG. 64.

The first figure at the end of each member—written parallel to the direction of the member—represents the fixed-end moment. Figures marked (2) are obtained by distributing the unbalanced fixed-end moment at each joint and changing the signs. Figures marked (3) are one-half the balanced moments (2), carried from one end of a member to the other. The sums of these first three figures represent the first approximate end moments at the joints. Figures marked (4) are obtained by distributing or balancing moments (3); and the underlined figures marked (5) are the one-half "carried-over" moments from (4), thus completing the second cycle of the computation and resulting in the first correction of the initial moment values. Figures marked (6) and (7) complete the third cycle of the operation or the second correction. The last figures, marked (8) on the diagram and obtained by summing up the preceding (7) lines of figures, indicate the final moments—corresponding to two cycles of corrections.

Unlike the usual procedure of the method, it is to be noted from the diagram that each cycle of operation ends with the "carried-over" moments, and that the accuracy of the solution at each cycle or stage of computation is measured by the degree of balance of summed-up moments at the end of that cycle. Division of cycles in this manner furnishes an important check upon the accuracy of the routine computations. This is readily seen by comparison to the solution in the preceding method, in which moments were obtained from deflection angles, each cycle of correction of moments shown in Fig. 64 corresponding to an angle increment in Table 3. It is also interesting to note, by comparing the two solutions, the relative length and ease of computation of each method.

36. Rectangular Frames, Side Sway Neglected.—When an unsymmetrical bent contains more than 3 bays, side sway due to vertical loading is generally small and often omitted from computations. With the omission of the deflection factor, the solution of moments in a frame of this type becomes identical with that of a symmetrical bent. Obviously, the accuracy of results thus obtained is not only dependent upon the accuracy of the routine computations, but also the relative magnitudes of the omitted lateral deflections.

PROBLEMS

21. The bent shown in Fig. 65 is subjected to a system of symmetrical vertical loading. Assuming the legs fixed at the bases, determine the factors of correction for joints A, B, E and F.

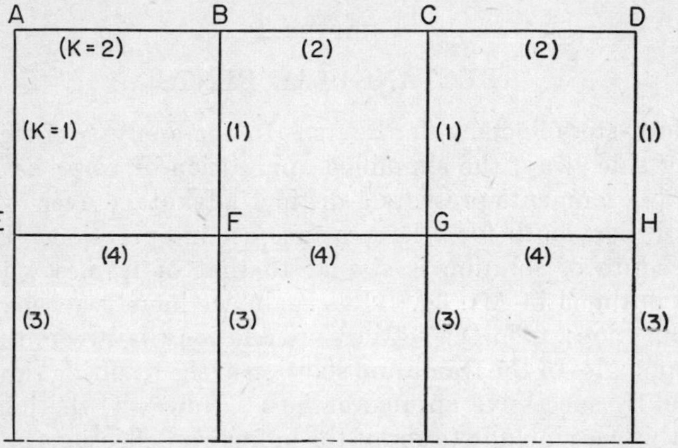

FIG. 65.

22. The bent shown in Fig. 63 is assumed to be hinged at the bases. Obtain the end moments, performing three corrections.

PART III. FRAMES INVOLVING SIDE SWAY

CHAPTER I

RECTANGULAR BENTS

37. Multi-story Rectangular Bents.—In the analysis of rigid frames involving side sway, the simplified application of *slope deflection* for determining moments presents a distinct advantage over other methods of solution, both for briefness and ease in operation. In general, the procedure of solution is similar to that of frames without side sway, as outlined in Art. 34. Here again, we have two separate steps of computation; namely, setting up relations between the various deflection angles of the frame and solution of the resulting simultaneous equations by successive approximations. However, the joint expressions in this case include terms of the unknown deflections and in order to reduce these equations to the general form containing only deflection angles and load constants, it becomes necessary, as an additional step, to first eliminate these terms from the expressions. This is accomplished by substituting for deflections in the joint expressions their values, in terms of the deflection angles and the load constants, obtained from the shear equation of each story. To illustrate, consider the bent shown in Fig. 66. The joint expression at D, for

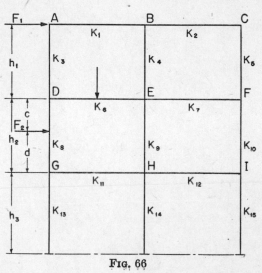

FIG. 66

example, obtained by summing up end moments of the members meeting at that joint is in the form

$$(K_3+K_6+K_8)D+K_3\frac{A}{2}+K_6\frac{E}{2}+K_8\frac{G}{2}-K_3R_1-K_8R_2+FM_D=0, \quad (82)$$

where R_1 and R_2 denote the deflections of the top and middle stories, and FM_D the algebraic sum of fixed-end moments $(FM_{DE}+FM_{DG})$ at D. The shear expressions of these two stories are given by the equations

$$M_{AD}+M_{DA}+M_{BE}+M_{EB}+M_{CF}+M_{FC}=1.5[K_3(A+D)$$
$$+K_4(B+E)+K_5(C+F)]-2(K_3+K_4+K_5)R_1=-F_1h_1 \quad . \quad (83)$$

and

$$M_{DG}+M_{GD}+M_{EH}+M_{HE}+M_{FI}+M_{IF}=1.5[K_8(D+G)$$
$$+K_{10}(F+I)]-2(K_8+K_9+K_{10})R_2+1.5K_9(E+H)$$
$$+FM_{DG}+FM_{GD}=-F_1h_2-F_2d; \quad . \quad . \quad . \quad . \quad . \quad . \quad . \quad . \quad (83a)$$

from which

$$R_1=\frac{3}{4}\left[\frac{K_3(A+D)+K_4(B+E)+K_5(C+F)}{K_3+K_4+K_5}\right]+\frac{F_1h_1}{2(K_3+K_4+K_5)}, \quad (84)$$

$$_2=\frac{3}{4}\left[\frac{K_8(D+G)+K_9(E+H)+K_{10}(F+I)}{K_8+K_9+K_{10}}\right]$$

$$+\frac{FM_{DG}+FM_{GD}+F_1h_2+F_2d}{2(K_8+K_9+K_{10})} \quad . \quad . \quad . \quad . \quad . \quad . \quad . \quad (84a)$$

Substituting these values of R_1 and R_2 in eq. (82), we have:

$$\left[K_3+K_6+K_8-\frac{3K_3^2}{4(K_3+K_4+K_5)}-\frac{3K_8^2}{4(K_8+K_9+K_{10})}\right]D$$

$$+\left[\frac{K_3}{2}-\frac{3K_3^2}{4(K_3+K_4+K_5)}\right]A-\frac{3K_3K_4}{4(K_3+K_4+K_5)}B$$

$$-\frac{3K_3K_5}{4(K_3+K_4+K_5)}C+\left[\frac{K_6}{2}-\frac{3K_3K_4}{4(K_3+K_4+K_5)}-\frac{3K_8K_9}{4(K_8+K_9+K_{10})}\right]E$$

$$-\left[\frac{3K_3K_5}{4(K_3+K_4+K_5)}+\frac{3K_8K_{10}}{4(K_8+K_9+K_{10})}\right]F$$

$$+\left[\frac{K_8}{2}-\frac{3K_8^2}{4(K_8+K_9+K_{10})}\right]G-\frac{3K_8K_9}{4(K_8+K_9+K_{10})}H$$

$$-\frac{3K_8K_{10}}{4(K_8+K_9+K_{10})}I+FM_D-\frac{K_3F_{11}h}{2(K_3+K+_4K_5)}$$

$$-\frac{K_8(FM_{DG}+FM_{GD}+F_1h_2+F_2d)}{2(K_8+K_9+K_{10})}=0 \quad . \quad . \quad . \quad . \quad . \quad . \quad . \quad . \quad (85)$$

Eq. (85) is the general joint expression for a rectangular bent with side sway, resulting from lateral loading, or dissymmetry of vertical loading or framing. It gives the typical relation existing between the deflection angle of a joint under consideration and those of the other joints in the two neighboring stories directly affecting its value. Unlike the joint expression of a bent without side sway, in which the relation is between adjacent joints only, here we find interdependency between all the joints of two adjacent stories. Despite its length, this equation is of a simple form and can easily be memorized. To formulate rules of construction, the various terms involved may be divided into three groups:

(a) The coefficient of the joint under consideration;
(b) The coefficients of the other joints of the two adjacent stories;
(c) The load constants.

Now, let F_D denote the sum of stiffness ratios of members forming the joint; K_{sa} the sum of the stiffness ratios of vertical members in the story above the joint; K_{sb} the sum of the stiffness ratios of vertical members in the story below the joint; and K_a and K_b the respective stiffness ratios of the vertical member directly above and below the joint. With these notations, for the joint coefficient at D we can write:

$$f_D = F_D - \frac{3K_a^2}{4K_{sa}} - \frac{3K_b^2}{4K_{sb}} \quad \cdots \cdots \cdot (86)$$

The forms of coefficients (b) vary in accordance with their positions relative to the joint under consideration, as shown diagrammatically in Fig. 67. If the joint is adjacent vertically (A and G in this case),

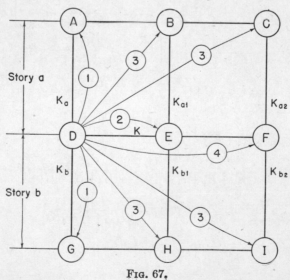

Fig. 67.

then the coefficient has the form

$$f_{1a} = \frac{K_a}{2} - \frac{3K_a^2}{4K_{sa}},$$

or

$$f_{1b} = \frac{K_b}{2} - \frac{3K_b^2}{4K_{sb}}. \qquad \right\} \qquad \dots\dots\dots (87)$$

If the joint is adjacent horizontally, such as E, the coefficient is in the form

$$f_2 = \frac{K}{2} - \frac{3K_a K_{a1}}{4K_{sa}} - \frac{3K_b K_{b1}}{4K_{sb}} \qquad \dots\dots (87a)$$

in which K indicates the stiffness ratio of the member between the two joints. For joints located diagonally, as shown by the arrows marked (3) in the diagram,

$$f_{3a} = - \frac{3K_a K_{u1}}{4K_{sa}},$$

or

$$f_{3b} = - \frac{3K_b K_{b1}}{4K_{sb}}. \qquad \right\} \qquad \dots\dots\dots (87b)$$

And, lastly, if the joint is non-adjacent but located on the same floor line, as F in Fig. 67, we have:

$$f_4 = - \frac{3K_a K_{a2}}{4K_{sa}} - \frac{3K_b K_{b2}}{4K_{sb}} \qquad \dots\dots (87c)$$

The load constants of the equation may be expressed in the more condensed form, and with symbol Q,

$$Q_D = FM_D - \frac{K_a H_a h_a}{2K_{sa}} - \frac{K_b H_b h_b}{2K_{sb}} - \frac{K_a FM_{sa}}{2K_{sa}} - \frac{K_b FM_{sb}}{2K_{sb}}, \quad \cdot \quad (88)$$

in which h and H indicate, respectively, the height and the total shear of the story, and FM_s the algebraic sum of fixed-end moments, that is, the fixed-end moments of the vertical members in each story when the lateral load is applied between the panel points.

It is interesting to note that by omitting all the negative terms in eq. (85), it reduces to the typical form of joint expression of a frame without side sway. Obviously, the same difference will appear in the respective forms of the coefficients of correction for the two cases of analysis.

Having obtained the typical joint expression, the second step of the computation, namely, the routine solution of the simultaneous equations thus resulting, is carried through in the usual tabular form, as illustrated in the following example.

ILLUSTRATIVE EXAMPLE

The three-story bent shown in Fig. 68 is subjected to a single lateral load of 4 kips, applied at the top panel. The framing is symmetrical and the legs are assumed to be fixed at the bases. Determine:

    (*a*) The coefficients of correction;

    (*b*) The values of the deflection angles;

    (*c*) The values of the deflection;

    (*d*) The moments at the joints.

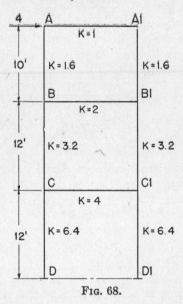

Fig. 68.

Solution: (*a*) Due to symmetry of framing, the deflection angles at joints *A*, *B* and *C* equal, respectively, those at *A*1, *B*1 and *C*1. The various factors *f* and *Q* for these three joints, obtained from eq. (85) or eqs. (87), are as follows:

Joint *A*:

$$f_A = 2.6 + \frac{1}{2} - 2 \times \frac{3}{8} \times 1.6 = 1.9;$$

$$f_b = \frac{1.6}{2} - 2 \times \frac{3}{8} \times 1.6 = -0.4;$$

$$f_{BA} = -\frac{f_b}{f_A} = -\left(\frac{-0.4}{1.9}\right) = 0.2105;$$

$$Q_A = -\frac{4 \times 10}{2 \times 2} = -10 \text{ ft.-kips.}$$

Joint B:

$$f_B = 6.8 + 1 - \frac{3}{4}(1.6 + 3.2) = 4\ 2;$$

$$f_a = -\frac{1.6}{4} = -0.4; \quad f_c = -\frac{3.2}{4} = -0.8;$$

$$f_{AB} = \frac{0.4}{4.2} = 0.0952; \quad f_{CB} = \frac{0.8}{4.2} = 0.1904;$$

$$Q_B = -\frac{4 \times 10}{4} - \frac{4 \times 12}{4} = -22 \text{ ft.-kips.}$$

Joint C:

$$f_C = 13.6 + 2 - \frac{3}{4}(3.2 + 6.4) = 8.4;$$

$$f_b = -\frac{3.2}{4} = -0.8;$$

$$f_{BC} = \frac{0.8}{8.4} = 0.0952;$$

$$Q_C = -\frac{4 \times 12}{4} - \frac{4 \times 12}{4} = -24 \text{ ft.-kips.}$$

(b) The values of the deflection angles, corresponding to four cycles of corrections, are shown in the last space of Table 4.

TABLE 4.
(For Bent shown in Fig. 68)

		A	B	C
1	f	$f_{AB} = 0.0952$	$f_{BA} = 0.2105$ $f_{BC} = 0.0952$	$f_{CB} = 0.1904$
2	α_1	5.263	5.238	2.857
3	$f\alpha_1$	1.103	0.501 0.544	0.499
4	α_2	1.103	1.045	0.499
5	$f\alpha_2$	0.220	0.105 0.095	0.099
6	α_3	0.220	0.200	0.099
7	$f\alpha_3$	0.042	0.021 0.019	0.019
8	α_4	0.042	0.040	0.019
9	$f\alpha_4$	0.008	0.004 0.004	0.004
10	α_5	0.008	0.008	0.004
11	α	6.636	6.531	3.478

(c) By substituting values of deflection angles in eqs. (84) and (84a), we obtain:

$$R_{AB} = \frac{3}{4}(6.636 + 6.531) + \frac{4 \times 10}{4 \times 1.6} = 16.126,$$

$$R_{BC} = \frac{3}{4}(6.531 + 3.477) + \frac{4 \times 12}{4 \times 3.2} = 11.257,$$

$$R_{CD} = \frac{3}{4}(3.478 + 0) \quad + \frac{4 \times 12}{4 \times 6.4} = 4.484.$$

(d) Moments:

Joint A:

$$M_{AA1} = 1(1.5 \times 6.636) = 9.954 \text{ ft.-kips},$$

$$M_{AB} = 1.6(6.636 + 3.266 - 16.126) = -9.959 \text{ ft.-kips};$$

Joint B:

$$M_{BA} = 1.6(6.531 + 3.318 - 16.126) = -10.043 \text{ ft.-kips},$$

$$M_{BC} = 3.2(6.531 + 1.739 - 11.257) = -9.558,$$

$$M_{BB1} = 2(1.5 \times 6.531) = 19.593;$$

Joint C:

$$M_{CB} = 3.2(3.478 + 3.266 - 11.257) = -14.442,$$

$$M_{CD} = 6.4(3.478 + 0 - 4.484) = -6.438,$$

$$M_{CC1} = 4(1.5 \times 3.478) = 20.868;$$

Base D:

$$M_{DC} = 6.4(0 + 1.739 - 4.484) = -17.568.$$

38. Single-story Rectangular Bents.—In the case of single-story rectangular bents of more than three bays, subjected to lateral loading applied at the top, an alternate method of solution, similar to that of frames without side sway, may result in further simplification in the computations. The procedure is as follows:

    (a) Considering the deflection term as the load constant of the joint equation, obtain values of deflection angles of the bent in terms of the common R, as if there were no side sway;

    (b) Determine the value of R from the shear expression of the bent; and

    (c) Obtain the final deflection angles by substituting the value of R in (a).

With this procedure, the number of coefficients of correction for a joint, and, consequently, the number of multiplications required in each cycle of correction, is reduced to a maximum of two, as compared to the total of joints in the bent, which is the number of necessary operations per joint and per cycle if the method of Art. 37 is directly applied. The bent shown in Fig. 69 will serve as an illustration.

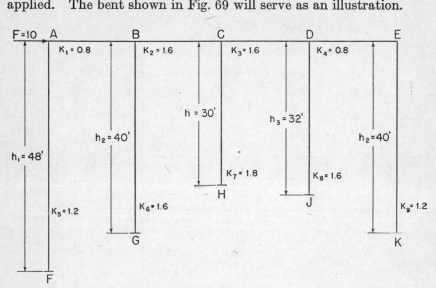

FIG. 69.

Since the true lateral deflection Δ is the same at all joints at the top (effect of axial shortenings being neglected), then for deflections $R\left(=\dfrac{6E\Delta}{h}\right)$ of the vertical members, expressed in terms of R of the shortest leg of the bent, we have:

$$R_{AF}=a_1R, \quad R_{DG}=R_{EK}=a_2R, \quad R_{DJ}=a_3R;$$

in which, $\qquad a_1=\dfrac{h}{h_1}, \quad a_2=\dfrac{h}{h_2}, \quad a_3=\dfrac{h}{h_3}.$

The typical joint expression, written at joint B, for example, is in the form, assuming the legs to be fixed at the bases,

$$(K_1+K_2+K_6)B+K_1\frac{A}{2}+K_2\frac{C}{2}-a_2K_6R=0 \quad . \quad . \quad . \quad . \quad (89)$$

The coefficients of correction at the same joint are:

$$f_{AB}\ (\text{from } A \text{ to } B)=-\frac{K_1}{2(K_1+K_2+K_6)}=-\frac{0.8}{8}=-0.1;$$

$$f_{CB}\ (\text{from } C \text{ to } B)=-\frac{1.6}{8}=-0.2.$$

And the first approximate value of B equals

$$\alpha_{1B} = \frac{a_2 K_6 R}{K_1 + K_2 + K_6} = \frac{0.75 \times 1.6R}{4} = 0.3R.$$

The remainder of computations is given in Table 5.

TABLE 5.

(For Bent shown in Fig. 69)

		A	B	C	D	E
1	f	$f_{AB}=-0.10$	$f_{BA}=-0.20$ $f_{BC}=-0.16$	$f_{CB}=-0.20$ $f_{CD}=-0.20$	$f_{DC}=-0.16$ $f_{DE}=-0.20$	$f_{ED}=-0.10$
2	α_1	0. 375R	0. 30R	0. 30R	0. 375R	0. 450R
3	$f\alpha_1$	−0. 06	−0. 0375 −0. 072	−0. 048 −0. 06	−0. 072 −0. 045	−0. 075
4	α_2	−0. 06	−0. 1095	−0. 108	−0. 117	−0. 075
5	$f\alpha_2$	0. 0219	0. 006 0. 0216	0. 0175 0. 0187	0. 0216 0. 0075	0. 0234
6	α_3	0. 0219	0. 2076	0. 0362	0. 0291	0. 0234
7	$f\alpha_3$	−0. 0055	−0. 0022 −0. 0072	−0. 0044 −0. 0046	−0. 0072 −0. 0023	−0. 0058
8	α_4	−0. 0055	−0. 0094	−0. 0090	−0. 0095	−0. 0058
9	$f\alpha_4$	0. 0019	0. 0006 0. 0018	0. 0015 0. 0015	0. 0018 0. 0006	0. 0019
10	α_5	0. 0019	0. 0024	0. 0030	0. 0024	0. 0019
11	a_R	0. 3333R	0. 2111R	0. 2822R	0. 2800R	0. 3945R

The shear expression for a bent of this type, with the legs fixed at the bases, has the form

$$1.5\left(K_5\frac{A}{h_1} + K_6\frac{B}{h_2} + K_7\frac{C}{h} + K_8\frac{D}{h_3} + K_9\frac{E}{h_2} \right)$$

$$-2R\left(K_5\frac{a_1}{h_1} + K_6\frac{a_2}{h_2} + K_7\frac{1}{h} + K_8\frac{a_3}{h_3} + K_9\frac{a_2}{h_2} \right) = -F \quad \ldots \quad (90)$$

or, substituting for the deflection angles their αR values,

$$2R\left[\frac{K_5}{h_1}(\tfrac{3}{4}\alpha_A - a_1) + \frac{K_6}{h_2}(\tfrac{3}{4}\alpha_B - a_2) + \frac{K_7}{h}(\tfrac{3}{4}\alpha_C - 1) + \frac{K_8}{h_3}(\tfrac{3}{4}\alpha_D - a_3) \right.$$

$$\left. + \frac{K_9}{h_2}(\tfrac{3}{4}\alpha_B - a_2) \right] = -F \quad \ldots \ldots \ldots \ldots \quad (91)$$

Substituting the numerical values for the terms a, K, h and α (as given in the last space of Table 5) in eq. (91), and solving for R,

$$R = 38.40$$

Then, for the final values of deflection angles and deflections we have:

.	A	B	C	D	E
α	12. 80	8. 10	10. 84	10. 75	15. 14
R	24. 00	28. 80	38. 40	36. 00	28. 80

PROBLEMS

23. The lateral load shown in Fig. 68 is applied midway between the joints A and B. Assuming the legs fixed at the bases, obtain the joint coefficients, coefficients of corrections and the load constants of the bent.

24. Derive the shear expression corresponding to eq. (91) for the bent shown in Fig. 69 with the legs assumed to be hinged at the bases.

Chapter II

TRAPEZOIDAL BENTS

39. Single-story Trapezoidal Bents.—When one or both vertical members of a rectangular panel are given certain inclinations, thus forming a trapezoidal panel, the lateral sway of these members will then produce corresponding deflections in the horizontal members. The single-story bents shown in Fig. 70 represent the simplest types

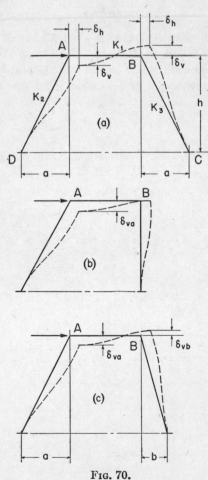

Fig. 70.

of a trapezoidal frame. In each case the panel is composed of a top horizontal and two leg members. The legs of the bent shown in Fig. 70 (a) have the same stiffness and inclination; the bent in (b) has one vertical and one sloping leg; and that in (c) illustrates the more general case of two legs with different inclinations. If the legs are assumed to be retained in position at the bases, that is, when there is no spread or settlement at the bases, then the deflections of the members, due to a lateral force or an unsymmetrical vertical loading, will conform to the exaggerated deformation outlines (shown with dotted lines) in the figure. Because of symmetry, the two legs of the bent in Fig. 70 (a) will have the same deflection. In swaying, the horizontal deflection δ_h of the left leg is accompanied by a vertical downward displacement δ_v, while that of the right leg causes an upward deflection of the same magnitude.

The vertical components of the displacements of the two upper joints in Fig. 70 (c) differ for the two sides, in accordance with the geometry of the figure. This geometric relation between component displacements is shown in Fig. 71, illustrating the deformation of an

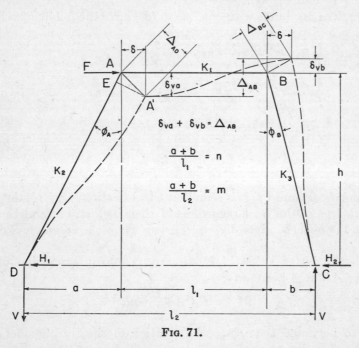

FIG. 71.

unsymmetrical trapezoidal panel subjected to a clockwise sway. Since the deflections resulting from axial stresses are neglected, the horizontal displacement of the joint A must equal that at the joint B.

With sufficient accuracy, the distance $\overline{AA'}$, representing the diagonal displacement of the joint A, may be considered as the true deflection of the leg AD. (By definition, the true deflection of the member AD is measured by the distance $\overline{A'E}$, normal to the unstrained position of the leg; however, the error involved in substituting the chord for the sine distance of a small angle is negligible.) Denoting this displacement by Δ_{AD}, we have:

$$\Delta_{AD} = \delta.\sec \phi_A; \quad \ldots \ldots \ldots \ldots \quad (a)$$

and for vertical component of the displacement,

$$\delta_{va} = \delta. \tan \phi_A = \Delta_{AD} \sin \phi_A \ldots \ldots \ldots \quad (b)$$

Similarly, at the joint B we have:

$$\Delta_{BC} = \delta.\sec \phi_B; \quad \ldots \ldots \ldots \ldots \ldots \quad (c)$$

$$\delta_{vb} = \delta.\tan \phi_B = \Delta_{BC} \sin \phi_B \ldots \ldots \ldots \quad (d)$$

The deflection terms R of the end moment expressions, equaling $6E$ times $\dfrac{\Delta}{l}$ (true deflection divided by the length) ratios of each member, in accordance with eqs. (a) to (d), have the following relative values:

$$\frac{1}{6E}R_{AD} = \frac{\Delta_{AD}}{l_{AD}} = \frac{\delta}{l_{AD}} \sec \phi_A = \frac{\delta}{h}; \quad \ldots \ldots \ldots \quad (e)$$

$$\frac{1}{6E}R_{BC} = \frac{\Delta_{BC}}{l_{BC}} = \frac{\delta}{l_{BC}} \sec \phi_B = \frac{\delta}{h}; \quad \ldots \ldots \ldots \quad (f)$$

$$\frac{1}{6E}R_{AB} = \frac{\Delta_{AB}}{l_{AB}} = \frac{\delta_{va}+\delta_{vb}}{l_{AB}} = \frac{\delta}{l_1} (\tan \phi_A + \tan \phi_B) = n\frac{\delta}{h}; \ldots \quad (g)$$

where

$$n = \frac{a+b}{l_1} = \frac{l_2-l_1}{l_1}.$$

From eqs. (e) and (f) it is seen that the deflection term R is the same for both legs of the bent regardless of their inclination; and that for the top member, as given by eq. (g), is n times the common R of the legs.

With the latter value of R, the end moment expression of the member AB at A becomes

$$M_{AB} = K_1\left(A + \frac{B}{2} + nR\right) \ldots \ldots \ldots \quad (92)$$

(It is to be noted that since the rotation of the top member is in opposite direction to that of the legs, the deflection term in eq. (92)

is given a plus sign, in lieu of the minus sign as used in the fundamental moment expression for an assumed clockwise rotation.)

The end moment expression for the legs does not differ from that of vertical members in rectangular panels. If the legs are assumed to be fixed at the bases, then the moment equation at A, for example, corresponding to a lateral force F at the same joint, is in the familiar form

$$M_{AD} = K_2(A - R).$$

And, in the case of hinged bases,

$$M_{AD} = K_2\left(\frac{3}{4}A - \frac{R}{2}\right).$$

Then, for the joint expression at A, with the bases fixed, we have:

$$(K_1 + K_2)A + \frac{K_1}{2}B + (nK_1 - K_2)R = 0; \quad \ldots \ldots \quad (93)$$

and, when the bases are hinged,

$$\left(K_1 + \frac{3}{4}K_2\right)A + \frac{K_1}{2}B + \left(nK_1 - \frac{K_2}{2}\right)R = 0 \quad \ldots \ldots \quad (94)$$

In writing the shear expression of the panel, we must consider both vertical and horizontal reactions at the bases. Denoting the former by V, in the case of hinged bases,

$$V = \frac{Fh}{l_2}; \quad \ldots \ldots \ldots \ldots \ldots \quad (h)$$

and, if the bases are fixed, its value may be obtained from the relation

$$M_{DA} + M_{CB} = Vl_2 - Fh. \quad \ldots \ldots \ldots \ldots \quad (k)$$

Accordingly, for the shear expression of the panel shown in Fig. 71, we have:

$$M_{AD} + M_{DA} + M_{BC} + M_{CB} = V(a + b) - Fh;$$

or,

$$M_{AD} + (1 - m)M_{DA} + M_{BC} + (1 - m)M_{CB} = (m - 1)Fh \quad \ldots \quad (95)$$

Substituting moment values in eq. (95), the shear expressions for the two conditions of support become:

(a) For fixed bases,

$$\left(\frac{3 - m}{2}\right)K_2A + \left(\frac{3 - m}{2}\right)K_3B - (2 - m)(K_2 + K_3)R = (m - 1)Fh. \quad (96)$$

(b) For hinged bases,

$$\frac{3}{4}K_2A + \frac{3}{4}K_3B - \frac{1}{2}(K_2 + K_3)R = (m - 1)Fh. \quad \ldots \quad (97)$$

from which

$$R_f = \frac{(3-m)(K_2A+K_3B)}{2(2-m)(K_2+K_3)} + \frac{(1-m)Fh}{(2-m)(K_2+K_3)}, \quad \cdots \quad (98)$$

$$R_h = \frac{3(K_2A+K_3B)}{2(K_2+K_3)} + \frac{2(1-m)Fh}{(K_2+K_3)} \quad \cdots \cdots \cdots (99)$$

Substituting these values for R in eqs. (93) and (94), the final form of the respective joint expression is obtained. Thus, for fixed bases,

$$\left[K_1+K_2+\frac{(3-m)(nK_1-K_2)K_2}{2(2-m)(K_2+K_3)}\right]A + \left[\frac{K_1}{2}+\frac{(3-m)(nK_1-K_2)K_3}{2(2-m)(K_2+K_3)}\right]B$$
$$= -\frac{(1-m)(nK_1-K_2)Fh}{(2-m)(K_2+K_3)}; \quad \cdots \cdots \cdots \cdots (100)$$

and, for hinged bases,

$$\left[K_1+\frac{3}{4}K_2+\frac{3(2nK_1-K_2)K_2}{4(K_2+K_3)}\right]A + \left[\frac{K_1}{2}+\frac{3(2nK_1-K_2)K_3}{4(K_2+K_3)}\right]B$$
$$= -\frac{(2nK_1-K_2)(1-m)Fh}{(K_2+K_3)} \quad \cdots \cdots \cdots \cdots (101)$$

Since these expressions contain only two unknowns, the values of the deflection angles are readily determined by simultaneous solution of the two joint equations of the bent, as illustrated in the following examples.

ILLUSTRATIVE EXAMPLES

1. The symmetrical bent shown in Fig. 72 is subjected to a lateral force of 8 kips, applied at the joint A. Assuming the legs to be fixed at the bases, determine the end moments.

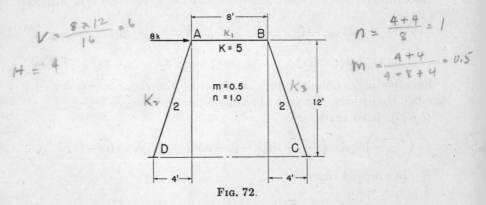

FIG. 72.

Solution: Due to the symmetry of the bent, the deflection angle at A equals that at B. The value of this single unknown is then obtained from eq. (100):

$$\left(1.5\times5+2+\frac{2.5\times3\times2}{1.5\times4}\right)A=-\frac{0.5\times3\times8\times12}{1.5\times4},$$

$$A=-\frac{24}{12}=-2.$$

Applying eq. (98),

$$R=-\frac{2.5\times2\times4}{2\times1.5\times4}+\frac{0.5\times8\times12}{1.5\times4}=\frac{19}{3}.$$

The end moments at the joint A are:

$$M_{AB}=5\left(-1.5\times2+\frac{19}{3}\right)=\frac{50}{3},$$

$$M_{AD}=2\left(-2-\frac{19}{3}\right)=-\frac{50}{3};$$

and at the base D,

$$M_{DA}=2\left(-1-\frac{19}{3}\right)=-\frac{44}{3}.$$

2. The lateral force of Fig. 72 is replaced with a vertical load of the same magnitude, applied 2 feet from the joint A, Fig. 73. Assuming again the bases to be fixed, determine the end moments.

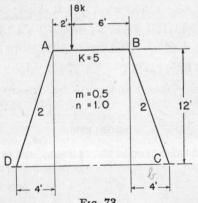

FIG. 73.

Solution: Since the load is eccentric, the bent will sway laterally. With due consideration to the changes of the load constants in the shear and joint expressions, eqs. (98) and (100), become, respectively:

$$R_f=\frac{(3-m)(K_2A+K_3B)}{2(2-m)(K_2+K_3)}+\frac{(me-b)P}{(2-m)(K_2+K_3)};\quad\ldots\ (98a)$$

and

$$\left[K_1+K_2+\frac{(3-m)(nK_1-K_2)K_2}{2(2-m)(K_2+K_3)}\right]A+\left[\frac{K_1}{2}+\frac{(3-m)(nK_1-K_2)K_3}{2(2-m)(K_2+K_3)}\right]B$$

$$=-FM_{AB}-\frac{(me-b)(nK_1-K_2)P}{(2-m)(K_2+K_3)}\quad\ldots\ldots\ (100a)$$

in which P is the vertical load and e its distance from the right base. The joint equations at A and B become:

$$\left(5+2+\frac{2.5\times3\times2}{2\times1.5\times4}\right)A+\left(2.5+\frac{2.5\times3\times2}{2\times1.5\times4}\right)B=9-\frac{1\times3\times8}{1.5\times4},$$

$$\left(5+2+\frac{2.5\times3\times2}{2\times1.5\times4}\right)B+\left(2.5+\frac{2.5\times3\times2}{2\times1.5\times4}\right)A=-3-\frac{1\times3\times8}{1.5\times4};$$

or,

$$8.25A+3.75B=5,$$

$$3.75A+8.25B=-7.$$

Solving for A and B,

$$A=1.25;\quad B=-1.417;$$

and, applying eq. (98a),

$$R=\frac{2.5\times2(1.25-1.417)}{2\times1.5\times4}+\frac{1\times8}{1.5\times4}$$

$$=-0.07+1.333=1.263.$$

Substitution of these values in the moment equation of each member will result in the following end moments:

$$M_{AB}=5(1.25-0.708+1.263)-9=0.025 \text{ ft.-kips,}$$
$$M_{AD}=2(1.25-1.263)=-0.026 \text{ ft.-kips;}$$

$$M_{BA}=5(-1.417+0.625+1.263)+3=5.355 \text{ ft.-kips,}$$
$$M_{BC}=2(-1.417-1.263)=-5.36 \text{ ft.-kips;}$$

$$M_{DA}=2(0.625-1.263)=-1.276 \text{ ft.-kips;}$$

$$M_{CB}=2(-0.708-1.263)=-3.942 \text{ ft.-kips.}$$

PROBLEMS

25. The symmetrical bent shown in Fig. 74 is subjected to a uniform lateral load of 1 kip per vertical foot. Assuming the legs to be fixed at the bases, determine the end moments.

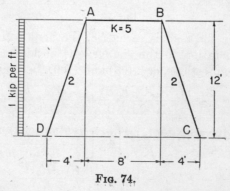

Fig. 74.

26. The bent shown in Fig. 75 is hinged to the bases.   Determine:

    (a) Moments at joints A and B;

    (b) Reactions at the bases.

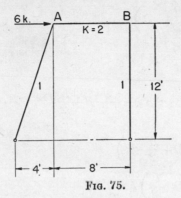

Fig. 75.

40. Single-story Bent with Bottom Member.—In the case of the closed panel, with a horizontal member both at top and bottom, the joint and shear expressions in Art. 39 are modified to include the effect of the added member.   As shown in Fig. 76, the top and leg

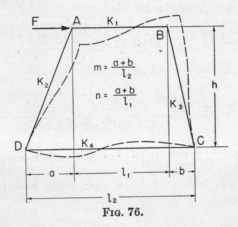

Fig. 76.

members are free to deflect under a lateral load, while the deflection R of the bottom member is dependent upon the relative position of the two lower joints.   If these joints are assumed to be hinged to unyielding supports, thus allowing them to rotate and yet preventing their relative displacement, then the deflection term of the bottom member DC reduces to zero.   The derivation of the top and bottom joint expressions, in accordance with this conception and for the loading shown in Fig. 76, follows:

Top joint A,

$$M_{AB}=K_1\left(A+\frac{B}{2}+nR\right)$$

$$M_{AD}=K_2\left(A+\frac{D}{2}-R\right)$$

$$M_{AB}+M_{AD}=(K_1+K_2)A+\frac{K_1}{2}B+\frac{K_2}{2}D+(nK_1-K_2)R=0 \ . \ \ (102)$$

Bottom joint D,

$$M_{DA}=K_2\left(D+\frac{A}{2}-R\right)$$

$$M_{DC}=K_4\left(D+\frac{C}{2}\right)$$

$$M_{DA}+M_{DC}=(K_2+K_4)D+\frac{K_2}{2}A+\frac{K_4}{2}C-K_2R=0 \ \ . \ . \ \ (103)$$

The shear expression of the panel, obtained by substituting the moment values in eq. (95), is in the form

$$\left(\frac{3-m}{2}\right)K_2A+\left(\frac{3-m}{2}\right)K_3B+\left(\frac{3-2m}{2}\right)K_2D+\left(\frac{3-2m}{2}\right)K_3C$$

$$-(2-m)(K_2+K_3)R=(m-1)Fh \ . \ . \ . \ . \ . \ . \ \ (104)$$

From which,

$$R=\frac{(3-m)(K_2A+K_3B)+(3-2m)(K_2D+K_3C)}{2(2-m)(K_2+K_3)}$$

$$+\frac{(1-m)Fh}{(2-m)(K_2+K_3)} \cdot \ . \ . \ . \ . \ . \ . \ . \ . \ . \ . \ \ (105)$$

Substituting this value of R in eqs. (102) and (103), the joint expressions become:

Joint A,

$$\left[K_1+K_2+\frac{(3-m)(nK_1-K_2)K_2}{2(2-m)(K_2+K_3)}\right]A+\left[\frac{K_1}{2}+\frac{(3-m)(nK_1-K_2)K_3}{2(2-m)(K_2+K_3)}\right]B$$

$$+\frac{(3-2m)(nK_1-K_2)K_3}{2(2-m)(K_2+K_3)}C+\left[\frac{K_2}{2}+\frac{(3-2m)(nK_1-K_2)K_2}{2(2-m)(K_2+K_3)}\right]D$$

$$+\frac{(1-m)(nK_1-K_2)Fh}{(2-m)(K_2+K_3)}=0 \ . \ . \ . \ . \ . \ . \ . \ . \ , \ , \ . \ . \ . \ \ (106)$$

Joint D,

$$\left[K_2+K_4-\frac{(3-2m)K_2^2}{2(2-m)(K_2+K_3)}\right]D+\left[\frac{K_2}{2}-\frac{(3-m)K_2^2}{2(2-m)(K_2+K_3)}\right]A$$

$$-\frac{(3-m)K_2K_3}{2(2-m)(K_2+K_3)}B+\left[\frac{K_4}{2}-\frac{(3-2m)K_2K_3}{2(2-m)(K_2+K_3)}\right]C$$

$$-\frac{(1-m)K_2Fh}{(2-m)(K_2+K_3)}=0 \quad . . . . \quad (107)$$

Similarly, at joint B,

$$\left[K_1+K_3+\frac{(3-m)(nK_1-K_3)K_3}{2(2-m)(K_2+K_3)}\right]B+\left[\frac{K_1}{2}+\frac{(3-m)(nK_1-K_3)K_2}{2(2-m)(K_2+K_3)}\right]A$$

$$+\frac{(3-2m)(nK_1-K_3)K_2}{2(2-m)(K_2+K_3)}D+\left[\frac{K_3}{2}+\frac{(3-2m)(nK_1-K_3)K_3}{2(2-m)(K_2+K_3)}\right]C$$

$$+\frac{(1-m)(nK_1-K_3)Fh}{(2-m)(K_2+K_3)}=0; \quad . . . . \quad (108)$$

and at joint C,

$$\left[K_3+K_4-\frac{(3-2m)K_3^2}{2(2-m)(K_2+K_3)}\right]C+\left[\frac{K_3}{2}-\frac{(3-m)K_3^2}{2(2-m)(K_2+K_3)}\right]B$$

$$-\frac{(3-m)K_2K_3}{2(2-m)(K_2+K_3)}A+\left[\frac{K_4}{2}-\frac{(3-2m)K_2K_3}{2(2-m)(K_2+K_3)}\right]D$$

$$-\frac{(1-m)K_3Fh}{(2-m)(K_2+K_3)}=0 \quad . . . . \quad (109)$$

For a symmetrical bent, that is, when $K_2=K_3$ and the lateral load is applied at the top, the deflection angles at A and D equal respectively those at B and C. In this case, eqs. (105), (106) and (107) assume the following simplified forms:

$$R=\frac{(3-m)A+(3-2m)D}{2(2-m)}+\frac{(1-m)Fh}{2(2-m)K_2}; \quad . . . \quad (105b)$$

$$\left[1.5K_1+K_2+\frac{(3-m)(nK_1-K_2)}{2(2-m)}\right]A+\left[\frac{K_2}{2}+\frac{(3-2m)(nK_1-K_2)}{2(2-m)}\right]D$$

$$+\frac{(1-m)(nK_1-K_2)Fh}{2(2-m)K_2}=0, \quad . . . . \quad (106b)$$

$$\left[K_2+1.5K_4-\frac{(3-2m)K_2}{2(2-m)}\right]D+\left[\frac{K_2}{2}-\frac{(3-m)K_2}{2(2-m)}\right]A$$

$$-\frac{(1-m)Fh}{2(2-m)}=0 \quad . . . . \quad (107b)$$

If the lateral load is applied between the panel points, as shown in Fig. 77, the load factors of the expressions are modified accordingly.

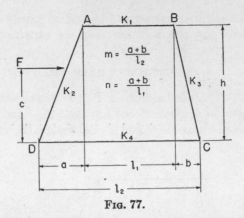

FIG. 77.

This change is made by replacing Fh with Fc and including the fixed-end moments FM_{AD} and FM_{DA} in the shear expression. Thus, eqs. (95) and (104) become:

$$M_{AD}+(1-m)M_{DA}+M_{BC}+(1-m)M_{CB}=(m-1)Fc \quad \ldots \ldots \quad (95a)$$

$$\frac{(3-m)}{2}K_2A+\frac{(3-m)}{2}K_3B+\frac{(3-2m)}{2}K_3C+\frac{(3-2m)}{2}K_2D$$
$$-(2-m)(K_2+K_3)R+FM_{AD}+(1-m)FM_{DA}=(m-1)Fc .(104a)$$

Then

$$R=\frac{(3-m)(K_2A+K_3B)+(3-2m)(K_3C+K_2D)}{2(2-m)(K_2+K_3)}$$
$$+\frac{FM_{AD}+(1-m)FM_{DA}+(1-m)Fc}{(2-m)(K_2+K_3)}; \quad \ldots \ldots \quad (105a)$$

and for the joint expressions at A and D we have:

Joint A,

$$\left[K_1+K_2+\frac{(3-m)(nK_1-K_2)K_2}{2(2-m)(K_2+K_3)}\right]A+\left[\frac{K_1}{2}+\frac{(3-m)(nK_1-K_2)K_3}{2(2-m)(K_2+K_3)}\right]B$$
$$+\frac{(3-2m)(nK_1-K_2)K_3}{2(2-m)(K_2+K_3)}C+\left[\frac{K_2}{2}+\frac{(3-2m)(nK_1-K_2)K_2}{2(2-m)(K_2+K_3)}\right]D$$
$$+FM_{AD}+\frac{(nK_1-K_2)}{(2-m)(K_2+K_3)}[FM_{AD}+(1-m)FM_{DA}+(1-m)Fc]$$
$$=0; \quad \ldots \ldots \ldots \ldots \ldots \ldots \ldots \ldots \quad (106a)$$

Joint D,

$$\left[K_2+K_4-\frac{(3-2m)K_2{}^2}{2(2-m)(K_2+K_3)}\right]D+\left[\frac{K_2}{2}-\frac{(3-m)K_2{}^2}{2(2-m)(K_2+K_3)}\right]A$$
$$-\frac{(3-m)K_2K_3}{2(2-m)(K_2+K_3)}B+\left[\frac{K_4}{2}-\frac{(3-2m)K_2K_3}{2(2-m)(K_2+K_3)}\right]C+FM_{DA}$$
$$-\frac{K_2}{(2-m)(K_2+K_3)}\left[FM_{AD}+(1-m)FM_{DA}+(1-m)Fc\right]=0. \quad \, (107a)$$

In general, the joint expressions of the panel involve four unknown deflection angles, and the solution may be obtained in the usual tabular form.

The unsymmetrical bent shown in Fig. 78 is subjected to a lateral load of 1,000 pounds, applied at the top joint A. Assuming the bent to be hinged to the supports C and D, determine the end moments of the members.

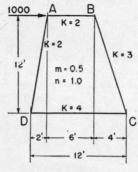

FIG. 78.

Solution: The various coefficients of the four joints are determined from eqs. (106), (107), (108) and (109), by substitution of the numerical constants. Thus:

Joint A,

$$f_A = 2 + 2 + \frac{(3-0.5)(2-2)2}{2(2-0.5)(2+3)} = 4;$$

$$f_b = 1 - \frac{(3-0.5)(2-2)3}{2(2-0.5)(2+3)} = 1; \quad f_{BA} = -\frac{1}{4} = -0.25;$$

$$f_c = \frac{(3-1.0)(2-2)3}{2(2-0.5)(2+3)} = 0; \quad f_{CA} = -\frac{f_c}{f_A} = 0;$$

$$f_d = 1 - \frac{(3-1.0)(2-2)2}{2(2-0.5)(2+3)} = 1; \quad f_{DA} = -\frac{1}{4} = -0.25;$$

$$Q_A = \frac{(1-0.5)(2-2)1000 \times 12}{(2-0.5)(2+3)} = 0.$$

Joint B,

$$f_B = 2 + 3 + \frac{(3-0.5)(2-3)3}{2 \times 1.5 \times 5} = 4.5; \quad Q_B = \frac{(1-0.5)(2-3)12000}{(2-0.5)5} = -800;$$

$$f_a = 1 + \frac{2.5(2-3)2}{2 \times 1.5 \times 5} = \frac{2}{3}; \quad f_{AB} = -\frac{2}{3 \times 4.5} = -0.148;$$

$$f_c = 1.5 + \frac{(3-1)(2-3)3}{2 \times 1.5 \times 5} = 1.1; \quad f_{CB} = -\frac{1.1}{4.5} = -0.2444;$$

$$f_d = \frac{(3-1)(2-3)2}{2 \times 1.5 \times 5} = -\frac{4}{15}; \quad f_{DB} = \frac{4}{15 \times 4.5} = 0.0593.$$

Joint C,

$$f_C = 3 + 4 - \frac{(3-1)3^2}{2 \times 1.5 \times 5} = 5.8; \quad Q_C = -\frac{(1-0.5)3 \times 12000}{1.5 \times 5} = -2400;$$

$$f_a = -\frac{(3-0.5)2 \times 3}{2 \times 1.5 \times 5} = -1; \quad f_{AC} = \frac{1}{5.8} = 0.1724;$$

$$f_b = 1.5 - \frac{(3-0.5)3^2}{2 \times 1.5 \times 5} = 0; \quad f_{BC} = 0;$$

$$f_d = 2 - \frac{(3-1)2 \times 3}{2 \times 1.5 \times 5} = 1.2; \quad f_{DC} = -\frac{1.2}{5.8} = -0.207.$$

Joint D,

$$f_D = 2 + 4 - \frac{(3-1)2^2}{2 \times 1.5 \times 5} = 5.467; \quad Q_D = -\frac{(1-0.5)2 \times 12000}{1.5 \times 5} = -1600;$$

$$f_a = 1 - \frac{(3-0.5)2^2}{2 \times 1.5 \times 5} = \frac{1}{3}; \quad f_{AD} = -\frac{1}{3 \times 5.467} = -0.061;$$

$$f_b = -\frac{(3-0.5)2 \times 3}{2 \times 1.5 \times 5} = -1; \quad f_{BD} = \frac{1}{5.467} = 0.183;$$

$$f_c = 2 - \frac{(3-1)2 \times 3}{2 \times 1.5 \times 5} = \frac{6}{5}; \quad f_{CD} = -\frac{6}{5 \times 5.467} = -0.2195.$$

Then, for the initial values of the deflection angles, we have:

$$\alpha_{A1} = 0; \quad \alpha_{B1} = \frac{800}{4.5} = 177.78;$$

$$\alpha_{C1} = \frac{2400}{5.8} = 413.79; \quad \alpha_{D1} = \frac{1600}{5.467} = 292.66.$$

The remainder of the computations is shown in Table 6, and final values of the deflection angles, corresponding to 4 cycles of corrections, are given in the last space of the table.

TABLE 6

(For Bent shown in Fig. 78)

	Joint	A	B	C	D
1	f	f_{AB} —0.148 f_{AC} 0.1724 f_{AD} —0.061	f_{BA} —0.25 f_{BC} 0. f_{BD} 0.183	f_{CA} 0. f_{CB} —0.2444 f_{CD} —0.2195	f_{DA} —0.25 f_{DB} 0.0593 f_{DC} —0.207
2	α_1	0.	177.78	413.79	292.66
3	$f\alpha_1$	—44.44 0. —73.14	0. —101.13 17.35	0. 0. —60.58	0. 32.53 —90.83
4	α_2	—117.58	—83.78	—60.58	—58.30
5	$f\alpha_2$	20.94 0. 14.57	17.4 14.82 —3.46	—20.3 0. 12.07	7.17 —15.35 13.3
6	α_3	35.51	28.76	—8.23	5.12
7	$f\alpha_3$	—7.19 0. —1.28	—5.26 2.01 0.31	6.12 0. —1.06	—2.17 5.27 1.80
8	α_4	—8.47	—2.94	5.06	4.90
9	$f\alpha_4$	0.74 0. —1.22	1.25 —1.24 0.29	—1.47 0. —1.01	0.52 —0.54 —1.10
10	α_5	—0.48	0.30	—2.48	—1.12
11	α	—91.02	120.12	347.56	243.26

Substituting these values in eq. (105),

$$R = \frac{2.5(-2\times91.02+3\times120.12)+2(2\times243.26+3\times347.56)}{2\times1.5\times5}$$
$$+\frac{0.5\times12000}{1.5\times5}=1033.61.$$

Accordingly, the end moments become:

$$M_{AB}=2(-91.02+60.06+1033.61)=2005.3,$$
$$M_{AD}=2(-91.02+121.63-1033.61)=-2006.0;$$

$$M_{BA}=2(120.12-45.51+1033.61)=2216.5,$$
$$M_{BC}=3(120.12+173.78-1033.61)=-2219.1;$$

$$M_{CB}=3(347.56+60.06-1033.61)=-1877.9,$$
$$M_{CD}=4(347.56+121.63)=1876.8;$$

$$M_{DA}=2(243.26-45.51-1033.61)=-1671.7,$$
$$M_{DC}=4(243.26+173.78)=1668.2.$$

27. The unsymmetrical bent shown in Fig. 79 is subjected to a vertical load, applied between the top joints.   Determine:

(*a*) Load constants for the joints *A*, *B*, *C*, and *D;*

(*b*) Load constant for the deflection *R* of the legs.

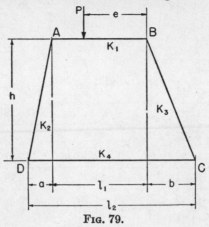

Fig. 79.

28. The symmetrical bent shown in Fig. 80 carries a lateral load of 10 kips— applied at the top joint.   Assuming the bent to be hinged to the bases, determine the end moments.

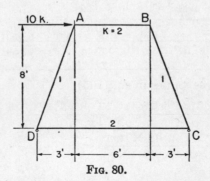

Fig. 80.

41. Multi-story Trapezoidal Bents.—The relative simplicity of the computations of single-story bents, as outlined in Arts. 39 and 40, is due to the definite relation of deflections of the members.   In a bent of more than one story, this relation cannot be easily determined and, hence, a direct solution is rather difficult to obtain.   However, by considering each panel of a multi-story bent separately, omitting the effect of adjacent panels, it becomes possible to compute a first set of approximate moment values.   The error involved is then adjusted in the next step by computing corrections or increments, resulting from the initial end moments of members directly adjacent to each panel. To illustrate, consider the three-story bent shown in Fig. 81 (a).

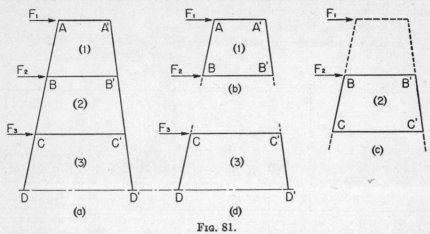

Fig. 81.

Starting at the top, panel 1 is severed from the original frame by insertion of two temporary hinges just below the joints B and B', thus resulting in the closed panel $AA'B'B$ shown in Fig. 81 (b). Similarly, panel 2 shown in Fig. 81 (c) is obtained by insertion of temporary hinges just above and below, respectively, the joints $B-B'$ and $C-C'$; and the bottom panel is isolated from the main frame through hinges placed just above the joints $C-C'$, as indicated in Fig. 81 (d). This arrangement, however, does not alter the loading condition of the separated panels, since the external overturning moment—taken about the respective base—to which each panel is subjected remains the same as in the original frame.

Proceeding with the solution, the moments for each panel are computed in accordance with the procedure of Arts. 39 and 40. These initial moment values will accordingly involve the following assumptions:

Panel 1,
$$R \text{ of member } BB'=0,$$
$$M_{BC}=0, \qquad M_{B'C'}=0;$$

Panel 2,
$$M_{BA}=0, \qquad M_{B'A'}=0,$$
$$M_{CD}=0; \qquad M_{C'D'}=0,$$
$$R \text{ of member } CC'=0;$$

Panel 3,
$$M_{CB}=0, \qquad M_{C'B'}=0.$$

Next, a first correction is made by substituting in each joint equation the end moment omitted in the first step. Considering this moment value as the new load constant of the joint equation, the routine solution of the first step is repeated, thus resulting in a second set of moment values which may be called the "first moment increment" of the panel.

By using the first moment increment, and repeating the second step, a second increment of moment for each panel is obtained.

If required, further corrections or moment increments may similarly be determined. However, since these increments diminish in magnitude rapidly, in most cases two corrections will provide a solution of sufficient accuracy.

Except for the load constants, eqs. (106) and (107) furnish the necessary data for computing the various coefficients of the tabular solution. The derivation of a general expression for this factor, corresponding to a system of loading and applicable to any panel regardless of its location, presents but little difficulty. In the case of the loading shown in Fig. 81, let M indicate the overturning moment of the external forces taken at the bottom of the panel under consideration; H, the shear of the panel, that is, the sum of the lateral forces above the panel; V, the vertical reaction couple just above the bottom joints of the panel; M_A and M_B, the end moments at the top and bottom, respectively, of the two legs; then, with other notations as given in Fig. 82, we have:

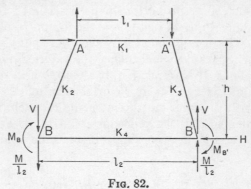

FIG. 82.

$$M_B + M_{B'} = Vl_2 - M, \quad \ldots \ldots \ldots \ldots \ldots \ldots \quad (a)$$

$$M_A + M_{A'} + M_B + M_{B'} = V(l_2 - l_1) - Hh \quad \ldots \ldots \quad (b)$$

Substituting the value of V from eq. (a) in eq. (b), and noting that

$$m = \frac{l_2 - l_1}{l_2},$$

$$M_A + M_{A'} + (1 - m)(M_B + M_{B'}) = mM - Hh \quad . \quad . \quad (c)$$

The right side of eq. (c) represents the load constant of the shear expression. Denoted by Q, the corresponding values in the equations for R and top and bottom joints will then assume the following forms:

$$Q \text{ of } R = \frac{Hh - mM}{(2-m)(K_2 + K_3)};$$

$$Q \text{ of top joint} = \frac{(nK_1 - K_2)(Hh - mM)}{(2-m)(K_2 + K_3)}; \left.\begin{array}{c}\\\\\\\\\end{array}\right\} \quad \cdots \quad (110)$$

$$Q \text{ of bottom joint} = \frac{K_2(mM - Hh)}{(2-m)(K_2 + K_3)};$$

in which n equals $\dfrac{l_1 - l_2}{l_1}$, and the Q values are written for the left side joints of the panel.

If the lateral load is applied between the joints of a panel, the load constant of that panel will need a further revision. The middle panel of the bent shown in Fig. 83 represents this particular case. With the

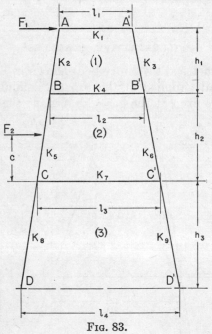

FIG. 83.

notations as indicated in the figure, the sheer expression, eq. (c), becomes

$$M_{BC} + M_{B'C'} + (1 - m_2)(M_{CB} + M_{C'B'}) = m_2 M_2 - H_2 h_2 \quad \cdots \quad (d)$$

in which

$$M_2 = F_1(h_1 + h_2) + F_2 c;$$

$$H_2 = F_1 + \frac{c}{h_2} F_2;$$

$$m_2 = \frac{l_3 - l_2}{l_3}.$$

Then, for the load constants of the deflection of the panel, R_2, and the joints B and C we can write:

$$Q \text{ of } R_2 = \frac{FM_{BC} + (1-m_2)FM_{CB} + H_2h_2 - m_2M_2}{(2-m_2)(K_5+K_6)};$$

$$Q \text{ of } B = FM_{BC} + \frac{(n_2K_4 - K_5)}{(2-m_2)(K_5+K_6)}\left[FM_{BC} + (1-m_2)FM_{CB} \right.$$
$$\left. + H_2h_2 - m_2M_2 \right];$$

$$Q \text{ of } C = FM_{CB} - \frac{K_5}{(2-m_2)(K_5+K_6)}\left[FM_{BC} + (1-m_2)FM_{CB} \right.$$
$$\left. + H_2h_2 - m_2M_2 \right];$$

(111)

in which n_2 equals $\dfrac{l_3 - l_2}{l_2}$.

ILLUSTRATIVE EXAMPLES

1. The unsymmetrical two-story bent shown in Fig. 84 is subjected to two lateral loads, applied at the top and middle joints. Assuming the bent to be fixed at the bases, determine the end moments.

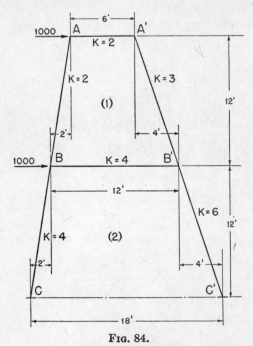

FIG. 84.

Solution: Since the top panel is identical with the single-story bent in the illustrative example of Art. 40 (Fig. 78), its coefficients are the same as those given in Table 6. The coefficients of the joints B and B' are determined from eq. (100), and the load constants from eq. (110). Thus:

Joint B,

$$m_2 = \frac{18-12}{18} = \frac{1}{3}; \quad n_2 = \frac{18-12}{12} = \frac{1}{2};$$

$$f_B = 4 + 4 + \frac{(3-\frac{1}{3})(2-4)4}{2(2-\frac{1}{3})(4+6)} = 7.36;$$

$$f_{b'} = 2 + \frac{(3-\frac{1}{3})(2-4)6}{2(2-\frac{1}{3})(4+6)} = 1.04; \quad f_{B'B} = \frac{1.04}{7.36} = -0.1413;$$

$$Q_B = \frac{(2-4)(2000 \times 12 - \frac{1}{3} \times 36000)}{(2-\frac{1}{3})(4+6)} = -1440.$$

Joint B',

$$f_{B'} = 4 + 6 + \frac{(3-\frac{1}{3})(2-6)6}{2(2-\frac{1}{3})(4+6)} = 8.08;$$

$$f_b = 2 + \frac{(3-\frac{1}{3})(2-6)4}{2(2-\frac{1}{3})(4+6)} = 0.72; \quad f_{BB'} = -\frac{0.72}{8.08} = -0.0891;$$

$$Q_{B'} = \frac{(2-6)(2000 \times 12 - \frac{1}{3} \times 36000)}{(2-\frac{1}{3})(4+6)} = -2880.$$

For the initial values of the deflection angles of these two joints we have:

$$\alpha_1 \text{ of } B = -\frac{Q_B}{f_B} = \frac{1440}{7.36} = 195.5;$$

$$\alpha_1 \text{ of } B' = -\frac{Q_{B'}}{f_{B'}} = \frac{2880}{8.08} = 356.$$

Table 7 contains the complete computations for the bent. Since the loading of the top panel is the same as that of the bent in Fig. 78, the final values of the deflection angles, the deflection and the end moments of that panel are obtained from the previous solution and listed in space 2 of the table, as the summary of the first set of moment

TABLE 7.

(For Bent shown in Fig. 84)

Panel	Joint	Top panel				Bottom panel		Panel	Joint	
		A	A'	B	B'	B	B'			
1	f	$A=4$	$A'=4.5$	$B=5.467$	$B'=5.8$	$B=7.36$	$B'=8.08$	f		1
		$A'-0.148$ $B-0.061$ B' 0.1724	$A-0.25$ B 0.183 B' 0	$A-0.25$ A' 0.0593 $B'-0.207$	A 0 $A'-0.2445$ $B-0.2195$	$B'-0.0891$	$B-0.1413$			
2	$-Q'$	0	800	1600	2400	1440	2880	$-Q'$		2
	α'	-91.02	120.12	243.26	347.56	195.5	356	α_1		
	R'	\multicolumn — $R'_{AB}=R'_{A'B'}=1033.61$				-50.3	-17.4	α_2		
	M'	$M'_{AB}=-2006$; $M'_{BA}=-1671.7$; $M'_{A'B'}=-2219.1$; $M'_{B'A'}=-1877.9$				2.5	4.5	α_3		
						-0.6	-0.2	α_4		
3	$-Q''$	0	0	3138.4	3532.8	147.1	342.9	α'		3
	α_1	0	0	573	609	$R'_{BC}=931.7$		R'		
	α_2	-143.2	-114.5	-133.7	-118.5	$M_{BC}=-3138.4$ $M_{B'C'}=-3532.8$		M'		
	α_3	62.0	42.3	13.7	3.0					
	α_4	-14.1	-9.1	3.4	7.8	1671.7	1877.9	$-Q''$		
	α_5	1.3	0.4	-2.5	-3.1	196.7	214.9	α''		
	α_6	0.5	0.4	0.7	0.3	$R''_{BC}=166.1$		R''		
	α''	-93.5	-80.5	454.6	498.5	$M''_{BC}=122.4$ $M''_{B'C'}=292.8$		M''		
	R''	$R''_{AB}=249.2$								
	M''	$M''_{AB}=-231$; $M''_{BA}=318$; $M''_{A'B'}=-242$; $M''_{B'A'}=627$				-318	-627	$-Q'''$		
						-32.7	-74.6	α'''		
4	$M'+M''$	$M_{AB}=M'_{AB}+M''_{AB}=-2237$ $M_{A'B'}=M'_{A'B'}+M''_{A'B'}=-2461.1$ $M_{BA}=M'_{BA}+M''_{BA}=-1353.7$ $M_{B'A'}=M'_{B'A'}+M''_{B'A'}=-1250.9$				$R'''_{BC}=-46.3$		R'''		4
						$M'''_{BC}=54.4$ $M'''_{B'C'}=169.8$		M''''		
						$M_{BC}=-2961.6$ $M_{B'C'}=-3070.2$		$M'+M''+M'''$		

calculations. With three corrections, the deflection angles B and B' of the bottom panel, as shown in space 2 of that panel with a symbol α', equal 147.1 and 342.9, respectively. Substituting these latter values in the R (eqs. 98 and 110) and moment expressions the following result:

$$R'_{BC}=\frac{(3-\tfrac{1}{3})(4\times147.1+6\times342.9)}{2(2-\tfrac{1}{3})(4+6)}+\frac{24000-12000}{(2-\tfrac{1}{3})(4+6)}=931.7;$$

$$M'_{BC}=4(147.1+0-931.7)=-3138.4;$$

$$M'_{B'C'}=6(342.9+0-931.7)=-3532.8;$$

$$M'_{CB}=4(0+73.55-931.7)=-3432.6;$$

$$M'_{C'B'}=6(0+171.45-931.7)=-4561.5.$$

Using the first moment values as new load constants, an initial correction is made to the moments of both panels, as shown in summary form in the spaces 3 of Table 7. For the top panel, the load constant at the joint B is $M'_{BC}(=-3138.4)$, and at B', $M'_{B'C'}(=-3532.8)$. In the bottom panel, these values at the joints B and B' are given by $M'_{BA}(=-1671.7)$ and $M'_{B'A'}(=-1877.9)$, respectively. (The values α'' of the top panel are obtained from 5 cycles of corrections, and, for brevity, only the final values of each cycle are shown in the table. Similarly, the three increments of α'' of the bottom panel, computed as in space 2, are omitted in space 3.)

The deflections R'', corresponding to the first moment increments, are determined from eqs. (98) and (105), noting that the load constant in each expression becomes zero. For R'' of the bottom panel, for example, we have:

$$R''_{BC} = \frac{(3-\frac{1}{3})(4\times196.7+6\times214.9)}{2(2-\frac{1}{3})(4+6)} = 166.1.$$

A second correction is made to the moments of the bottom panel by using the second set moments, $M''_{BA}(=318)$ and $M''_{B'A'} (=627)$, as load constants, Q''', for the joints B and B'. The resulting values are shown in space 4 of that panel in the table.

The final end moments are indicated in the last spaces of the table. In the case of the bottom panel, these values represent the sums of three moment sets, that is, $M'+M''+M'''$; while in the top panel, only two sets are used.

The end moments of the horizontal members of the bent may be obtained by adding up the two leg-member moments at the respective joints. Thus:

$$M_{A'A} = -M_{A'B'} = 2461.1;$$

$$M_{AA'} = -M_{AB} = 2237.0;$$

$$M_{BB'} = -(M_{BA}+M_{BC}) = 4315.3;$$

$$M_{B'B} = -(M_{B'A'}+M_{B'C'}) = 4321.1.$$

2. Fig. 85 represents the bent of Kinzua Viaduct. Assuming the legs to be fixed at the bases, determine the end moments due to the wind loading shown on the sketch.

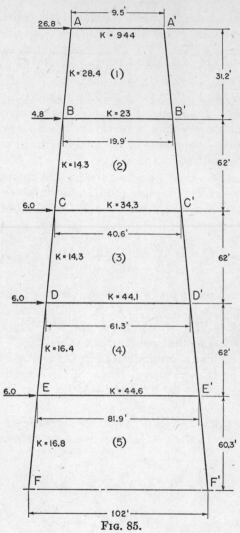

Fig. 85.

Solution: Since the bent is symmetrical and the lateral loading applied at the panel points, the deflection angles of the joints at the left side equal the respective angles at the right side joints. Accordingly, the computations of the panels 1 to 4 involve only two unknowns each, and the bottom panel has only one unknown. First, the shear H, the external overturning moment M and the constants m and n for each panel are computed and listed as shown below.

Panel	1	2	3	4	5
Shear H	26. 8	31. 6	37. 6	43. 6	49. 6
Moment M	835. 4	2794. 6	5125. 8	7829. 0	10820. 0
m	0. 522	0. 51	0. 338	0. 252	0. 197
n	1. 095	1. 04	0. 51	0. 336	0. 246

TABLE 8.

(For Bent shown in Fig. 85)

Panel	Joint	1		2		3		4		5	
		A	B	B	C	C	D	D	E	E	F
1	f_j	2287.0	44.14	56.84	56.24	68.31	70.45	81.31	71.6	79.17	∞
	f_e	0.2175	−0.297	0.0845	−0.2405	0.061	−0.1375	0.0656	−0.0894		
2	$-Q'$	−4780.0	135.0	−121.0	180.0	−40.3	180.0	204	209.0		0
	α'	−2.818	2.446	−2.843	2.960	−0.934	2.503	−0.009	2.919	1.042	
	R'	4.007		12.185		13.604		1.800		15.010	−243.5
	M'	−159.2	−84.4	−193.8	−152.3	−190.0	−165.5	−210.0	−194.7	−234.7	0
3	$-Q''$	0	193.8	84.4	190.0	152.3	219.0	160.5	234.7	194.7	0
	α''	−1.223	4.124	0.658	3.434	1.788	3.219	−0.832	3.391	2.460	
	R''	1.706		2.835		3.680		−0.860		1.910	
	M''	−24.7	51.3	−6.6	13.3	−4.2	6.2	−4.5	7.3	9.2	−11.4
4	$-Q'''$	0	6.6	−51.3	4.2	−13.3	5.5	−4.2	−9.2	−7.3	0
	α''	−0.042	0.141	−0.903	0	−0.204	0.065	−0.064	−0.112	−0.092	
	R''	0.058		−0.754		−0.117		−0.130		−0.072	
	M''	−0.9	1.8	−2.1	4.3	−0.8	1.2	8.2	−0.2	−0.3	0.1
	$M'+M''+M'''$	−184.8	−31.3	−202.5	−134.7	−195.0	−158.1	−227.3	−187.6	−225.8	−254.8
	M by Maugh	185.0	31.0	202.4	134.4	196.0	159.2	227.6	186.6	226.6	255.4
	M by Grimm	185.2	30.3	202.4	133.7	196.8	157.7	227.1	189.4	217.1	
	Location of M	M_{AB}	M_{BA}	M_{BC}	M_{CB}	M_{CD}	M_{DC}	M_{DB}	M_{BD}	M_{BF}	M_{FB}

Next, the joint coefficients and coefficients of correction of the joints are determined from eqs. (106b) and (107b). These values, denoted with the symbols f_j and f_c, respectively, are given in space 1 of Table 8 which contains the summary of the computations. The load constants Q', corresponding to the initial moment values of the panels, are obtained from eqs. (110), and the resulting deflection angles α' determined in the usual manner. (For brevity, only the final values of α are given in the table.) The deflections R' of this set are computed from eqs. (105b) and (110); and substitution of the values α' and R' in the fundamental moment expression results in the first set moments M'. The résumé of the computations for the first moment increments, constituting the second set moments M'', is given in space 3 of the table. (The Q'' values of this first correction are merely the end moments of the preceding set.) The third set moments M''', resulting from a second increment or correction, are indicated in space 4 of the table. The final moments, corresponding to the initial set and two increments, are represented by the sums $M'+M''+M'''$.

For comparison of results, values obtained by two other methods of solution are given in the table. One of these is the original solution by Grimm,[1] based on the method of Least Work; and the other is based on a European method, adapted by Professor Maugh[2] and applicable to symmetrical bents only.

Since each panel contains only two unknown deflection angles (except for the bottom panel), the values of the unknowns may also be determined by simultaneous solution of the two joint equations of each panel. However, once the coefficients f are computed, an operation consisting of a series of simple multiplications, as shown in space 2 for the bottom panel in Table 7, becomes more convenient.

PROBLEMS

29. Assuming the legs of the bent shown in Fig. 83 to be fixed at the bases D and D', determine the following load constants for the bottom panel:

    (a) Q of R_{CD};
    (b) Q of C;
    (c) Q of C'.

---

[1] Transactions, A. S. C. E., Vol. XLVI (1901), pp. 21-77.
[2] Engineering News-Record, March 14, 1935, p. 379.

30. The symmetrical bent shown in Fig. 86 is assumed to be fixed at the bases. Determine the end moments by computing the initial values and two increments. Give the summary of the computations in a form similar to Table 8.

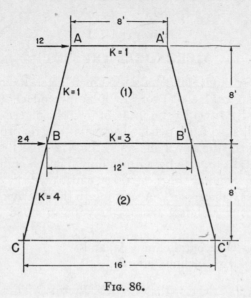

Fig. 86.

Chapter III

VIERENDEEL TRUSSES

42. Trusses without Diagonals.—Named after its originator, the eminent Belgian engineer, Prof. Arthur Vierendeel, the Vierendeel truss is essentially a two-legged multi-story bent placed in a horizontal position. Unlike a truss with diagonals, where principal stresses are direct or axial, the panel shears in the Vierendeel truss are transmitted to the end supports by the bending of chord and web members, thus producing bending fiber stresses which are, in general, much larger than the axial stresses. According to the relative position of the two chords, the Vierendeel trusses may be grouped in two general classes:

(*a*) Trusses with parallel chords; and

(*b*) Trusses with inclined chords.

43. Vierendeel Truss with Parallel Chords.—The parallel-chord Vierendeel truss differs but little from a rectangular bent subjected to lateral loading. First, consider the simplest type, that of a symmetrical truss having a system of symmetrical loading. The four-bay truss shown in Fig. 87, subjected to a single force applied at midspan,

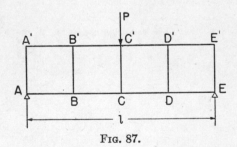

Fig. 87.

represents such a case. Obviously, the reactions at the two supports equal $\frac{P}{2}$, and, since the member CC' coincides with the vertical axis of symmetry of the truss, the deflection angles at the joints C and C' become zero, while the deflection angles of the four joints in the left half of the truss equal those of the respective joints in the right half with opposite signs. The solution of the four angles is then obtained

in the same manner as that of a two-story bent, fixed at the bases
and subjected to a single load at the top, as shown in Fig. 88.

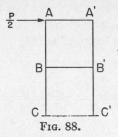

FIG. 88.

If the truss has an odd number of panels, and the symmetry of
loading and framing is kept, as in Fig. 89 (a), the deflection angles of

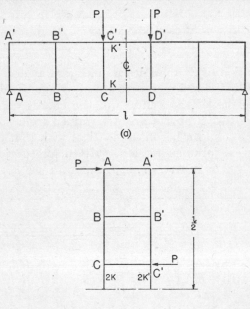

FIG. 89.

joints symmetrically located with respect to the vertical axis at midspan again remain equal and of opposite sign. Noting also that the
joints C and D, and C' and D' have the same deflections (by virtue
of the symmetrical bending), the deflection terms R of the members
CD and $C'D'$ become zero. Accordingly, the left half of the truss
may be considered as a three-story bent, Fig. 89 (b), fixed at the bases,
the K values of the two legs in the bottom story being twice the values
of the corresponding members in the truss, and the shear in the same
story equaling zero.

In the more general case, resulting from dissymmetry of loading
and/or framing, the deflection angles and deflections of the truss no
longer possess definite relations with respect to each other. However,
the analogy between truss and bent is not altered. For example, a
shift of the load in Fig. 87 from C' to B', as indicated in Fig. 90, will

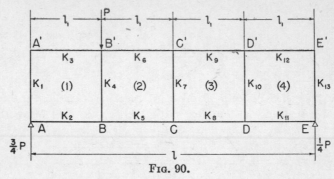

Fig. 90.

require the solution of five unknown deflection angles, provided that
the top and bottom chord members are of symmetrical stiffness, and
ten unknown angles, if the stiffness of the chords differ. After the
reactions at the two supports are determined from statics—as in a
simple truss, the solution becomes identical with that of a four-story
bent. The typical joint expression, written for the joint B, for instance, and derived as in Art. 37, is in the form

$$\left[K_2+K_4+K_5-\frac{3K_2^2}{4(K_2+K_3)}-\frac{3K_5^2}{4(K_5+K_6)}\right]B+\left[\frac{K_2}{2}-\frac{3K_2^2}{4(K_2+K_3)}\right]A$$

$$-\frac{3K_2K_3}{4(K_2+K_3)}A'+\left[\frac{K_4}{2}-\frac{3K_2K_3}{4(K_2+K_3)}-\frac{3K_5K_6}{4(K_5+K_6)}\right]B'$$

$$+\left[\frac{K_5}{2}-\frac{3K_5^2}{4(K_5+K_6)}\right]C-\frac{3K_5K_6}{4(K_5+K_6)}C'=\frac{K_2H_1l_1}{2(K_2+K_3)}$$

$$+\frac{K_5H_2l_1}{2(K_5+K_6)}=-Q_B \dots \dots \dots \dots \dots \dots \quad (112)$$

in which H_1 and H_2 denote the shears in panels 1 and 2, and in this case
equal $+\frac{3}{4}P$ and $-\frac{1}{4}P$, respectively. (It is to be noted that in eq.
(112) the load constant, Q_B, is transferred to the right side of the
equation, hence the minus sign; and the sign of the panel shear accordingly is governed by the rotation of the shear couple—the plus sign
corresponding to a clockwise rotation.)

Except for the load constants, eq. (112) is typical for any parallel-
chord truss, independent of the loading and panel lengths. If the
top and bottom chord members are of the same stiffness, as in Fig. 91,

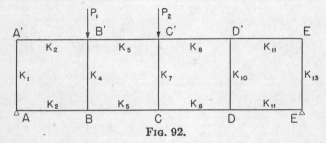

Fig. 91.

then eq. (112) reduces to the following form:

$$\left[\frac{5}{8}K_2+K_4+\frac{5}{8}K_5\right]B+\frac{1}{8}K_2A-\frac{3}{8}K_2A'+\left[\frac{K_4}{2}-\frac{3}{8}K_2-\frac{3}{8}K_5\right]B'$$

$$+\frac{1}{8}K_5C-\frac{3}{8}K_5C'=-Q_B \quad \cdots \cdots \quad (113)$$

When the loads are applied at the panel points, as indicated in Fig. 92, the deflection angles of the top chord joints become equal to the

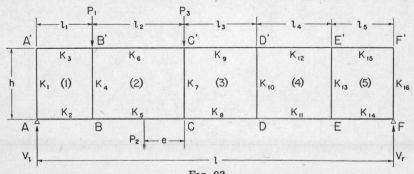

Fig. 92.

corresponding angles of the bottom chord joints, resulting in a further simplified joint expression

$$\left(\frac{1}{4}K_2+\frac{3}{2}K_4+\frac{1}{4}K_5\right)B-\frac{1}{4}K_2A-\frac{1}{4}K_5C=-Q_B \quad \cdots \quad (114)$$

The derivation of a general expression for the load constant applicable to any system of loading, is equally simple. For this purpose, consider the truss shown in Fig. 93. The panels are of different lengths, and one of the loads is applied between the lower chord joints B and C. For the deflection R_1 of panel (1) we have:

$$R_1 = \frac{3K_2(A+B)}{4(K_2+K_3)} + \frac{3K_3(A'+B')}{4(K_2+K_3)} + \frac{H_1 l_1}{2(K_2+K_3)} \quad \dots \quad (115)$$

in which H_1 is the shear in the first panel and equals the vertical reaction of the left support. Similarly, the deflection R_2 of panel (2) is in the form

$$R_2 = \frac{3K_5(B+C)}{4(K_5+K_6)} + \frac{3K_6(B'+C')}{4(K_5+K_6)} + \frac{H_2 l_2}{2(K_5+K_6)} + \frac{FM_{BC}+FM_{CB}}{2(K_5+K_6)} \dots (115a)$$

where H_2 is the shear in the second panel and equals $\left(V_l - P_1 - \frac{e}{l_2}P_2\right)$.

Likewise,

$$\left. \begin{aligned} R_3 &= \frac{3K_8(C+D)}{4(K_8+K_9)} + \frac{3K_9(C'+D')}{4(K_8+K_9)} + \frac{H_3 l_3}{2(K_8+K_9)}, \\ R_4 &= \frac{3K_{11}(D+E)}{4(K_{11}+K_{12})} + \frac{3K_{12}(D'+E')}{4(K_{11}+K_{12})} + \frac{H_4 l_4}{2(K_{11}+K_{12})}; \end{aligned} \right\} \quad \dots \quad (115b)$$

in which, for this particular loading, the shears H_3 and H_4 each equal the reaction at the right support with a minus sign.

Now, to obtain the load constant for any joint equation, we have only to add to the sum of the fixed-end moments at the joint K times the numerical constant of R of the two chord members meeting at the joint. Thus, at joint A, for example, the load constant becomes

$$\left. \begin{aligned} -Q_A &= \frac{K_2 H_1 l_1}{2(K_2+K_3)}. \\[4pt] \text{Similarly,} \quad & \\[4pt] -Q_{A'} &= \frac{K_3 H_1 l_1}{2(K_2+K_3)}, \\[4pt] -Q_B &= -FM_{BC} + \frac{K_5(FM_{BC}+FM_{CB})}{2(K_5+K_6)} + \frac{K_2 H_1 l_1}{2(K_2+K_3)} + \frac{K_5 H_2 l_2}{2(K_5+K_6)}, \\[4pt] -Q_{B'} &= -\frac{K_6(FM_{BC}+FM_{CB})}{2(K_5+K_6)} + \frac{K_3 H_1 l_1}{2(K_2+K_3)} + \frac{K_6 H_2 l_2}{2(K_5+K_6)}, \\[4pt] -Q_C &= -FM_{CB} + \frac{K_5(FM_{BC}+FM_{CB})}{2(K_5+K_6)} + \frac{K_5 H_2 l_2}{2(K_5+K_6)} + \frac{K_8 H_3 l_3}{2(K_8+K_9)}, \\[4pt] -Q_{C'} &= \frac{K_6(FM_{BC}+FM_{CB})}{2(K_5+K_6)} + \frac{K_6 H_2 l_2}{2(K_5+K_6)} + \frac{K_9 H_3 l_3}{2(K_8+K_9)}, \\[4pt] -Q_D &= \frac{K_8 H_3 l_3}{2(K_8+K_9)} + \frac{K_{11} H_4 l_4}{2(K_{11}+K_{12})}, \end{aligned} \right\} \quad (116)$$

in which,

$$H_1 = +V_l; \quad H_2 = +V_l - P_1 - \frac{e}{l_2}P_2; \quad H_3 = V_r.$$

The joint coefficients and the load constants thus obtained, the unknown deflection angles and the deflections are determined in the usual manner, as illustrated in the following examples.

ILLUSTRATIVE EXAMPLES

1. The four-panel truss shown in Fig. 94 is subjected to a symmetrical loading concentrated at the panel points. Determine the end moments.

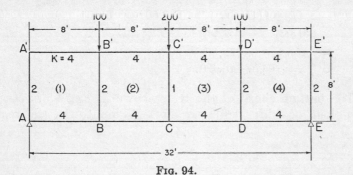

FIG. 94.

Solution: Since the top and bottom chord members have the same stiffness ratio, the following relations exist:

$$A = A' = -E = -E'; \quad B = B' = -D = -D';$$
$$C = C' = 0; \quad R_1 = -R_4; \quad R_2 = -R_3.$$

The values of the two unknown deflection angles A and B are then obtained from simultaneous solution of the two joint equations. By applying eqs. (114) and (116) we have:

$$(3+1)A - 1B = \frac{4 \times 200 \times 8}{2(4+4)} = 400;$$

$$(1+3+1)B - 1A = \frac{4 \times 200 \times 8}{2(4+4)} + \frac{4 \times 100 \times 8}{2(4+4)} = 600.$$

From which,

$$A=\frac{2600}{19},\ B=\frac{2800}{19};$$

and applying eqs. (115),

$$R_1=\frac{3(2600+2800)}{4\times19}+\frac{200\times8}{2(4+4)}=313.16;$$

$$R_2=\frac{3(2800+0)}{4\times19}+\frac{100\times8}{2(4+4)}=160.53.$$

The end moments become:

$$M_{AA'}=2(1.5\times136.84)=410.52,$$
$$M_{AB}=4(130.84+73.68-313.16)=-410.56;$$

$$M_{BA}=4(147.37+68.42-313.16)=-389.48,$$
$$M_{BC}=4(147.37+0-160.53)=-52.64,$$
$$M_{BB'}=2(1.5\times147.37)=442.10;$$

$$M_{CB}=4(0+73.68-160.53)=-347.40,$$
$$M_{CC'}=1(0+0)=0.$$

2. The bottom chord of the truss shown in Fig. 95 is carrying a uniform load of 1 kip per linear foot. Compute the end moments.

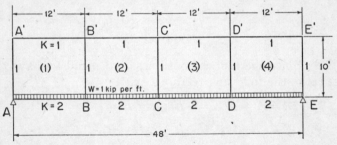

FIG. 95.

Solution: Due to the symmetry of loading and framing, the deflection angles of the joints in the left half of the truss are equal and of opposite sign to those of the corresponding joints in the right half. Also, $C=C'=O$; and $R_1=-R_4$; $R_2=-R_3$. The joint equations of the four unknown deflection angles A, A', B and B' are obtained from eqs. (112) and (116):

$$2A-0.5B'=84,$$
$$1.75A'-0.5B+0.25B'=36,$$
$$3B-0.5B'-0.5A'=96,$$
$$2.5B'-0.5A+0.25A'-0.5B=48.$$

The solution for the unknowns is given in Table 9.

TABLE 9

(For Truss shown in Fig. 95)

	Joint	A	A'	B	B'
1	f	B' 0.2	B ⅙ $B'-0.1$	A' 2/7 B' 0.2	A 0.25 A' $-\frac{1}{7}$ B ⅙
2	$-Q$	84	36	96	48
3	α_1	42	20.57	32	19.2
4	$f\alpha_1$	4.8	9.14 −2.74	3.43 3.2	8.4 −2.06 6 4
5	α_2	4.8	6.40	6.63	12.74
6	$f\alpha_2$	3.18	1.90 −1.82	1.07 2.12	0.96 −0.64 1.33
7	α_3	3.18	0.08	3.19	1.65
8	$f\alpha_3$	0.41	0.91 −0.24	0.01 0.27	0.63 −0.01 0.64
9	α_4	0.41	0.67	0.28	1.26
10	$f\alpha_4$	0.31	0.08 −0.18	0.21 0.12	0.08 −0.07 0.06
11	α_5	0.31	−0.10	0.33	0.07
12	$f\alpha_5$	0.02	0.09 −0.01	−0.02 0.01	0.06 0.01 0.06
13	α_6	0.02	0.08	−0.01	0.13
14	α	50.72	27.70	42.42	35.05

The deflections are obtained from eq. (115):

$$R_1 = 46.57 + 15.71 + 36 = 98.28,$$
$$R_2 = 21.22 + 8.76 + 12 = 41.98;$$

The end moments become:

$$M_{AA'}=1(50.72+13.85)=64.57,$$
$$M_{AB}=2(50.72+21.21-98.28)-12=-64.70;$$

$$M_{A'A}=1(27.70+25.36)=53.06,$$
$$M_{A'B'}=1(27.70+17.53-98.28)=-53.05;$$

$$M_{BA}=2(42.42+25.36-98.28)+12=-49.00,$$
$$M_{BC}=2(42.42+0-41.98)-12=-11.12,$$
$$M_{BB'}=1(42.42+17.53)=59.95;$$

$$M_{B'A'}=1(35.06+13.85-98.28)=-49.37,$$
$$M_{B'C'}=1(35.06+0-41.98)=-6.92,$$
$$M_{B'B}=1(35.06+21.21)=56.27;$$

$$M_{CB}=2(0+21.21-41.98)+12=-29.54;$$
$$M_{CC'}=1(0+0)=0;$$

$$M_{C'B'}=1(0+17.53-41.98)=-24.45;$$
$$M_{C''C}=1(0+0)=0.$$

PROBLEMS

31. Obtain the load constant for the joint equations of the truss shown in Fig. 96.

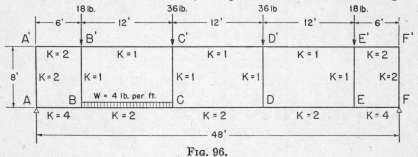

Fig. 96.

32. All members of the truss shown in Fig. 97 have the same stiffness ratio. Assuming the common K as unity, determine the deflection angles, deflections and end moments.

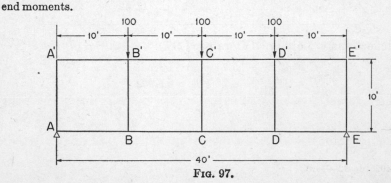

Fig. 97.

44. Vierendeel Trusses with Inclined Chords.—The inclined-chord Vierendeel truss is fundamentally a multi-story trapezoidal bent; hence the procedure of solution, outlined in Arts. 40 and 41, for the latter type of framing is equally valid in this case. As in the parallel-chord truss, the similarity is at once seen by considering the ends of the truss as the tops of two bents bending about a common base. For a truss of symmetrical framing and loading, having an even number of panels, illustrated in Fig. 98 (a), the web member located

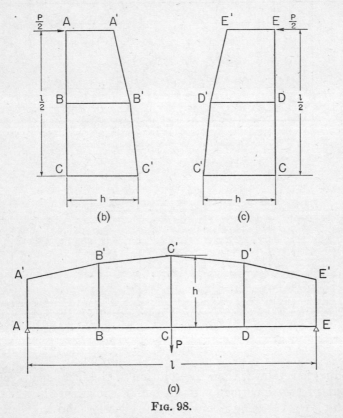

FIG. 98.

at mid-span becomes the axis of rotation, and the two halves of the truss may be regarded as two identical vertical bents, bending in opposite directions. Since the loading in this particular case consists of a single force P, each reaction, $\frac{P}{2}$, constitutes the loading in the respective bent; and since the joints C and C' are located on the line of symmetry and rotation, their deflection angles become zero, thus providing fixed bases for the equivalent two bents in Fig. 98 (*b*) and (*c*).

If the truss is composed of an odd number of panels, as, for example, the five-bay truss shown in Fig. 99 (*a*), and the symmetry of framing

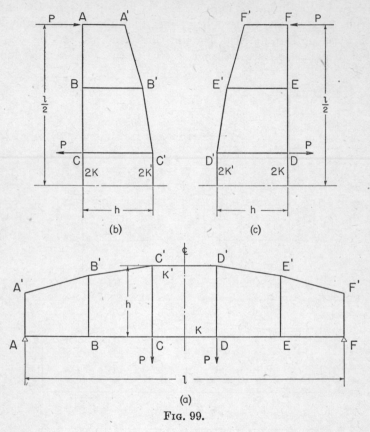

Fig. 99.

and loading is retained, then the solution of the truss again coincides with that of two identical vertical bents, shown in (*b*) and (*c*), in which the lateral loading is made of the reaction and the load in the respective half of the truss. The joints *C* and *D* having the same deflection, the deflection term *R* of that panel is zero and $C = -D$. This condition is simulated in the equivalent vertical bent by assuming its two legs in the bottom story to be one-half as long as the corresponding members in the truss and the legs fixed at the bases.

In the more general case of unsymmetrical loading, indicated in Fig. 100, the truss may again be considered as composed of two

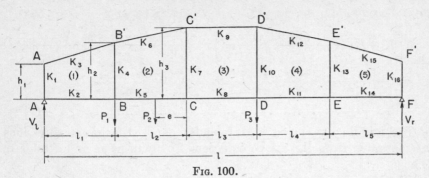

vertical bents in which, unlike the preceding special cases, the deflections and deflection angles of the two parts differ. For the common base of the two bents we may choose either the member CC' or DD' which limit the middle bay of the truss. This consideration being intended to establish a similarity between the truss and a trapezoidal bent, it is clear that any other web member may serve as reference line; in fact, the truss may be regarded as a single vertical bent, in which one end post constitutes the top strut of the bent and the other its base. It is more convenient, however, to use for reference base a web member located near the center of the truss.

The typical joint expressions, written for the panel (1), and derived as in Art. 40, are in the following forms:

Joint A,

$$\left[K_1+K_2+\frac{(3-m)(nK_1-K_2)K_2}{2(2-m)(K_2+K_3)}\right]A+\left[\frac{K_1}{2}+\frac{(3-m)(nK_1-K_2)K_3}{2(2-m)(K_2+K_3)}\right]A'$$

$$+\left[\frac{K_2}{2}+\frac{(3-2m)(nK_1-K_2)K_2}{2(2-m)(K_2+K_3)}\right]B+\left[\frac{(3-2m)(nK_1-K_2)K_3}{2(2-m)(K_2+K_3)}\right]B'$$

$$=-Q_A; \quad \ldots \ldots \ldots \ldots \ldots \ldots \quad (117)$$

Joint A',

$$\left[K_1+K_3+\frac{(3-m)(nK_1-K_3)K_3}{2(2-m)(K_2+K_3)}\right]A'+\left[\frac{K_1}{2}+\frac{(3-m)(nK_1-K_3)K_2}{2(2-m)(K_2+K_3)}\right]A$$

$$+\left[\frac{K_3}{2}+\frac{(3-2m)(nK_1-K_3)K_3}{2(2-m)(K_2+K_3)}\right]B'+\left[\frac{(3-2m)(nK_1-K_3)K_2}{2(2-m)(K_2+K_3)}\right]B$$

$$=-Q_{A'}; \quad \ldots \ldots \ldots \ldots, \ldots \ldots \quad (117a)$$

Joint B,

$$\left[K_2+K_4-\frac{(3-2m)K_2^2}{2(2-m)(K_2+K_3)}\right]B+\left[\frac{K_2}{2}-\frac{(3-m)K_2^2}{2(2-m)(K_2+K_3)}\right]A$$

$$+\left[\frac{K_4}{2}-\frac{(3-2m)K_2K_3}{2(2-m)(K_2+K_3)}\right]B'-\left[\frac{(3-m)K_2K_3}{2(2-m)(K_2+K_3)}\right]A'$$

$$=-Q_B; \quad \ldots \ldots \ldots \ldots \ldots \ldots \quad (118)$$

Joint B',

$$\left[K_3+K_4-\frac{(3-2m)K_3^2}{2(2-m)(K_2+K_3)}\right]B'+\left[\frac{K_3}{2}-\frac{(3-m)K_3^2}{2(2-m)(K_2+K_3)}\right]A'$$

$$+\left[\frac{K_4}{2}-\frac{(3-2m)K_2K_3}{2(2-m)(K_2+K_3)}\right]B-\left[\frac{(3-m)K_2K_3}{2(2-m)(K_2+K_3)}\right]A$$

$$=-Q_{B'}; \quad \dots \dots \dots \dots \dots \dots \dots \dots \dots \dots (118a)$$

The middle bay being a rectangular panel, the joint expressions are obtained from the above equations by equating m and n to zero, Thus:

Joint C,

$$\left[K_7+K_8-\frac{3K_8^2}{4(K_8+K_9)}\right]C+\left[\frac{K_7}{2}-\frac{3K_8K_9}{4(K_8+K_9)}\right]C'+\left[\frac{K_8}{2}-\frac{3K_8^2}{4(K_8+K_9)}\right]D$$

$$-\frac{3K_8K_9}{4(K_8+K_9)}D'=-Q_C \quad \dots \dots \dots (119)$$

Joint D,

$$\left[K_8+K_{10}-\frac{3K_8^2}{4(K_8+K_9)}\right]D+\left[\frac{K_{10}}{2}-\frac{3K_8K_9}{4(K_8+K_9)}\right]D'$$

$$+\left[\frac{K_8}{2}-\frac{3K_8^2}{4(K_8+K_9)}\right]C-\frac{3K_8K_9C'}{4(K_8+K_9)}=-Q_D \quad \dots (119a)$$

The deflections R of the panels are expressed by the following typical equations, written for the panels (1) and (3):

$$R1=\frac{(3-m)(K_2A+K_3A')+(3-2m)(K_2B+K_3B')}{2(2-m)(K_2+K_3)}+Q_{R1}. \quad (120)$$

$$R3=\frac{3(K_8C+K_9C')+3(K_8D+K_9D')}{4(K_8+K_9)}+Q_{R3} \quad \dots \dots (121)$$

For the load constants Q of the joint and deflection expressions we have:

Panel (1),

$$Q_{R1}=\frac{H_1l_1-mM_1}{(2-m)(K_2+K_3)}=\frac{(1-m)V_l l_1}{(2-m)(K_2+K_3)}, \quad \dots \dots (110a)$$

$$-Q_A=\frac{(nK_1-K_2)(mM_1-H_1l_1)}{(2-m)(K_2+K_3)}=\frac{(nK_1-K_2)(m-1)V_l l_1}{(2-m)(K_2+K_3)}, \quad (110b)$$

$$-Q_{A'}=\frac{(nK_1-K_3)(mM_1-H_1l_1)}{(2-m)(K_2+K_3)}=\frac{(nK_1-K_3)(m-1)V_l l_1}{(2-m)(K_2+K_3)}, \quad (110c)$$

$$-Q_B=\frac{K_2(H_1l_1-mM_1)}{(2-m)(K_2+K_3)}=\frac{K_2(1-m)V_l l_1}{(2-m)(K_2+K_3)}, \quad \dots \dots (110d)$$

$$-Q_{B'}=\frac{K_3(H_1l_1-mM)}{(2-m)(K_2+K_3)}=\frac{K_3(1-m)V_l l_1}{(2-m)(K_2+K_3)}; \quad \dots \dots (110e)$$

Panel (2),

$$Q_{R2} = \frac{FM_{BC} + (1-m_2)FM_{CB} + H_2 l_2 - m_2 M_2}{(2-m_2)(K_5+K_6)}, \quad \ldots \ldots \ldots \quad (111a)$$

$$-Q_B = -FM_{BC} - \frac{(n_2 K_4 - K_5)}{(2-m_2)(K_5+K_6)}[FM_{BC}$$

$$+ (1-m_2)FM_{CB} + H_2 l_2 - m_2 M_2], \ldots \ldots \ldots \quad (111b)$$

$$-Q_C = -FM_{CB} + \frac{K_5}{(2-m_2)(K_5+K_6)}[FM_{BC}$$

$$+ (1-m_2)FM_{CB} + H_2 l_2 - m_2 M_2], \quad \ldots \ldots \ldots \quad (111c)$$

$$-Q_{B'} = -\frac{(n_2 K_4 - K_6)}{(2-m_2)(K_5+K_6)}[FM_{BC} + (1-m_2)FM_{CB} + H_2 l_2 - m_2 M_2], (111d)$$

$$-Q_{C'} = \frac{K_6}{(2-m_2)(K_5+K_6)}[FM_{BC} + (1-m_2)FM_{CB} + H_2 l_2 - m_2 M_2]; . \quad (111e)$$

Panel (3),

$$\left.\begin{array}{l} Q_{R3} = \dfrac{H_3 l_3}{2(K_8+K_9)}, \\[2ex] -Q_C = -Q_D = \dfrac{K_8 H_3 l_3}{2(K_8+K_9)}, \\[2ex] -Q_{C'} = -Q_{D'} = \dfrac{K_9 H_3 l_3}{2(K_8+K_9)}. \end{array}\right\} \quad \ldots \ldots \quad (122)$$

H_1, H_2 and H_3 in the above equations denote the shears of panels (1), (2) and (3), respectively; M_1 and M_2 the moments, taken above the base of the respective panel. Both H and M are assumed to be positive, that is, rotating in a clockwise direction. For the truss and loading shown in Fig. 100 we have:

$$H_1 = V_l, \ H_2 = V_l - P_1 - \frac{e}{l_2}P_2, \ H_3 = V_l - P_1 - P_2, \ H_4 = H_5 = -V_r;$$

$$M_1 = V_l l_1, \ M_2 = V_l(l_1+l_2) - P_1 l_2 - eP_2, \ M_4 = -V_r(l_4+l_5), \ M_5 = -V_r l_5;$$

$$m = \frac{h_2 - h_1}{h_2}, \ m_2 = \frac{h_3 - h_2}{h_3}; \ n = \frac{h_2 - h_1}{h_1}, \ n_2 = \frac{l_3 - h_2}{h_2}.$$

If the top and bottom chord members in a panel have the same stiffness ratio, and no load is applied between the joints, as shown in Fig. 101, then the deflection angles of top chord joints equal those of

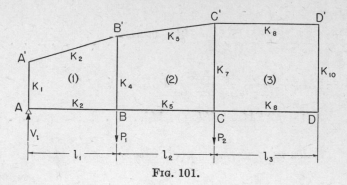

FIG. 101.

the respective joints in the bottom chord, and the joint and deflection
equations become:

Panel (1), joint A,

$$\left[1.5K_1+K_2+\frac{(3-m)(nK_1-K_2)}{2(2-m)}\right]A$$

$$+\left[\frac{K_2}{2}+\frac{(3-2m)(nK_1-K_2)}{2(2-m)}\right]B=-Q_A; \ \cdot \ \cdot \ \cdot \ (117c)$$

Panel (1), joint B,

$$\left[K_2+1.5K_4-\frac{(3-2m)K_2}{2(2-m)}\right]B+\left[\frac{K_2}{2}-\frac{(3-m)K_2}{2(2-m)}\right]A=-Q_B; \ (118c)$$

$$R1=\frac{(3-m)A+(3-2m)B}{2(2-m)}+Q_{R1}; \ \cdot \ \cdot \ \cdot \ \cdot \ \cdot \ (120a)$$

Panel (3),

$$\left.\begin{aligned} \left(1.5K_7+\frac{K_8}{4}\right)C-\frac{K_8}{4}D=-Q_C, \\ \left(1.5K_{10}+\frac{K_8}{4}\right)D-\frac{K_8}{4}C=-Q_D; \end{aligned}\right\} \ \cdot \ \cdot \ \cdot \ \cdot \ \cdot \ (119c)$$

$$R3=\frac{3}{4}(C+D)+C_{R3};$$

in which

$$\left.\begin{aligned} -Q_A=\frac{(nK_1-K_2)(mM_1-H_1l_1)}{2(2-m)K}, \\ -Q_B=\frac{(H_1l_1-mM_1)}{2(2-m)}; \end{aligned}\right\} \ \cdot \ \cdot \ \cdot \ \cdot \ \cdot \ (110f)$$

$$Q_{R1} = \frac{H_1 l_1 - m M_1}{2(2-m)K_2};$$

$$-Q_C = -Q_D = \frac{H_3 l_3}{4};$$

$$Q_{R3} = \frac{H_3 l_3}{4 K_8} = \frac{(V_l - P_1 - P_2)l_3}{4 K_8}$$

. . . . . . (122a)

Having obtained the joint and deflection expressions, the remainder of the solution is made in the usual manner. In the first step, the end moments are computed for each panel as a separate unit—assumed to be hinged to the members of the adjacent panels. The error thus made is then adjusted in the next step. By considering the initial moments of the first step as the new load constants in the joint equations, the solution is repeated, resulting in a first set of moment increments or corrections. If necessary, additional corrections are similarly obtained. The following example will illustrate the procedure of solution in detail.

ILLUSTRATIVE EXAMPLE

The five-bay truss shown in Fig. 102 carries a single load placed at the third joint of the lower chord. The truss is symmetrical about its vertical axis and the chords have the same stiffness ratio in each panel. Determine the end moments by computing the initial values and then applying two corrections.

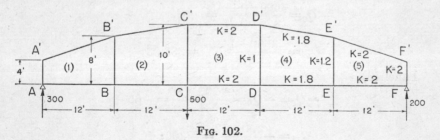

Fig. 102.

Solution: Since the top and bottom chord members are of equal stiffness, and the load is applied at the panel point, the deflection angles of the top chord joints equal those of the corresponding joints in the bottom chord. However, the loading being unsymmetrical, the values of deflection angles for joints symmetrically located—with respect to the vertical axis of symmetry of the truss—differ, and it will be necessary to compute the moments in all five panels.

Assuming the web member DD' as the base for the two halves of the truss, the various panel constants are given in the following table:

Panel	1	2	3	4	5
m	0.5	0.20	0	0.20	0.5
n	1.0	0.25	0	0.25	1.0
H	300	300	-200	-200	-200
M	3600	7200		-4800	-2400

The load constants are obtained by substituting these values in eqs (110f) and (122a). Thus:

Panel (1),

$$-Q_A = \frac{(2-2)(1800-3600)}{4(2-0.5)} = 0,$$

$$-Q_B = \frac{3600-1800}{2(2-0.5)} = 600,$$

$$Q_{R1} = \frac{3600-1800}{4(2-0.5)} = 300;$$

Panel (2) (base CC'),

$$-Q_B = \frac{(0.3-1.8)(1440-3600)}{2 \times 1.8(2-0.2)} = 500,$$

$$-Q_C = \frac{3600-1440}{2(2-0.2)} = 600;$$

$$Q_{R2} = \frac{3600-1440}{2 \times 1.8(2-0.2)} = 333.33$$

Panel (3),

$$-Q_C = -Q_D = \frac{-200 \times 12}{4} = -600;$$

$$Q_{R3} = -\frac{200 \times 12}{4 \times 2} = -300;$$

Panel (4) (base DD'),

$$-Q_B = -\frac{1.5(2400-960)}{2 \times 1.8 \times 1.8} = -333.33,$$

$$-Q_D = -\frac{2400-960}{2 \times 1.8} = -400;$$

$$Q_{R4} = -\frac{2400-960}{2 \times 1.8 \times 1.8} = -222.22;$$

Panel (5) (base EE'),

$$-Q_F=0; \quad -Q_E=-\frac{2400-1200}{2\times1.5}=-400;$$

$$Q_{R5}=-\frac{2400-1200}{4\times1.5}=-200.$$

Applying eqs. (117c) and (118c), for the joint equations of panel (1) we have:

$$\left[3+2+\frac{2.5(2-2)}{2\times1.5}\right]A+\left[1+\frac{2(2-2)}{2\times1.5}\right]B=0,$$

$$\left[2+1.8-\frac{2\times2}{2\times1.5}\right]B+\left[1-\frac{2.5\times2}{2\times1.5}\right]A=600;$$

or,

$$5A+B=0,$$

$$-0.67A+2.47B=600;$$

from which

$$A=-46.15, \quad B=230.77;$$

and

$$R1=\frac{-2.5\times46.15+2\times230.77}{2\times1.5}+300=415.39.$$

Then the initial moments of the panel are:

$$M_{AB}=2(-46.15+115.38-415.39)=-692.32,$$

$$M_{BA}=2(-23.07+230.77-415.39)=-415.38.$$

Similarly, for the joint equations of panel (2) we have:

$$2.433B-0.183C=500,$$

$$-0.5B+2.0C=600;$$

from which

$$C=358.11, \quad B=232.44;$$

and

$$R2=\frac{2.8\times232.44+2.6\times358.11}{2\times1.8}+333.33=772.75.$$

With these values, initial moments of panel (2) become:

$$M_{BC}=1.8(232.44+179.06-772.75)=-650.26,$$

$$M_{CB}=1.8(116.22+358.11-772.75)=-537.16.$$

Panel (3) being rectangular and of symmetrical stiffness, the two joint equations, obtained from eqs. (119c), are of identical form:

$$2.0C - 0.5D = -600,$$
$$2.0D - 0.5C = -600;$$

hence

$$C = D = -400;$$
$$R_3 = -1.5 \times 400 - 300 = -900;$$

and

$$M_{CD} = M_{DC} = 2(-1.5 \times 400 + 900) = 600.$$

Due to the symmetry in framing of the truss, panels (4) and (5) have the same joint equations, excepting the load constants, as panels (2) and (1), respectively. The panel shear and moment in the former being two thirds of the latter (with opposite signs), the load constants and, consequently, the initial end moments will also vary in the same ratio. Thus:

Panel (4),

$$M_{DE} = -\frac{2}{3}M_{CB} = 358.31,$$

$$M_{ED} = -\frac{2}{3}M_{BC} = 433.11;$$

Panel (5),

$$M_{EF} = -\frac{2}{3}M_{BA} = 276.92$$

$$M_{FE} = -\frac{2}{3}M_{AB} = 461.55.$$

This completes the calculations of the initial end moments of the five panels. To apply a first correction to the moments of panel (1), the initial moment M_{BC}, originally assumed to be zero, is substituted for the load constant in the joint equation of B and the solution repeated as follows:

$$5A + 1B = 0,$$
$$-0.67A + 2.47B = 650.26;$$

from which

$$A = -50.02, \quad B = 250.10;$$

and the load constant of the deflection equation being zero,

$$R_1 = \frac{-2.5 \times 50.02 + 2 \times 250.1}{2 \times 1.5} = 125.08.$$

Then the first moment increments or corrections of the panel, obtained from these values, are:

$$M_{AB}=2(-50.02+125.05-125.08)=-100.10,$$
$$M_{BA}=2(-25.01+250.10-125.08)=200.02.$$

Similarly, in panel (2), using the initial moments M_{BA} and M_{CD} as load constants for joint equations B and C, respectively, we have:

$$2.433B-0.183C=415.38,$$
$$-0.5B+2.0C=-600.0;$$

from which

$$B=151.12, \quad C=-262.22;$$
$$R2=\frac{2.8\times151.12-2.6\times262.22}{2\times1.8}=-71.28;$$

and

$$M_{BC}=1.8(151.12-131.11\mid71.28)=164.32,$$
$$M_{CB}=1.8(75.56-262.22+71.28)=-207.68.$$

Likewise, panel (3),

$$2.0C-0.5D=537.16,$$
$$-0.5C+2.0D=-358.11;$$

$$C=238.74, \quad D=-119.37;$$
$$R3=\frac{3}{4}(238.74-119.37)=89.53;$$

$$M_{CD}=2(238.74-59.68-89.53)=179.06,$$
$$M_{DC}=2(119.37-119.37-89.53)=-179.06.$$

Panel (4),

$$2.433E-0.183D=-276.92,$$
$$-0.5E+2.0\ D=-600.0.$$

$$D=-334.72, \quad E=-138.88;$$
$$R4=-\frac{2.8\times138.88+2.6\times334.72}{2\times1.8}=-349.76;$$

$$M_{ED}=1.8(-138.88-167.36+349.76)=78.34,$$
$$M_{DE}=1.8(-69.44-334.72+349.76)=-97.92.$$

Panel (5),

$$5.0F+1.0E=0,$$
$$-0.67F+2.47E=-433.51;$$

therefore,

$$M_{EF}=-\frac{2}{3}M_{BA}=-133.35,$$

$$M_{FE}=-\frac{2}{3}M_{AB}=66.73.$$

The results of the second correction, similarly obtained from the first moment increments, are shown in Table 10. This table contains the summary of computations and the final chord moments. The end moments of the web members are obtained by adding up the two chord moments at each joint.

TABLE 10.

(For Truss shown in Fig. 102)

	Panel	(1)		(2)		(3)		(4)		(5)	
	Joint	A	B	B	C	C	D	D	E	E	F
Initial values	$-Q$	0	600	500	600	−600	−600	−400	−333.33	−400	0
	α	−46.15	230.77	232.44	358.11	−400	−400				
	R	415.39		772.75		−900					
	M'	−692.32	−415.38	−650.26	−537.16	600	600	358.11	433.51	276.92	461.55
1st increment	$-Q$	0	650.26	415.38	−600	537.16	−358.11	−600	−276.92	−433.51	0
	α	−50.02	250.10	151.2	−262.22	238.74	−119.37				
	R	125.08		−71.28		89.53					
	M''	−100.10	200.02	164.32	−207.68	179.06	−179.06	−97.92	78.34	−133.35	66.73
2d increment	$-Q$	0	−164.32	−200.02	−179.06	207.68	97.92	179.06	133.35	−78.34	0
	α	12.64	−63.20	−90.60	−112.18	123.82	79.92	105.20	62.68	−30.13	6.03
	R	−31.60		−151.48		152.80		124.73		−15.07	
	M'''	25.28	−50.56	8.62	−10.8	21.95	−21.95	21.26	−17.01	−24.1	12.08
M', M'', M'''		−767.14	−265.92	−477.32	−755.64	801.0	399.0	281.45	494.84	119.47	540.36
Location of M		M_{AB}	M_{BA}	M_{BC}	M_{CB}	M_{CD}	M_{DC}	M_{DE}	M_{ED}	M_{EF}	M_{FE}

PROBLEMS

33. Determine the joint equations for panel (2) of the truss shown in Fig. 103. The stiffness of top and bottom chord members vary.

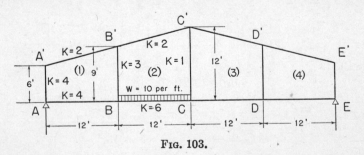

FIG. 103.

34. The loading of the five-bay truss shown in Fig. 104 is symmetrical. Obtain the end moments by first computing the initial values in each panel and then performing two corrections. Give the results in a tabular form similar to Table 10.

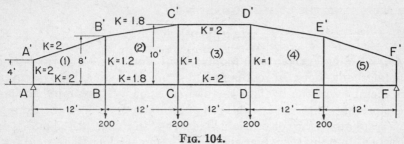

FIG. 104.

CHAPTER IV

GABLE BENTS

45. Building Frames with Sloping Roof Members.—In a rigid-frame
building bent, a gabled roof is provided merely by inclining the upper
two members of the bent to the desired slope. This simple arrangement presents distinct advantages of economy in design and graceful
appearance over the conventional truss type framing. Used mostly for
industrial buildings, such as shops and hangars, the gabled rigid bent,
built either in concrete or steel, constitutes an ideal architectural
medium for framings of auditoriums, assembly halls, theaters, churches,
and similar buildings where the esthetical consideration is of prime
importance. According to their outline, these bents may be classed in
three general groups:

(a) Single-span, single-story bents;

(b) Single-span, two-story bents; and

(c) Single-story bents of more than one span.

**46. Single-span, Single-story Symmetrical Bents with Symmetrical
Loading.**—In Fig. 105 there are shown three types of symmetrical

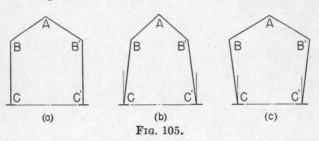

(a)   (b)   (c)

Fig. 105.

bents. The legs of the bent in (a) are vertical, those of the bents n
(b) and (c) are inclined; in the former sloping inward and in the
latter outward.

In general, the determination of moments for these bents, when
subjected to a system of loading, will require the solution of deflection
angles of the three upper joints, the deflections of the top and leg
members and the vertical and horizontal reactions at the bases.
With proper elimination, however, the number of the unknowns is
reduced to three, that is, the deflection angles of the joints A, B, and

146

B'—as given by the respective joint expressions. The procedure for obtaining these joint equations is similar to that used in the derivation of joint expressions for other types of bents as outlined in the preceding chapters.

Due to its relative simplicity, we will consider first the bent with vertical legs, having a symmetrical loading. Fig. 106 represents such

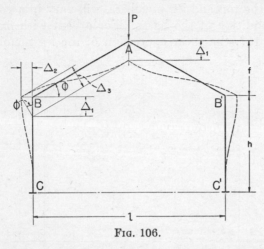

FIG. 106.

a case. As seen from the exaggerated deformation diagram of the bent, the downward deflection, Δ_1, of the top joint is accompanied by the lateral displacements, Δ_2, of the joints B and B'. The interrelation of the deflections is governed by the angle of inclination of the top members. In deflecting, the lengths of the members remain unchanged (the effect of axial stresses is neglected), and their true deflections, that is, the displacements normal to each member, equal

$$\Delta_{AB} = \Delta_{AB'} = \Delta_3 = \Delta_2 \, csc\phi, \quad \ldots \ldots \ldots \ldots (a)$$

where ϕ indicates the slope of the top members. Then, the deflection terms R of the members become:

$$R = R_{BC} = \frac{\Delta_2}{h} = -R_{B'C'} = -R', \quad \ldots \ldots \ldots (b)$$

$$R_{AB} = \frac{\Delta_{AB}}{f} \cdot \sin\phi = \frac{\Delta_2}{f} = -R_{AB'}; \quad \ldots \ldots \ldots (c)$$

from which, noting that the rotation of AB is in opposite direction to that of BC,

$$R_{AB} = -\frac{h}{f}R = -R_{AB'} = \frac{h}{f}R' \quad \ldots \ldots \ldots (123)$$

(It is to be noted from the deformation diagram that the sign of R_{BC} is minus. However, R being an algebraic quantity, and serving as the basis of Rs of the other members, it is more convenient to consider it as positive. This, of course, does not alter the correct signs of the rotations which result from the final solution.)

The value of the horizontal reaction, H, obtained from the shear expressions of the top and leg members, will vary in accordance with the support condition at the bases. For a bent with fixed bases, as shown in Fig. 107, the shear expression of the leg member BC is in

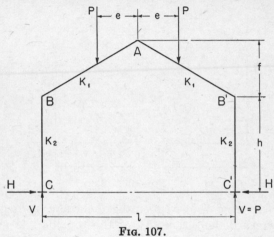

FIG. 107.

the form

$$M_{BC}+M_{CB}-Hh=1.5K_2B-2K_2R-Hh=\frac{1.5K_2}{h}B-\frac{2K_2}{h}R-H=0 \ .. \ (d)$$

Similarly, for the shear expression of the top member AB we have:

$$M_{AB}+M_{BA}+\frac{Vl}{2}-Pe-Hf=1.5K_1B+\frac{2hK_1}{f}R+FM_{AB}$$

$$+FM_{BA}+P\Big(\frac{l}{2}-e\Big)-Hf=\frac{1.5K_1}{f}B+\frac{2hK_1}{f^2}R$$

$$+\frac{1}{f}(FM_{AB}+FM_{BA})+\frac{P}{f}\Big(\frac{l}{2}-e\Big)-H=0 \ . \ . \ . \ . \ . \ . \ . \ . \ (e)$$

Subtracting eq. (e) from eq. (d), and solving for R,

$$\Big(\frac{2K_2}{h}+\frac{2hK_1}{f^2}\Big)R=\frac{3}{2}\Big(\frac{K_2}{h}-\frac{K_1}{f}\Big)B-\frac{1}{f}(FM_{AB}+FM_{BA})-\frac{P}{f}\Big(\frac{l}{2}-e\Big),$$

or,

$$R=-\frac{3f(hK_1-fK_2)}{4(h^2K_1+f^2K_2)}B-\frac{fh(FM_{AB}+FM_{BA})}{2(h^2K_1+f^2K_2)}-\frac{fhP(l-2e)}{4(h^2K_1+f^2K_2)}\cdot \ (124)$$

The loading being symmetrical, the deflection angle at A is zero, and the value at B is obtained from the joint expression of B. Thus,

$$M_{BA}+M_{BC}=(K_1+K_2)B+\left(\frac{h}{f}K_1-K_2\right)R+FM_{BA}=0 \quad . \quad . \quad (f)$$

Substituting for R in eq. (f) its value from eq. (124),

$$\left[K_1+K_2-\frac{3(hK_1-fK_2)^2}{4(h^2K_1+f^2K_2)}\right]B=-FM_{BA}+\frac{h(hK_1-fK_2)}{2(h^2K_1+f^2K_2)}(FM_{AB}+FM_{BA})$$

$$+\frac{hP(hK_1-fK_2)(l-2e)}{4(h^2K_1+f^2K_2)}=-Q_B \quad . \quad . \quad . \quad . \quad . \quad . \quad (125)$$

If the bases of the bent are assumed to be hinged, the shear expression of the member BC changes to the following form:

$$M_{BC}-Hh=\frac{3}{4}K_2B-\frac{K_2}{2}R-Hh=\frac{3K_2}{1h}B-\frac{K_2}{2h}R-H=0 \quad . \quad . \quad . \quad (g)$$

and the corresponding joint and deflection equations become:

$$\left[K_1+\frac{3}{4}K_2-\frac{3(2hK_1-fK_2)^2}{4(4h^2K_1+f^2K_2)}\right]B=-FM_{BA}$$

$$+\frac{h(2hK_1-fK_2)}{(4h^2K_1+f^2K_2)}(FM_{AB}+FM_{BA})+\frac{hP(2hK_1-fK_2)(l-2e)}{2(4h^2K_1+f^2K_2)}=-Q_B . \quad (126)$$

$$R=-\frac{3f(2hK_1-fK_2)}{2(4h^2K_1+f^2K_2)}B-\frac{2fh(FM_{AB}+FM_{BA})}{(4h^2K_1+f^2K_2)}-\frac{fhP(l-2e)}{(4h^2K_1+f^2K_2)} \quad . \quad (127)$$

The relation between the deflections of top and leg members of the bent with vertical legs, as given by eq. (123), applies also to bents with inclined legs, the deformations being similar to that shown in Fig. 106. Accordingly, the joint and deflection equations of the bent shown in Fig. 108, the legs of which slope inward, will differ from the

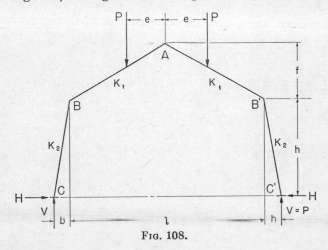

FIG. 108.

expressions of the preceding case only by an additional term—the moment of the vertical reaction at top of the leg, Vb, affecting the shear expression of that member. Assuming the legs to be fixed at the bases, the shear equation is in the form

$$M_{BC} + M_{CB} + Vb - Hh = 1.5K_2B - 2K_2R + Pb - Hh$$

$$= \frac{3K_2}{2h}B - \frac{2K_2}{h}R + \frac{Pb}{h} - H = 0 \quad \cdots \quad (h)$$

The shear expression of the top member, eq. (e), remains unchanged, and the deflection and joint equations become:

$$R = -\frac{3f(hK_2 - fK_2)}{4(h^2K_1 + f^2K_2)}B - \frac{fh(FM_{AB} + FM_{BA})}{2(h^2K_1 + f^2K_2)} - \frac{fh(l - 2e)P}{4(h^2K_1 + f^2K_2)}$$

$$+ \frac{f^2bP}{2(h^2K_1 + f^2K_2)}; \quad \cdots \quad (124a)$$

$$\left[K_1 + K_2 - \frac{3(hK_1 - fK_2)^2}{4(h^2K_1 + f^2K_2)}\right]B = -FM_{BA} + \frac{h(hK_1 - fK_2)}{2(h^2K_1 + f^2K_2)}(FM_{AB} + FM_{BA})$$

$$+ \frac{h(hK_1 - fK_2)(l - 2e)P}{4(h^2K_1 + f^2K_2)} - \frac{bf(hK_1 - fK_2)P}{2(h^2K_1 + f^2K_2)} = -Q_B \quad (125a)$$

If the bases are hinged,

$$M_{BC} + Vb - Hh = \frac{3K_2}{4h}B - \frac{K_2R}{2h} + \frac{Pb}{h} - H = 0, \quad \cdots \quad (i)$$

and

$$R = -\frac{3f(2hK_1 - fK_2)}{2(4h^2K_1 + f^2K_2)}B - \frac{2fh(FM_{AB} + FM_{BA})}{4h^2K_1 + f^2K_2} - \frac{fh(l - 2e)P}{4h^2K_1 + f^2K_2}$$

$$+ \frac{2bf^2P}{4h^2K_1 + f^2K_2}, \quad \cdots \quad (126a)$$

$$\left[K_1 + \frac{3}{4}K_2 - \frac{3(2hK_1 - fK_2)^2}{4(4h^2K_1 + f^2K_2)}\right]B = -FM_{BA}$$

$$+ \frac{h(2hK_1 - fK_2)}{4h^2K_1 + f^2K_2}(FM_{AB} + FM_{BA}) + \frac{h(2hK_1 - fK_2)(l - 2e)P}{2(4h^2K_1 + f^2K_2)}$$

$$- \frac{bf(2hK_1 - fK_2)P}{4h^2K_1 + f^2K_2} = -Q_B \quad \cdots \quad (127a)$$

In the case of the bent shown in Fig. 109, where the legs slope out-

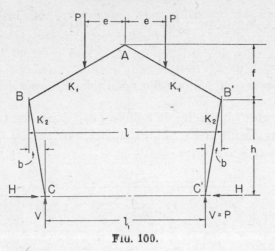

Fiu. 100.

ward, the shear expression of BC, for the fixed base condition, is in the form

$$M_{BC} + M_{CB} - Vb - Hh = 1.5K_2B - 2K_2R - Pb - Hh$$

$$= \frac{3K_2}{2h}B - \frac{2K_2}{h}R - \frac{Pb}{h} - H = 0 \quad \ldots \ldots \quad (j)$$

Eq. (e), the shear expression of the top member AB, remaining un-altered, the deflection and joint equations become:

$$R = -\frac{3f(hK_1 - fK_2)}{4(h^2K_1 + f^2K_2)}B - \frac{fh(FM_{AB} + FM_{BA})}{2(h^2K_1 + f^2K_1)} - \frac{fh(l - 2e)P}{4(h^2K_1 + f^2K_2)}$$

$$- \frac{bf^2P}{2(h^2K_1 + f^2K_2)} \quad \ldots \quad (124b)$$

$$\left[K_1 + K^2 - \frac{3(hK_1 - fK_2)^2}{4(h^2K_1 + f^2K_2)}\right]B = -FM_{BA} + \frac{h(hK_1 - fK_2)}{2(h^2K_1 + f^2K_2)}(FM_{AB} + FM_{BA})$$

$$+ \frac{h(hK_1 - fK_2)(l - 2e)P}{4(h^2K_1 + f^2K_2)} + \frac{bf(hK_1 - fK_2)P}{2(h^2K_1 + f^2K_2)} = -Q_B \ldots \quad (125b)$$

Similarly, if the bases are hinged,

$$M_{BC} - Vb - Hh\frac{3K_2}{4h} = B - \frac{K_2R}{2h} - \frac{Pb}{h} - H = 0 \quad \ldots \ldots \quad (k)$$

and

$$R = -\frac{3f(2hK_1 - fK_2)}{2(4h^2K_1 + f^2K_2)}B - \frac{2fh(FM_{AB} + FM_{BA})}{4h^2K_1 + f^2K_2} - \frac{fh(l - 2e)P}{4h^2K_1 + f^2K_2}$$

$$- \frac{2bf^2P}{4h^2K_1 + f^2K_2} \quad \ldots \quad (126b)$$

$$\left[K_1 + \frac{3}{4}K_2 - \frac{3(2hK_1 - fK_2)^2}{4(4h^2K_1 + f^2K_2)}\right]B = -FM_{BA} + \frac{h(2hK_1 - fK_2)}{4h^2K_1 + f^2K_2}(FM_{AB} + FM_{BA})$$

$$+ \frac{h(2hK_1 - fK_2)(l - 2e)P}{2(4h^2K_1 + f^2K_2)} + \frac{bf(2hK_1 - fK_2)P}{4h^2K_1 + f^2K_2} = -Q_B \quad \ldots \quad (127b)$$

It is interesting to note from these equations that the deflections and deflection angles of the bent with vertical legs are larger than those for the bent with inward-sloping legs, and smaller (by the same amount) as compared to the bent having outward-battering legs, provided, of course, the dimensions and the stiffnesses are the same in all three bents.

When the vertical loading is uniform, say w per linear foot of roof projection, as shown in Fig. 110, the load constants of the equations

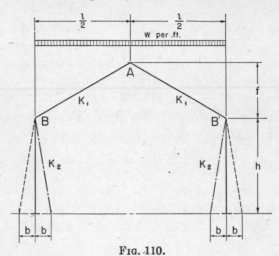

Fig. 110.

assume simplified forms as a result of the following relations:

$$FM_{AB}+FM_{BA}=0; \quad (l-2e)P=\frac{wl^2}{4}; \quad V=\frac{wl}{2}; \quad FM_{BA}=-\frac{wl^2}{48} \quad \cdots \quad (l)$$

Accordingly, for the load constants of the bent with vertical legs and fixed bases we can write:

$$-Q_B=\frac{wl^2}{48}+\frac{h(hK_1-fK_2)}{16(h^2K_1+f^2K_2)}\,wl^2; \quad Q_R=-\frac{fhwl^2}{16(h^2K_1+f^2K_2)} \quad \cdots \quad (128)$$

and for hinged bases,

$$-Q_B=\frac{wl^2}{48}+\frac{h(2hK_1-fK_2)}{8(4h^2K_1+f^2K_2)}wl^2; \quad Q_R=-\frac{fhwl^2}{4(4h^2K_1+f^2K_2)} \quad \cdots \quad (129)$$

In the case of the bent with inclined legs, the load constants become:

(a) Fixed bases,

$$\left.\begin{aligned}-Q_B&=\frac{wl^2}{48}+\frac{h(hK_1-fK_2)}{16(h^2K_1+f^2K_2)}wl^2\mp\frac{bf(hK_1-fK_2)}{4(h^2K_1+f^2K_2)}wl,\\Q_R&=-\frac{fhwl^2}{16(h^2K_1+f^2K_2)}\pm\frac{bf^2wl}{4(h^2K_1+f^2K_2)}\end{aligned}\right\} \quad \cdots \quad (128a)$$

(b) Hinged bases,

$$
\left.
\begin{aligned}
-Q_B &= \frac{wl^2}{48} + \frac{h(2hK_1-fK_2)wl^2}{8(4h^2K_1+f^2K_2)} \mp \frac{bf(2hK_1-fK_2)}{2(4h^2K_1+f^2K_2)}wl, \\
Q_R &= -\frac{fhwl^2}{4(4h^2K_1+f^2K_2)} \pm \frac{bf^2wl}{4h^2K_1+f^2K_2}.
\end{aligned}
\right\} \;\; \text{. . } (129a)
$$

in which the top sign of the last term in each expression corresponds to the bent having inward sloping legs.

ILLUSTRATIVE EXAMPLES

1. The symmetrical bent shown in Fig. 111 is carrying a uniform vertical roof load of 1 kip per lin. ft. of horizontal projection.   Assuming the legs to be fixed at the bases, determine:

(a) End moments at the joints,

(b) Reactions at the bases.

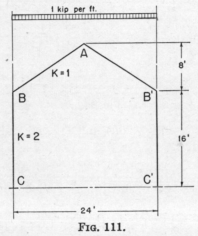

FIG. 111.

Solution: Since the loading is symmetrical, $A=0$, and $B=-B'$. Applying eqs. 124, 125 and 128, we have:

$$
\left[1+2-\frac{3(16-16)^2}{4(16^2+2\times8^2)}\right]B = 12+\frac{16(16-16)24^2}{16(16^2+2\times8^2)}, B=\frac{12}{3}=4;
$$

$$
R = -\frac{3\times8(16-16)4}{4(16^2+2\times8^2)} - \frac{8\times16\times24^2}{16(16^2+2\times8^2)} = -12; \; R_{AB}=\frac{16}{8}\times12=24.
$$

Then, (a)

$$M_{AB}=1(0+2-24)+12=-10 \text{ ft.-kips,}$$

$$M_{BA}=1(4+0-24)-12=-32 \text{ ft.-kips,}$$

$$M_{BC}=2(4+0+12)=32 \text{ ft.-kips,}$$

$$M_{CB}=2(2+0+12)=28 \text{ ft.-kips;}$$

(b)

$$V = 12 \text{ kips};$$

$$H = \frac{32+28}{16} = 3.75 \text{ kips.}$$

2. The symmetrical bent with inclined legs shown in Fig. 112 is subjected to a single vertical load of 2 kips, applied at the crown joint. Assuming the legs to be hinged at the bases, determine the end moments.

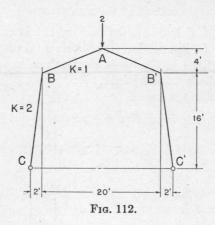

FIG. 112.

Solution: Applying eqs. (126a) and (127a), and noting that (e) is zero and P equals 1,

$$\left[1 + 1.5 - \frac{3(32-8)^2}{4(4\times16^2+32)}\right] B = \frac{(32-8)(20\times16-4\times4)}{2(4\times16^2+32)},$$

$$B = \frac{76}{46} = 1.652;$$

$$R = -\frac{3\times4(32-8)}{2(4\times16^2+32)} \times \frac{76}{46} - \frac{4\times16\times20-4\times4^2}{4\times16^2+32}$$

$$= -1.377; \; R_{AB} = \frac{16}{4}\times1.377 = 5.508.$$

With these values, the end moments become:

$$M_{AB} = 1(0+0.826-5.508) = -4.682 \text{ ft.-kips;}$$

$$M_{BA} = 1(1.652+0-5.508) = -3.856 \text{ ft.-kips,}$$

$$M_{BC} = 2(1.239+0.689) = 3.856 \text{ ft.-kips;}$$

$$M_{CB} = 0$$

PROBLEMS

35. The legs of the bent shown in Fig. 113 have symmetrical brackets. Following the procedure in Art. 46, derive the deflection and joint expressions corresponding to two conditions of support:

(a) Fixed bases;
(b) Hinged bases.

Denote the fixed and hinged-end moments by their symbols.

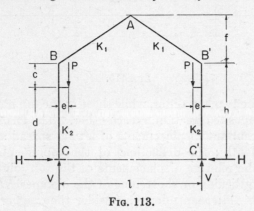

FIG. 113.

36. The loading and the framing of the bent shown in Fig. 114 are symmetrical. Assuming the legs to be hinged to the bases, determine:

(a) End Moments;
(b) Reactions at the bases.

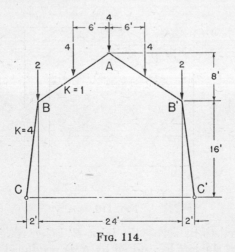

FIG. 114.

47. Single-span, Single-story Symmetrical Bents with Unsymmetrical Loading.—When the loading of a gabled bent is unsymmetrical with respect to the vertical axis, as shown in Fig. 115, then the

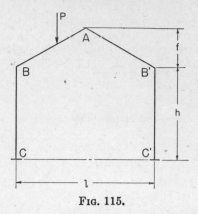

FIG. 115.

deflections of the two legs differ, while those of the top members remain
equal and in opposite direction to each other.   The former deflections,
representing resultant displacements of lateral spread and side sway,
vary independently; the deflections of the top members, however,
depend upon the relative displacements of the top joints of the legs,
that is, the lengthening or shortening of the distance $\overline{BB'}$ in Fig. 115.
To illustrate this interdependency, consider the exaggerated displacement diagram shown in Fig. 116.   Here the deflection of the right leg

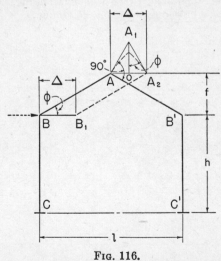

FIG. 116.

$(B'C')$ is assumed to be zero—the joint B' being retained in position.
The deflection of the left leg, noted by Δ, is produced by the displacement of the joint B to its deflected position B_1.   Since the lengths of
the members remain unchanged (the effect of axial stresses neglected),
the new position of the crown joint A is then established by the inter-

section of two arcs, having their centers at B' and B_1, and for radius the common length of the members $BA(=\overline{B_1A_2})$ and $B'A$. However, noting that these displacements are small, and unlike the distorted representation in the figure, we can substitute the two tangent distances $\overline{AA_1}$ and $\overline{A_2A_1}$ for the respective arcs, and consider their intersection point A_1 as the deflected position of the crown joint A. The triangle AA_1A_2 thus formed graphically indicates the interrelation of the true deflections of the three members: $\overline{AA_2}(=\overline{BB_1})$ being the deflection of the leg BC, and the two sides $\overline{AA_1}$ and $\overline{A_2A_1}$ representing the deflections of the top members AB' and AB, respectively. It is also noted that the angles OA_1A and OA_1A_2 being equal to ϕ (the slope of the top members), for the deflections $\overline{AA_1}$ and $\overline{A_1A_2}$ we can write:

$$\overline{AA_1}=\Delta_{AB'}=\frac{\Delta}{2\sin\phi}=\Delta_{AB}; \quad \ldots \ldots \quad (a)$$

and the deflection terms R become:

$$R_{BC}=R=6E\frac{\Delta}{h}; \ R_{B'C'}=0 \ \ldots \ldots \ldots \ldots \quad (b)$$

$$\left.\begin{array}{l} R_{AB'}=6E\dfrac{\Delta_{AB}{}'}{f}\sin\phi=6E\dfrac{\Delta}{2f}=\dfrac{h}{2f}R, \\[2mm] R_{AB}=-R_{AB'}=-\dfrac{h}{2f}R. \end{array}\right\} \ldots \ldots \quad (c)$$

Similarly, if the top of the right leg, joint B, is displaced a distance Δ', and the left leg is prevented from deflecting, for the corresponding deflections of the top members we have:

$$\Delta_{AB}=\frac{\Delta'}{2\sin\phi}=-\Delta_{AB'};$$

and

$$R_{B'C'}=R'=6E\frac{\Delta'}{h}; \ R_{BC}=0,$$

$$R_{AB}=\frac{h}{2f}R', \ \ R_{AB'}=-\frac{h}{2f}R' \ \ldots \ldots \ldots \quad (d)$$

If both legs of the bent are allowed to deflect, and the deflection terms of the left and right legs be indicated by R and R', then the corresponding terms of the top members, obtained from eqs. (c) and (d), become:

$$R_{AB}=\frac{h}{2f}(R'-R), \ R_{AB'}=\frac{h}{2f}(R-R') \ \ldots \ldots \quad (130)$$

Eqs. (130) are the general expressions relating the deflection terms of top and leg members of a bent in unsymmetrical bending. When the two legs sway in the same direction and distance, R_{AB} and $R_{AB'}$ reduce to zero; and when the deflections of the legs are the same but sway in opposite directions, then eqs. (130) become

$$R_{AB} = \frac{h}{f} R = -R_{AB'},$$

which is the relation corresponding to symmetrical bending, as given by eq. (123) in the preceding article.

Having obtained the general deflection relation, the joint expressions of the bent are derived in a manner similar to that outlined in Art. 46.

First, consider the loading shown in Fig. 117. Assuming the legs

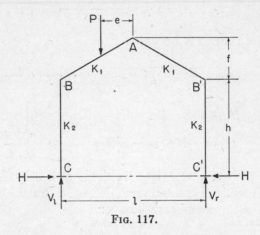

Fig. 117.

of the bent to be fixed at the bases, for the shear expressions of the members AB and BC we can write:

$$M_{AB} + M_{BA} - Hf + V_l \frac{l}{2} - Pe = 0,$$

$$M_{BC} + M_{CB} - Hh = 0.$$

Noting that

$$V_l l = -(M_{BA} + M_{B'A}) + P\left(e + \frac{l}{2}\right),$$

and eliminating H,

$$\frac{1}{f} M_{AB} + \frac{1}{2f}(M_{BA} - M_{B'A}) - \frac{1}{h}(M_{BC} + M_{CB}) + \frac{P}{4f}(l - 2e) = 0 \quad \cdots \quad (e)$$

But

$$M_{AB}=K_1\left[A+\frac{B}{2}-\frac{h}{2f}(R'-R)\right]+FM_{AB};$$

$$M_{BA}=K_1\left[\frac{A}{2}+B-\frac{h}{2f}(R'-R)\right]+FM_{BA};$$

$$M_{B'A}=K_1\left[\frac{A}{2}+B'+\frac{h}{2f}(R'-R)\right];$$

$$M_{BC}=K_2(B-R);$$

$$M_{CB}=K_2\left(\frac{B}{2}-R\right).$$

Substituting these values for the end moments in eq. (e),

$$\left(\frac{hK_1}{f^2}+\frac{2K_2}{h}\right)R-\frac{hK_1}{f^2}R'=-\frac{K_1}{f}A+\left(\frac{3K_2}{2h}-\frac{K_1}{f}\right)B+\frac{K_1}{2f}B'$$

$$-\frac{1}{f}\left(FM_{AB}+\frac{1}{2}FM_{BA}\right)-(l-2e)\frac{P}{4f}=s \quad\ldots\ldots\quad (131)$$

Similarly, from the shear expressions of the members AB' and $B'C'$ we have:

$$-\frac{hK_1}{f^2}R+\left(\frac{hK_1}{f^2}+\frac{2K_2}{h}\right)R'=-\frac{K_1}{f}A+\frac{K_1}{2f}B+\left(\frac{3K_2}{2h}-\frac{K_1}{f}\right)B'$$

$$+\frac{1}{2f}FM_{BA}+(l-2e)\frac{P}{4f}=s' \quad\ldots\ldots\ldots\quad (131a)$$

Solving eqs. (131) and (131a) simultaneously for R and R',

$$R=\frac{us+u's'}{K_2}\ ;\ R'=\frac{u's+us'}{K_2} \quad\ldots\ldots\ldots\quad (132)$$

in which

$$u=\frac{h\left(1+\frac{2f^2K_2}{h^2K_1}\right)}{4\left(1+\frac{f^2K_2}{h^2K_1}\right)}\ ;\ u'=\frac{h}{4\left(1+\frac{f^2K_2}{h^2K_1}\right)}\ ;\ u+u'=\frac{h}{2}\quad\ldots\quad (133)$$

In writing the joint expression at A, it is to be noted that the sum of deflection terms for the members AB and AB' becomes zero. At joint B, for the deflection terms of the members BA and BC we have;

$$\frac{hK_1}{2f}(R'-R)+K_2R=ts+t's' \quad\ldots\ldots\ldots\quad (f)$$

and at B',

$$\frac{hK_1}{2f}(R-R')+K_2R'=t's+ts' \quad\ldots\ldots\ldots\quad (g)$$

in which

$$t=\frac{h\left(1+\dfrac{2f^{2}K}{h^{2}K_{1}}\right)-f}{4\left(1+\dfrac{f^{2}K_{2}}{h^{2}K_{1}}\right)}; \quad t'=\frac{f+h}{4\left(1+\dfrac{f^{2}K_{2}}{h^{2}K_{1}}\right)}; \quad t+t'=\frac{h}{2}. \quad . . \quad (134)$$

Substituting these values for the deflection terms, the joint equations become:
Joint A,

$$2K_{1}A+\frac{K_{1}}{2}B+\frac{K_{1}}{2}B'=-FM_{AB}; \quad . . . . \quad (135)$$

Joint B,

$$\left[K_{1}+K_{2}-\frac{t'K_{1}}{2f}+t\left(\frac{K_{2}}{f}-\frac{3K_{2}}{2h}\right)\right]B+\frac{(f+h)}{2f}K_{1}A+\left[t'\left(\frac{K_{1}}{f}-\frac{3K_{2}}{2h}\right)\frac{tK_{1}}{2f}\right]B'$$
$$=-FM_{BA}-\frac{t}{f}\left(FM_{AB}+\frac{1}{2}FM_{BA}\right)+\frac{t'}{2f}FM_{BA}$$
$$-(t-t')(l-2e)\frac{P}{4f}=-Q_{B}; \quad . . . . \quad (136)$$

Joint B',

$$\left[K_{1}+K_{2}-\frac{t'K_{1}}{2f}+t\left(\frac{K_{1}}{f}-\frac{3K_{2}}{2h}\right)\right]B'+\frac{(f+h)}{2f}K_{1}A+\left[t'\left(\frac{K_{1}}{f}-\frac{3K_{2}}{2h}\right)-\frac{tK_{1}}{2f}\right]B$$
$$=\frac{t}{2f}FM_{BA}-\frac{t'}{f}\left(FM_{AB}+\frac{1}{2}FM_{BA}\right)+(t-t')(l-2e)\frac{P}{4f}=-Q_{B'}. \quad . \quad 137)$$

In the case of the bent with hinged bases, Fig. 118, the vertical reac-

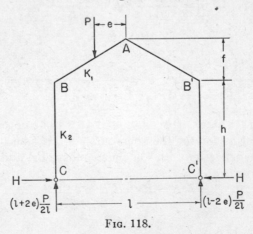

FIG. 118.

tions are determinate. From the shear expressions of the members AB and BC we have:

$$M_{AB}+M_{BA}-Hf+(l+2e)\frac{P}{4}-Pe=0,$$

$$M_{BC}-Hh=0.$$

Eliminating H,

$$\frac{1}{f}(M_{AB}+M_{BA})-\frac{1}{h}M_{BC}+(l-2e)\frac{P}{4f}=0;$$

or

$$\left(\frac{hK_1}{f^2}+\frac{K_2}{2h}\right)R-\frac{hK_1}{f^2}R'=-\frac{3K_1}{2f}A+\left(\frac{3K_2}{4h}-\frac{3K_1}{2f}\right)B$$

$$-\frac{1}{f}(FM_{AB}+F'M_{BA})-(l-2e)\frac{P}{4f}=s \quad \ldots \ldots \quad (138)$$

From the shear expressions of the members AB' and $B'C'$,

$$\left(\frac{hK_1}{f^2}+\frac{K_2}{2h}\right)R'-\frac{hK_1}{f^2}R=-\frac{3K_1}{2f}A+\left(\frac{3K_2}{4h}-\frac{3K_1}{2f}\right)B'+(l-2e)\frac{P}{4f}=s'. \,(138a)$$

Solving for R and R',

$$R=\frac{us+u's'}{K_2}; \; R'=\frac{u's+us'}{K_2}; \quad \ldots \ldots \quad (132a)$$

in which

$$u=\frac{2h\left(2+\frac{f^2K_2}{h^2K_1}\right)}{4+\frac{f^2K_2}{h^2K_1}}, \quad u'=\frac{4h}{4+\frac{f^2K_2}{h^2K_1}}; \quad u+u'=2h \ldots \ldots (139)$$

Let

$$t=\frac{h\left(2+\frac{f^2K_2}{h^2K_1}\right)-f}{4+\frac{f^2K_2}{h^2K_1}}, \quad t'=\frac{f+2h}{4+\frac{f^2K_2}{h^2K_1}}; \quad t+t'=h; \ldots \ldots (140)$$

then

$$\frac{hK_1}{2f}(R'-R)+\frac{K_2}{2}R=ts+t's',$$

$$\frac{hK_1}{2f}(R-R')+\frac{K_2}{2}R'=t's+ts';$$

and the joint equations become:

Joint A,

$$2K_1A+\frac{K_1}{2}B+\frac{K_1}{2}B'=-FM_{AB}; \quad \ldots \ldots \quad (141)$$

Joint B,

$$\left[K_1+\frac{3}{4}K_2+t\left(\frac{3K_1}{2f}-\frac{3K_2}{4h}\right)\right]B+\frac{(f+3h)}{2f}K_1A+t'\left(\frac{3K_1}{2f}-\frac{3K_2}{4h}\right)B'$$

$$=-FM_{BA}-\frac{t}{f}(FM_{AB}+FM_{BA})-(t-t')(l-2e)\frac{P}{4f}=-Q_B; \quad . \quad (142)$$

Joint B',

$$\left[K_1+\frac{3}{4}K_2+t\left(\frac{3K_1}{2f}-\frac{3K_2}{4h}\right)\right]B'+\frac{(f+3h)}{2f}K_1A+t'\left(\frac{3K_1}{2f}-\frac{3K_2}{4h}\right)B$$

$$=-\frac{t'}{f}(FM_{AB}+FM_{BA})+(t-t')(l-2e)\frac{P}{4f}=-Q_{B'} \quad . \quad . \quad . \quad . \quad (143)$$

The joint and deflection equations derived above are typical, except for the load constants. These latter factors for some other loading conditions follow:

(1) Uniform vertical loading, w per lin. ft. of horizontal projection, Fig. 119:

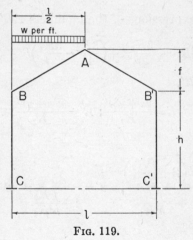

FIG. 119.

(a) Bases fixed:

$$q=\text{load constant in eq. of } s$$

$$=-\frac{7}{96}\cdot\frac{wl^2}{f},$$

$$q'=\frac{5}{96}\cdot\frac{wl^2}{f};$$

$$-Q_B=\frac{wl^2}{48}-\frac{7}{96}\cdot\frac{t}{f}wl^2+\frac{5}{96}\cdot\frac{t}{f}wl^2,$$

$$-Q_{B'}=\frac{5}{96}\cdot\frac{t}{f}wl^2-\frac{7}{96}\cdot\frac{t'}{f}wl^2.$$

(*b*) Bases hinged:

$$q = -\frac{wl^2}{16f}, \ q' = \frac{wl^2}{10f};$$

$$-Q_B = \frac{wl^2}{48} - (t - t')\frac{wl^2}{16f},$$

$$-Q_{B'} = (t - t')\frac{wl^2}{10f}.$$

(2) Single horizontal load, applied to top member, Fig. 120:

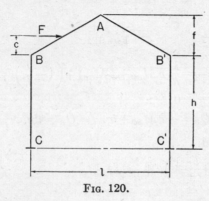

FIG. 120.

(*a*) Bases fixed:

$$q = -\frac{1}{f}\Big(FM_{AB} + \frac{1}{2}FM_{BA}\Big) + \frac{(2f-c)}{2f}F,$$

$$q' = \frac{1}{2f}FM_{BA} + \frac{cF}{2f} \ \ ;$$

$$-Q_B = -FM_{BA} + tq + t'q',$$

$$-Q_{B'} = tq' + t'q.$$

(*b*) Bases hinged:

$$q = -\frac{1}{f}(FM_{AB} + FM_{BA}) + \Big(1 - \frac{c-h}{2f}\Big)F,$$

$$q' = \frac{(c+h)}{2f}F;$$

$$-Q_B = -FM_{BA} + tq + t'q',$$

$$-Q_{B'} = tq' + t'q.$$

(3) Single horizontal load, applied to the leg, Fig. 121:

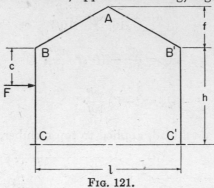

FIG. 121.

(a) Bases fixed:

$$q = \frac{1}{h}(FM_{BC} + FM_{CB}) + \left(1 - \frac{c}{h}\right)F,$$

$$q' = 0;$$

$$-Q_B = -FM_{BC} + tq, \quad -Q_{B'} = t'q.$$

(b) Bases hinged:

$$q = \left(\frac{h-c}{h} + \frac{h-c}{2f}\right)F + \frac{1}{h}HM_{BC},$$

$$q' = \frac{(h-c)}{2f}F;$$

$$-Q_B = -HM_{BC} + tq + t'q', \quad -Q_{B'} = t'q + tq'.$$

(4) Uniform horizontal load, w per lin. ft. of vertical projection, applied to the top member, Fig. 122:

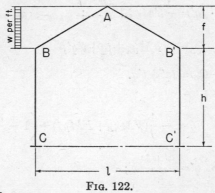

FIG. 122.

(a) Bases fixed:

$$q = \frac{17}{24}wf, \quad q' = \frac{5}{24}wf;$$

$$-Q_B = \frac{wf^2}{12} + tq + t'q', \quad -Q_{B'} = tq' + t'q.$$

(*b*) Bases hinged:

$$q=\left(\frac{3}{4}f+\frac{h}{2}\right)w, \quad q'=\left(\frac{f}{4}+\frac{h}{2}\right)w;$$

$$-Q_B=\frac{wf^2}{12}+tq+t'q', \quad -Q_{B'}=tq'+t'q.$$

(5) Uniform horizontal load, *w* per lin. ft., applied to the leg, Fig. 123:

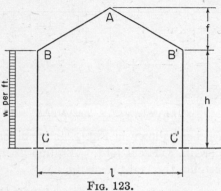

FIG. 123.

(*a*) Bases fixed:

$$q=\frac{wh}{2}, \quad q'=0;$$

$$-Q_B=-FM_{BC}+tq, \quad -Q_{B'}=t'q.$$

(*b*) Bases hinged:

$$q=\frac{wh^2}{4f}+\frac{5}{8}wh, \quad q'=\frac{wh^2}{4f};$$

$$-Q_B=-HM_{BC}+tq+t'q',$$

$$-Q_{B'}=t'q+tq'.$$

(6) Uniform horizontal load, *w* per lin. ft. of vertical projection, applied to both top member and the leg, Fig. 124:

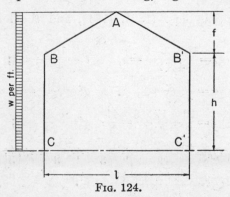

FIG. 124.

(a) Bases fixed:

$$q=\frac{wh}{2}+\frac{17}{24}wf, \quad q'=\frac{5}{24}wf;$$

$$-Q_B=\frac{w}{12}(f^2-h^2)+tq+t'q',$$

$$-Q_{B'}=tq'+t'q.$$

(b) Bases hinged:

$$q=\left[\frac{f}{2}+\frac{5}{8}h+\frac{(f+h)^2}{4f}\right]w, \quad q'=\frac{(f+h)^2}{4f}w;$$

$$-Q_B=\frac{wf^2}{12}-\frac{wh^2}{8}+tq+t'q', \quad -Q_{B'}=tq'+t'q.$$

ILLUSTRATIVE EXAMPLE

The symmetrical bent shown in Fig. 124a is subjected to a uniform load of one kip per lin. vertical foot. Assuming the legs to be fixed at the bases, determine the end moments.

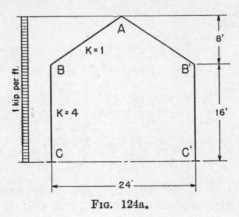

FIG. 124a.

Solution: Applying eqs. (133), (134), and the load constants in (6)(a),

$$t=\frac{16\times3-8}{4\times2}=5, \qquad t'=\frac{16+8}{4\times2}=3;$$

$$u=\frac{16\times3}{4\times2}=6, \qquad u'=\frac{16}{4\times2}=2;$$

$$q=\frac{16}{2}+\frac{17\times8}{24}=\frac{41}{3}, \quad q'=\frac{5\times8}{24}=\frac{5}{3};$$

$$-Q_B=\frac{(64-256)}{12}+\frac{5\times41}{3}+\frac{3\times5}{3}=57\frac{1}{3},$$

$$-Q_{B'}=\frac{5\times5}{3}+\frac{3\times41}{3}=49\frac{1}{3}.$$

Substituting these values for the load factors in the joint eqs. (135)—(137),

$$2A + \frac{1}{2}B + \frac{1}{2}B' = -5\frac{1}{3},$$

$$\frac{3}{2}A + \frac{57}{16}B - \frac{17}{16}B' = 57\frac{-}{3},$$

$$\frac{3}{2}A - \frac{17}{16}B + \frac{57}{16}B' = 49\frac{1}{3};$$

From which

$$A = -19.051, \quad B = 33.632, \quad B' = 31.904.$$

Applying eqs. (131) and (132),

$$s' = 2.381 + 2.102 + 7.976 + 1.667 = 14.126,$$
$$s = 2.381 + 1.994 + 8.408 + 13.667 = 26.450;$$
$$R = \frac{6 \times 26.45 + 2 \times 14.126}{4} = 46.738,$$
$$R' = \frac{2 \times 26.45 + 6 \times 14.126}{4} = 34.414;$$
$$R_{AB} = -46.738 + 34.414 = -12.324.$$

The end moments become:

$$M_{AB} = 1(-19.051 + 16.816 + 12.324) + 5.33 = 15.42,$$
$$M_{AB} = 1(-19.051 + 15.952 - 12.324) = -15.42;$$

$$M_{BA} = 1(33.632 - 9.525 + 12.324) - 5.33 = 31.11,$$
$$M_{BC} = 4(33.632 + 0 - 46.738) + 21.33 = -31.10;$$

$$M_{B'A} = 1(31.904 - 9.525 - 12.324) = 10.05,$$
$$M_{B'C'} = 4(31.904 + 0 - 34.414) = -10.04;$$

$$M_{CB} = 4(0 + 16.816 - 46.738) - 21.33 = -141.02;$$

$$M_{C'B'} = 4(0 + 15.952 - 34.414) = -73.85.$$

PROBLEMS

37. The top member AB of the bent shown in Fig. 125 is carrying a uniform vertical load of 1 kip per linear foot of horizontal projection. Assuming the legs to be fixed at the bases, determine the end moments.

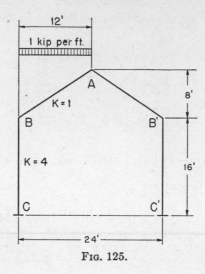

FIG. 125.

38. The left leg of the symmetrical bent shown in Fig. 126 is subjected to a bracket loading. Determine the load constants q and Q for two conditions of support:

    (a) Fixed bases;
    (b) Hinged bases.

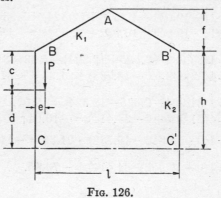

FIG. 126.

48. Symmetrical Bent with Inclined Legs, Unsymmetrical Loading.—The general relation of deflections, eq. (130), as derived in the preceding article for bents with vertical legs, is equally applicable for bents with inclined legs. The procedure in obtaining the joint and deflection expressions is also identical for the two cases. Consider, for example, the bent shown in Fig. 127. The legs of the bent slope

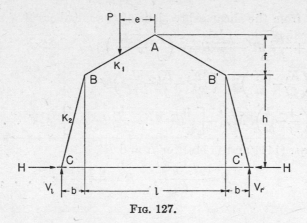

FIG. 127.

inward. For the fixed base condition, the shear expression of the leg member BC is in the form

$$M_{BC}+M_{CB}+V_l b-Hh=0;$$

and that of the top member AB,

$$M_{AB}+M_{BA}+V_l\frac{l}{2}-Pe-Hf=0.$$

Noting that

$$V_l l=-(M_{BA}+M_{B'A})+\left(e+\frac{l}{2}\right)P,$$

and eliminating H,

$$\frac{1}{f}M_{AB}+\left(\frac{1}{2f}+\frac{b}{hl}\right)M_{BA}+\left(\frac{b}{hl}-\frac{1}{2f}\right)M_{B'A}-\frac{1}{h}(M_{BC}+M_{CB})$$

$$+\left[\frac{1}{4f}(l-2e)-\frac{b}{2hl}(2e+l)\right]P=0 \ . \ . \ . \ (a)$$

Substituting the values of the end moments in eq. (a),

$$\left(\frac{hK_1}{f^2}+\frac{2K_2}{h}\right)R-\frac{hK_1}{f^2}R'=-\left(\frac{K_1}{f}+\frac{bK_1}{hl}\right)A$$

$$+\left(\frac{3K_2}{2h}-\frac{K_1}{f}-\frac{bK_1}{hl}\right)B+\left(\frac{K_1}{2f}-\frac{bK_1}{hl}\right)B'-\frac{1}{f}FM_{AB}$$

$$-\left(\frac{1}{2f}+\frac{b}{hl}\right)FM_{BA}+\left[\frac{b}{2hl}(2e+l)-\frac{1}{4f}(l-2e)\right]P=s \ . \ . \ . \ . \ (144)$$

Similarly, from the shear expressions of the members AB' and $B'C'$,

$$\left(\frac{hK_1}{f^2}+\frac{2K_2}{h}\right)R'-\frac{hK_1}{f^2}R=-\left(\frac{K_1}{f}+\frac{bK_1}{hl}\right)A$$

$$+\left(\frac{K_1}{2f}-\frac{bK_1}{hl}\right)B+\left(\frac{3K_2}{2h}-\frac{K_1}{f}-\frac{bK_1}{hl}\right)B'$$

$$+\left(\frac{1}{2f}-\frac{b}{hl}\right)FM_{BA}+\left[\frac{1}{4f}(l-2e)-\frac{b}{2hl}(l-2e)\right]P=s' \quad \cdots \quad (144a)$$

Solving eqs. (144) and (144a) for R and R',

$$R=\frac{us+u's'}{K_2}, \quad R'=\frac{u's+us'}{K_2}; \quad \cdots \cdots \quad (132)$$

in which

$$u=\frac{h\left(1+\frac{2f^2K_2}{h^2K_1}\right)}{4\left(1+\frac{f^2K_2}{h^2K_1}\right)}, \quad u'=\frac{h}{4\left(1+\frac{f^2K_2}{h^2K_1}\right)}; \quad u+u'=\frac{h}{2} \quad \cdots \quad (133)$$

Letting

$$t=\frac{h\left(1+\frac{2f^2K_2}{h^2K_1}\right)-f}{4\left(1+\frac{f^2K_2}{h^2K_1}\right)}, \quad t'=\frac{f+h}{4\left(1+\frac{f^2K_2}{h^2K_1}\right)}, \quad t+t'=\frac{h}{2}, \quad \cdots \quad (134)$$

the joint equations become:
    Joint A,

$$2K_1A+\frac{K_1}{2}B+\frac{K_1}{2}B'=-FM_{AB}; \quad \cdots \cdots \quad (135)$$

    Joint B,

$$\left| \quad _1+K_2-t'\left(\frac{K_1}{2f}-\frac{bK_1}{hl}\right)-t\left(\frac{3K_2}{2h}-\frac{K_1}{f}-\frac{bK_1}{hl}\right)\right]B$$

$$+\left[\frac{K_1}{2}+\frac{h}{2}\left(\frac{K_1}{f}+\frac{bK_1}{hl}\right)\right]A-\left[t\left(\frac{K_1}{2f}-\frac{bK_1}{hl}\right)+t'\left(\frac{3K_2}{2h}-\frac{K_1}{f}-\frac{bK_1}{hl}\right)\right]B'$$

$$=-FM_{BA}+tq+t'q'=-Q_B; \quad \cdots \cdots \cdots \quad (145)$$

    Joint B',

$$\left[K_1+K_2-t'\left(\frac{K_1}{2f}-\frac{bK_1}{hl}\right)-t\left(\frac{3K_2}{2h}-\frac{K_1}{f}-\frac{bK_1}{hl}\right)\right]B'$$

$$+\left[\frac{K_2}{2}+\frac{h}{2}\left(\frac{K_1}{f}+\frac{bK_1}{hl}\right)\right]A-\left[t\left(\frac{K_1}{2f}-\frac{bK_1}{hl}\right)+t'\left(\frac{3K_2}{2h}-\frac{K_1}{f}-\frac{bK_1}{hl}\right)\right]B$$

$$=tq'+t'q=-Q_{B'}; \quad \cdots \cdots \cdots \cdots \quad (145a)$$

in which q and q' indicate the load constants of s and s', eqs. (144) and (144a), and equal:

$$q=-\frac{1}{f}FM_{AB}-\left(\frac{1}{2f}+\frac{b}{hl}\right)FM_{BA}+\left[\frac{b}{2hl}(2e+l)-\frac{1}{4f}(l-2e)\right]P,\quad (b)$$

$$q'=\left(\frac{1}{2f}-\frac{b}{hl}\right)FM_{BA}+\left(\frac{1}{4f}-\frac{b}{2hl}\right)(l-2e)P\quad .\ .\ .\ .\ .\ .\ .\ .\ (c)$$

If the legs are assumed to be hinged to the bases, as in Fig. 128,

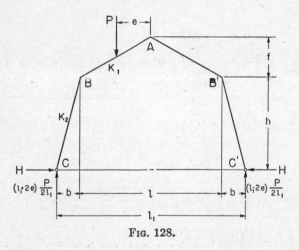

FIG. 128.

then the two vertical reactions become determinate. For the shear expressions of the members AB and BC we can write:

$$M_{BC}-Hh+\frac{b}{2l_1}(l_1+2e)P=0,$$

$$M_{AB}+M_{BA}-Hf+\frac{l(l_1+2e)-4el_1}{4l_1}P=0.$$

Eliminating H,

$$\frac{1}{f}(M_{AB}+M_{BA})-\frac{1}{h}M_{BC}+\left[\frac{l(l_1+2e)-4el_1}{2f}-\frac{b}{h}(l_1+2e)\right]\frac{P}{2l_1}=0;$$

or

$$\left(\frac{hK_1}{f_2}+\frac{K_2}{2h}\right)R-\frac{hK_1}{f^2}R'=-\frac{3K_1}{2f}A+\left(\frac{3K_2}{4h}-\frac{3K_1}{2f}\right)B$$

$$-\frac{1}{f}(FM_{AB}+FM_{BA})-\left[\frac{l(l_1+2e)-4el_1}{2f}-\frac{b}{h}(l_1+2e)\right]\frac{P}{2l_1}=s.\ .\ (146)$$

Similarly, from the shear expressions of the members AB' and $B'C'$,

$$\left(\frac{hK_1}{f^2}+\frac{K_2}{2h}\right)R'-\frac{hK_1}{f^2}R=-\frac{3K_1}{2f}A+\left(\frac{3K_2}{4h}-\frac{3K_1}{2f}\right)B'$$

$$+\left(\frac{l}{2f}-\frac{b}{h}\right)(l_1-2e)\frac{P}{2l_1}=s' \quad \ldots \ldots \ldots \ldots \quad (146a)$$

Solving eqs. (146) and (146a) for R and R',

$$R=\frac{us+u's'}{K_2}, \quad R'=\frac{u's+us'}{K_2} \quad \ldots \ldots \quad (132a)$$

in which

$$u=\frac{2h\left(2+\frac{f^2K_2}{h^2K_1}\right)}{4+\frac{f^2K_2}{h^2K_1}}, \quad u'=\frac{4h}{4+\frac{f^2K_2}{h^2K_1}}; \quad u+u'=2h \quad \ldots \quad (139)$$

Let

$$t=\frac{h\left(2+\frac{f^2K_2}{h^2K_1}\right)-f}{4+\frac{f^2K_2}{h^2K_1}}, \quad t'=\frac{f+2h}{4+\frac{f^2K_2}{h^2K_1}}, \quad t+t'=h; \quad \ldots \quad (140)$$

$$q=-\frac{1}{f}(FM_{AB}+FM_{BA})-\left[\frac{l(l_1+2e)-4el_1}{2f}-\frac{b}{h}(l_1+2e)\right]\frac{P}{2l_1}, \quad (d)$$

$$q'=\left(\frac{l}{2f}-\frac{b}{h}\right)(l_1-2e)\frac{P}{2l_1} \quad \ldots \ldots \ldots \ldots \ldots \ldots \ldots \quad (e)$$

then, for the joint equations of the bent we have:
Joint A,

$$2K_1A+\frac{K_1}{2}B+\frac{K_1}{2}B'=-FM_{AB}; \quad \ldots \ldots \quad (141)$$

Joint B,

$$\left[K_1+\frac{3}{4}K_2-t\left(\frac{3K_2}{4h}-\frac{3K_1}{2f}\right)\right]B+\frac{(f+3h)}{2f}K_1A-t'\left(\frac{3K_2}{4h}-\frac{3K_1}{2f}\right)B'$$

$$=-FM_{BA}+tq+t'q'=-Q_B; \quad \ldots \ldots \quad (147)$$

Joint B',

$$\left[K_1+\frac{3}{4}K_2-t\left(\frac{3K_2}{4h}-\frac{3K_1}{2f}\right)\right]B'+\frac{(f+3h)}{2f}K_1A-t'\left(\frac{3K_2}{4h}-\frac{3K_1}{2f}\right)B$$

$$=t'q+tq'=-Q_{B'}. \quad \ldots \ldots \quad (147a)$$

It will be noted that these joint equations differ from the corresponding expressions for the bent with vertical legs only by the factors containing the term b. By reversing the signs of these factors in the above equations, we obtain the joint expressions for a bent having outward-battering legs, as shown in Fig. 129.

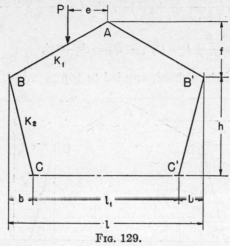

FIG. 129.

Except for the load constants q and Q, the joint equations are typical. These factors for some other loading conditions are given below:

(1) Uniform vertical loading, w per linear foot of horizontal projection, Fig. 130:

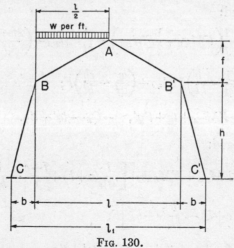

FIG. 130.

(a) Bases fixed:

$$q=\left(\frac{19b}{hl}-\frac{7}{2f}\right)\frac{wl^2}{48},$$

$$q'=\left(\frac{5}{2f}-\frac{5b}{hl}\right)\frac{wl^2}{48};$$

$$-Q_B=\frac{wl^2}{48}+tq+t'q', \quad -Q_{B'}=t'q+tq'.$$

(*b*) Bases hinged:

$$q=\left(\frac{2b}{h}-\frac{l^2}{2fl_1}+\frac{bl}{hl_1}\right)\frac{wl}{8},\ q'=\left(\frac{l}{2f}-\frac{b}{h}\right)\left(\frac{l_1}{2}-\frac{l}{4}\right)\frac{wl}{2l_1};$$

$$-Q_B=\frac{wl^2}{48}+tq+t'q',\ -Q_{B'}=t'q+tq'.$$

(2) Single horizontal load, applied to top member, Fig. 131,

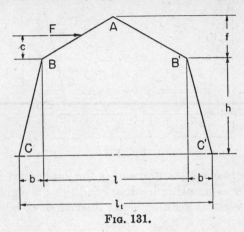

FIG. 131.

(*a*) Bases fixed:

$$q=-\frac{1}{f}\left(FM_{AB}+\frac{1}{2}FM_{BA}\right)-\frac{b}{hl}FM_{BA}+\left(\frac{2f-c}{2f}-\frac{cb}{hl}\right)F,$$

$$q'=\left(\frac{1}{2f}-\frac{b}{hl}\right)FM_{BA}+\left(\frac{c}{2f}-\frac{cb}{hl}\right)F;$$

$$-Q_B=-FM_{BA}+tq+t'q',\ \ -Q_{B'}-tq'+t'q.$$

(*b*) Bases hinged:

$$q=-\frac{1}{f}(FM_{AB}+FM_{BA})+\left[\frac{l}{2fl_1}(c+h)+\frac{f-c}{f}-\frac{b}{hl_1}(c+h)\right]F,$$

$$q'=\left[\frac{l}{2fl_1}(c+h)-\frac{b}{hl_1}(c+h)\right]F;$$

$$-Q_B=-FM_{BA}+tq+t'q',\ -Q_{B'}=tq'+t'q.$$

(3) Single horizontal load applied to the leg, Fig. 132:

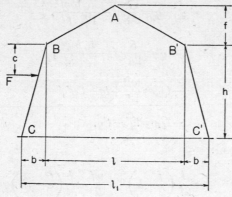

Fig. 132.

(a) Bases fixed:

$$q=\frac{1}{h}(FM_{BC}+FM_{CB})+\left(\frac{h-c}{h}\right)F, \quad q'=0;$$

$$-Q_B=-FM_{BC}+tq, \quad -Q_{B'}=t'q.$$

(b) Bases hinged:

$$q=\frac{1}{h}HM_{BC}+\left[\frac{h-c}{h}+\frac{l}{2fl_1}(h-c)-\frac{b}{hl_1}(h-c)\right]F,$$

$$q'=\left[\frac{l}{2fl_1}(h-c)-\frac{b}{hl_1}(h-c)\right]F;$$

$$-Q_B=-HM_{BC}+tq+t'q', \quad -Q_{B'},=tq'+t'q.$$

(4) Uniform horizontal load, w per lin. ft. of vertical projection, applied to the top member, Fig. 133:

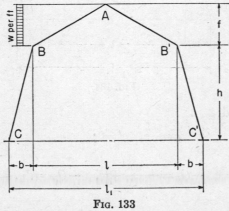

Fig. 133

(*a*) Bases fixed:

$$q = \frac{17}{24}wf - \frac{5}{12} \cdot \frac{bwf^2}{hl},$$

$$q' = \frac{5}{24}wf - \frac{5}{12} \cdot \frac{bwf^2}{hl};$$

$$-Q_B = \frac{wf^2}{12} + tq + t'q',$$

$$-Q_B = tq' + t'q.$$

(*b*) Bases hinged:

$$q = \frac{l}{2l_1}\left(\frac{f}{2} + h\right)w + \frac{wf}{2} - \frac{b}{hl_1}\left(\frac{f^2}{2} + fh\right)w,$$

$$q' = \frac{l}{2l_1}\left(\frac{f}{2} + h\right)w - \frac{b}{hl_1}\left(\frac{f^2}{2} + fh\right)w;$$

$$-Q_B = \frac{wf^2}{12} + tq + t'q', \quad -Q_{B'} = tq' + t'q.$$

(5) Uniform horizontal load, *w* per lin. ft. of vertical projection, applied to the leg, Fig. 134:

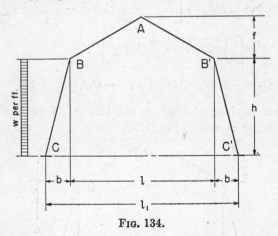

FIG. 134.

(*a*) Bases fixed:

$$q = \frac{wh}{2}, \quad q' = 0;$$

$$-Q_B = -\frac{wh^2}{12} + tq, \quad -Q_{B'} = t'q.$$

(*b*) Bases hinged:

$$q = \frac{5}{8}wh + \frac{lwh^2}{4fl_1} - \frac{bwh}{2l_1},$$

$$q' = \frac{lwh^2}{4fl_1} - \frac{bwh}{2l_1};$$

$$-Q_B = -\frac{wh^2}{8} + tq + t'q', \quad -Q_{B'} = t'q + tq'.$$

(6) Uniform horizontal load, *w* per linear foot of vertical projection, applied to top member and the leg, Fig. 135:

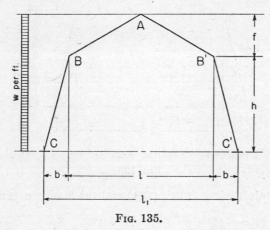

FIG. 135.

(*a*) Bases fixed:

$$q = \frac{17}{24}wf - \frac{5}{12} \cdot \frac{bwf^2}{hl} + \frac{wh}{2},$$

$$q' = \frac{5}{24}wf - \frac{5}{12} \cdot \frac{bwf^2}{hl};$$

$$-Q_B = \frac{w}{12}(f^2 - h^2) + tq + t'q',$$

$$-Q_{B'} = t'q + tq';$$

(*b*) Bases hinged:

$$q = \frac{l}{2l_1}\left(\frac{f}{2} + h + \frac{h^2}{2f}\right)w + \frac{wf}{2} - \frac{b}{2l_1}\left(\frac{f^2}{h} + 2f + h\right)w + \frac{5}{8}wh,$$

$$q' = \frac{l}{2l_1}\left(\frac{f}{2} + h + \frac{h^2}{2f}\right)w - \frac{b}{2l_1}\left(\frac{f^2}{h} + 2f + h\right)w;$$

$$-Q_B = \frac{wf^2}{12} - \frac{wh^2}{8} + tq + t'q', \quad -Q_{B'} = tq' + t'q.$$

The top member AB of the symmetrical bent shown in Fig. 136 is carrying a vertical load of one kip per lin. ft. of horizontal projection. Assuming the legs to be fixed at the bases, determine:

(a) End moments;
(b) Reactions at the bases.

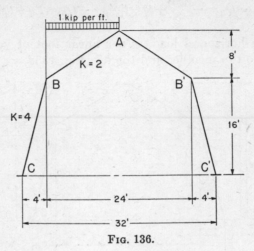

1 kip per ft.

FIG. 136.

Solution. Applying eqs. (133), (134) and the load constants in (1) (a):

$$u=\frac{16(1+1)}{4\times1.5}=\frac{16}{3}, \qquad u'=\frac{16}{4\times1.5}=\frac{8}{3};$$

$$t=\frac{16\times2-8}{4\times1.5}=4, \qquad t'=\frac{8+16}{4\times1.5}=4;$$

$$q=\left(\frac{19\times4}{16\times24}-\frac{7}{16}\right)12=-\frac{23}{8}, \qquad q'=\left(\frac{5}{16}-\frac{5\times4}{16\times24}\right)12=\frac{25}{8};$$

$$-Q_B=12-\frac{4\times23}{8}+\frac{4\times25}{8}=13, \qquad -Q_{B'}=\frac{4\times25}{8}-\frac{4\times23}{8}=1.$$

Substituting these values in eqs. (135), (145) and (145a), the joint equations become:

$$4A+B+B'=-12,$$

$$\frac{19}{6}A+\frac{31}{6}B-\frac{5}{6}B'=13,$$

$$\frac{19}{6}A-\frac{5}{6}B+\frac{31}{6}B'=1.$$

From which,

$$A=-6, \qquad B=7, \qquad B'=5.$$

Also, applying eqs. (144), (144a) and (132),

$$s=\left(\frac{1}{4}+\frac{1}{48}\right)6+\left(\frac{3}{8}-\frac{1}{4}-\frac{1}{48}\right)7+\left(\frac{1}{8}-\frac{1}{48}\right)5-\frac{23}{8}=0,$$

$$s'=\left(\frac{1}{4}+\frac{1}{48}\right)6+\left(\frac{1}{8}-\frac{1}{48}\right)7+\left(\frac{3}{8}-\frac{1}{4}-\frac{1}{48}\right)5+\frac{25}{8}=6;$$

$$R=\frac{8\times6}{3\times4}=4, \qquad R'=\frac{16\times6}{3\times4}=8;$$

$$R_{AB}=\frac{16}{2\times8}(8-4)=4, \qquad R_{AB'}=-4.$$

(a) The end moments become:

$$M_{AB}=2(-6+3.5-4)+12=-1 \text{ ft.-kip,}$$
$$M_{AB'}=2(-6+2.5+4)=1 \text{ ft.-kip;}$$

$$M_{BA}=2(7-3-4)-12=-12 \text{ ft.-kips,}$$
$$M_{BC}=4(7-4)=12 \text{ ft.-kips;}$$

$$M_{B'A}=2(5-3+4)=12 \text{ ft.-kips,}$$
$$M_{B'C'}=4(5-8)=-12 \text{ ft.-kips;}$$

$$M_{CB}=4(3.5-4)=-2 \text{ ft.-kips;}$$

$$M_{C'B'}=4(2.5-8)=-22 \text{ ft.-kips.}$$

(b) The reactions are:

$$V_l=\frac{M_{BA}+M_{B'A}-12\times18}{24}=\frac{-12+12-12\times18}{24}=9 \text{ kips;}$$
$$V_r=12-9=3 \text{ kips;}$$
$$H=\frac{M_{BC}+M_{CB}+4V_l}{16}=\frac{12-2+36}{16}=2\frac{7}{8} \text{ kips.}$$

PROBLEMS

39. The left leg of the symmetrical bent shown in Fig. 137 is subjected to a single concentrated load P.   Determine the load constants q, and Q for:

(a) Fixed bases;
(b) Hinged bases.

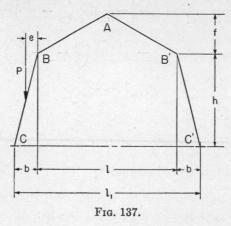

FIG. 137.

40- The symmetrical bent shown in Fig. 138 is subjected to a uniform load of one kip per linear vertical foot.   Assuming the legs to be fixed at the bases, determine the end moments.

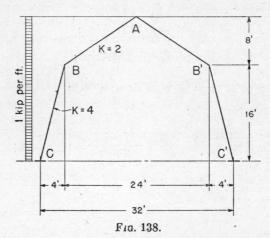

FIG. 138.

49. Two-story Symmetrical Bent with Symmetrical Loading.—The solution of moments for the bent shown in Fig. 139 differs but little

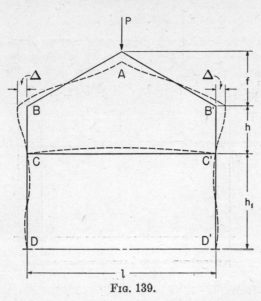

FIG. 139.

from that of the single-story bent discussed in Art. 46. The similarity is seen at once by considering the bent as composed of two component frames: (a), the top panel $CBAB'C'$, which in itself is a single-story gabled bent, and (b), the bottom rectangular panel $DCC'D'$. These two panels are interrelated by the common deflection angles at joints C and C'. The exaggerated joint displacements of the bent are indicated on the diagram in dotted lines. Since the loading is symmetrical (and neglecting the effect of the axial stresses), the bottom rectangular panel $DCC'D'$ will have no side sway. The top panel $CBAB'C'$ will sway as shown in Fig. 106; that is, the apex joint A moves down, and the joints B and B' spread out laterally equal distances, Δ. The relation between the deflections of the top and leg members of a single-story gabled bent, as derived in Art. 46, is directly applicable for this panel. Here again denoting the deflection term $\left(=6E\frac{\Delta}{h}\right)$ of the top leg BC by R, for the corresponding term of the top member AB we have:

$$R_{AB}=-\frac{h}{f}R \quad . \quad . \quad . \quad . \quad . \quad . \quad . \quad . \quad . \quad . \quad (123)$$

The deflection and the joint expressions of the bent are derived in the usual manner. Consider, for example, the loading shown in Fig. 140. The shear expression of the leg member BC in the top

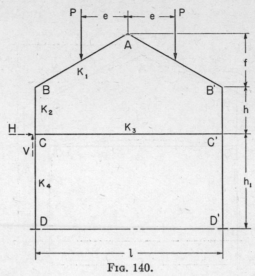

FIG. 140.

panel is in the form

$$M_{BC}+M_{CB}-Hh=\frac{3K_2}{2}(B+C)-2K_2R-Hh=\frac{3K_2}{2h}(B+C)$$

$$-\frac{2K_2}{h}R-H=0; \ldots \ldots \ldots \ldots (a)$$

in which H is the shear or horizontal reaction just above the joint C. Similarly, for the shear expression of the member AB we have:

$$M_{AB}+M_{BA}-Pe+\frac{Vl}{2}-Hf=\frac{3K_1}{2}B+\frac{2hK_1}{f}R+FM_{AB}+FM_{BA}$$

$$+P\left(\frac{l}{2}-e\right)-Hf=\frac{3K_1}{2f}B+\frac{2hK_1}{f^2}R+\frac{1}{f}(FM_{AB}+FM_{BA})$$

$$+\frac{P}{f}\left(\frac{l}{2}-e\right)-H=0 \ldots \ldots \ldots \ldots \ldots (b)$$

Subtracting eq. (a) from eq. (b), and solving for R,

$$\left(\frac{2hK_1}{f^2}+\frac{2K_2}{h}\right)R=\frac{3}{2}\left(\frac{K_2}{h}-\frac{K_1}{f}\right)B+\frac{3K_2}{2h}C-\frac{1}{f}(FM_{AB}+FM_{BA})-\frac{P}{f}\left(\frac{l}{2}-e\right),$$

or

$$R=\frac{3f(fK_2-hK_1)}{4(h^2K_1+f^2K_2)}B+\frac{3f^2K_2C}{4(h^2K_1+f^2K_2)}-\frac{fh(FM_{AB}+FM_{BA})}{2(h^2K_1+f^2K_2)}$$

$$-\frac{fh(l-2e)P}{4(h^2K_1+f^2K_2)} \ldots \ldots \ldots \ldots (148)$$

For the joint expression at B, obtained by summing up the end moments at that joint, we have:

$$M_{BA}+M_{BC}=(K_1+K_2)B+\frac{K_2}{2}C+\left(\frac{hK_1}{f}-K_2\right)R+FM_{BA}=0 \quad . \quad (c)$$

Substituting for R in eq. (c) its value from eq. (148),

$$\left[K_1+K_2-\frac{3(hK_1-fK_2)^2}{4(h^2K_1+f^2K_2)}\right]B+\left[\frac{K_2}{2}+\frac{3fK_2(hK_1-fK_2)}{4(h^2K_1+f^2K_2)}\right]C$$

$$=-FM_{BA}+\frac{h(hK_1-fK_2)}{2(h^2K_1+f^2K_2)}(FM_{AB}+FM_{BA})$$

$$+\frac{h(hK_1-fK_2)(l-2e)P}{4(h^2K_1+f^2K_2)}=-Q_B \quad . \quad . \quad . \quad . \quad . \quad . \quad . \quad . \quad (149)$$

Equations (148) and (149) are independent of the restraint condition at the bases, which condition affects the moment expressions of the bottom story columns and, consequently, the joint expressions at C and C' only. Assuming fixed bases at D and D', the derivation for joint C follows:

$$M_{CB}=K_2\left(C+\frac{B}{2}-R\right), \quad M_{CC'}=\frac{K_3}{2}C, \quad M_{CD}=K_4C;$$

$$M_{CB}+M_{CC'}+M_{CD}=\left(K_2+\frac{K_3}{2}+K_4\right)C+\frac{K_2}{2}B-K_2R=0, \quad . \quad . \quad (d)$$

and substituting for R its value as given by eq. (148),

$$\left[K_2+\frac{K_3}{2}+K_4-\frac{3f^2K_2^2}{4(h^2K_1+f^2K_2)}\right]C+\left[\frac{K_2}{2}-\frac{3fK_2(fK_2-hK_1)}{4(h^2K_1+f^2K_2)}\right]B$$

$$=-\frac{fhK_2(FM_{AB}+FM_{BA})}{2(h^2K_1+f^2K_2)}-\frac{fhK_2(l-2e)P}{4(h^2K_1+f^2K_2)}=-Q_C \quad . \quad . \quad . \quad (150)$$

If the legs CD and $C'D'$ are assumed to be hinged to the bases, the end moment M_{CD} equals $\frac{3}{4}K_4C$, and the corresponding joint expression at C becomes

$$\left[K_2+\frac{K_3}{2}+\frac{3}{4}K_4-\frac{3f^2K_2^2}{4(h^2K_1+f^2K_2)}\right]C+\left[\frac{K_2}{2}-\frac{3fK_2(fK_2-hK_1)}{4(h^2K_1+f^2K_2)}\right]B$$

$$=-\frac{fhK_2(FM_{AB}+FM_{BA})}{2(h^2K_1+f^2K_2)}-\frac{fhK_2(l-2e)P}{4(h^2K_1+f^2K_2)}=-Q_C \quad . \quad . \quad . \quad (150a)$$

In the case of uniform vertical loading, shown in Fig. 141, the load

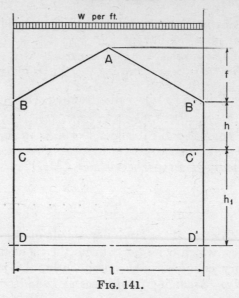

Fig. 141.

constants of eqs. (148) to (150a) assume the following simplified forms:

$$
\left.
\begin{aligned}
Q_R &= -\frac{fhwl^2}{16(h^2K_1+f^2K_2)}; \\
-Q_B &= +\frac{wl^2}{48}+\frac{h(hK_1-fK_2)wl^2}{16(h^2K_1+f^2K_2)}; \\
-Q_C &= -\frac{K_2fhwl^2}{16(h^2K_1+f^2K_2)}.
\end{aligned}
\right\} \quad \cdots \cdots \cdots (151)
$$

A symmetrical vertical loading, acting on the member CC', Fig. 142, will affect only the joint expression at C. This change is made by

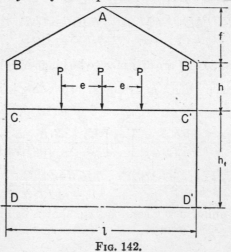

Fig. 142.

merely adding the fixed-end moment of the member $(-FM_{CC'})$ to the load constant.

It is also to be noted that the load constants of R and B equations, eqs. (148) and (149), corresponding to the loading shown in Fig. 142, become zero.

ILLUSTRATIVE EXAMPLES

1. The top members of the symmetrical bent shown in Fig. 143 carry a uniform vertical load of 1 kip per linear foot of horizontal projection. Assuming fixed bases at D and D', determine the end moments.

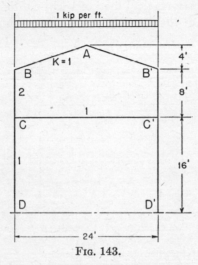

FIG. 143.

Solution: Applying eqs. (149), (150) and (151),

$$3B+C=12,$$

$$B+3C=-24;$$

from which

$$B=7.5, C=-10.5.$$

Substituting these values in eq. (148),

$$R=-\frac{3\times16\times2}{4\times96}\times10.5-\frac{4\times8\times24^2}{16\times96}=-14.625;$$

and

$$R_{AB}=\frac{8}{4}\times14.625=29.25,$$

The end moments become:

$$M_{AB}=(3.75 \quad 29.25) \mid 12 = -13.50;$$

$$M_{BA}=(7.5-29.25)-12=-33.75,$$
$$M_{BC}=2(7.5-5.25+14.625)=33.75,$$

$$M_{CB}=2(-10.5+3.75+14.625)=15.75,$$
$$M_{CC'}=-5.25;$$

$$M_{CD}=-10.50;$$

$$M_{DC}=-5.25.$$

2. The member CC' of the symmetrical frame shown in Fig. 143a is loaded with a uniform vertical load of 1 kip per linear foot. Assuming the legs to be fixed at the bases D and D', determine the end moments.

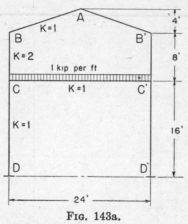

Fig. 143a.

Solution: The joint expression, at B and C differ from those of the preceding example by only the load constants Q. Since there is no load acting on the top members AB and AB', Q_B becomes zero. The load constant for C, Q_C, is simply the fixed-end moment of the member CC'. Thus

$$3B+C=0,$$
$$B+3C=48;$$
$$B=-6, \quad R=4.5,$$
$$C=18; \quad R_{AB}=-9.$$

The end moments become:

$$M_{AB}=-3+9=6; \qquad M_{DC}=9;$$

$$M_{BA}=-6+9=3, \qquad M_{CB}=2(18-3-4.5)=21,$$

$$M_{BC}=2(-6+9-4.5)=-3; \quad M_{CC'}=9-48=-39,$$

$$M_{CD}=18.$$

PROBLEMS

41. The bottom legs of the two-story symmetrical bent shown in Fig. 144 are subjected to two symmetrically placed bracket loadings. Derive the deflection and joint expressions corresponding to two conditions of support:

(a) Fixed bases;
(b) Hinged bases.

Denote the fixed and hinged-end moments by their symbols.

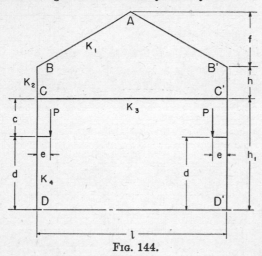

Fig. 144.

42. The roof members AB and AB' of the symmetrical bent shown in Fig. 145 are carrying three concentrated loads, placed symmetrically with respect to the apex. Assuming fixed bases at D and D', determine the end moments.

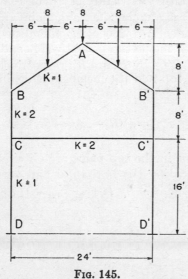

Fig. 145.

50. Two-story Symmetrical Bent with Unsymmetrical Loading.—
As in the case of symmetrical loading, the concept of deformations of
a two-story bent, subjected to an unsymmetrical loading, is greatly
simplified by considering the two stories of the frame separately.
These deformations are shown in Fig. 146.   In the upper story, the

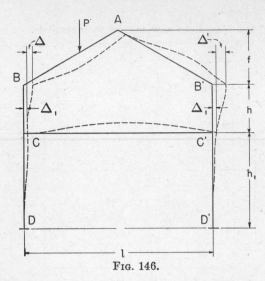

Fɪɢ. 146.

panel $CBAB'C'$ deflects in the same way as a single-story gabled bent;
that is, the crown joint A moves downward and laterally, while the
displacements of the joints B and B', indicated by Δ and Δ' in the
figure, result from both sway and spread of the legs BC and BC'.
The bottom panel is rectangular; hence the joints C and C' sway laterally the same distance Δ_1.   Denoting the deflection terms of the
members AB and AB' in the top panel by R_{AB} and $R_{AB'}$, and those of
the columns BC and $B'C'$ by R and R', respectively, the interrelation
of deflections of the top and leg members is again given by the previously derived expression

$$R_{AB}=\frac{h}{2f}(R'-R)=-R_{AB'} \quad . \ . \ . \ . \ . \ . \ . \quad (130)$$

The joint equations in the top panel are obtained in the same way
as in Art. 47.   Indicating the horizontal and vertical reactions just
above the joint C (Fig. 147) by H and V, for the shear expressions of

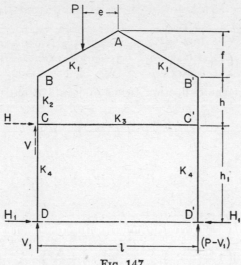

FIG. 147.

the members AB and BC we can write:

$$M_{AB}+M_{BA}-Hf+V\frac{l}{2}-Pe=0,$$

$$M_{BC}+M_{CB}-Hh=0.$$

Noting that

$$Vl=-(M_{BA}+M_{B'A})+P\left(e+\frac{l}{2}\right),$$

and eliminating H,

$$\frac{1}{f}M_{AB}+\frac{1}{2f}(M_{BA}-M_{B'A})-\frac{1}{h}(M_{BC}+M_{CB})+\frac{P}{4f}(l-2e)=0.$$

Substituting the values of the end moments,

$$\left(\frac{hK_1}{f^2}+\frac{2K_2}{h}\right)R-\frac{hK_1}{f^2}R'=-\frac{K_1}{f}A+\left(\frac{3K_2}{2h}-\frac{K_1}{f}\right)B+\frac{K_1}{2f}B'+\frac{3K_2}{2h}C$$

$$-\frac{1}{f}\left(FM_{AB}+\frac{1}{2}FM_{BA}\right)-(l-2e)\frac{P}{4f}=s \quad \ldots \ldots \quad (152)$$

Similarly, from the shear expressions of the members AB' and $B'C'$ we have:

$$-\frac{hK_1}{f^2}R+\left(\frac{hK_1}{f^2}+\frac{2K_2}{h}\right)R'=-\frac{K_1}{f}A+\frac{K_1}{2f}B+\left(\frac{3K_2}{2h}-\frac{K_1}{f}\right)B'$$

$$+\frac{3K_2}{2h}C'+\frac{1}{2f}FM_{BA}+(l-2e)\frac{P}{4f}=s' \quad \ldots \ldots \quad (152a)$$

Solving eqs. (152) and (152a) for R and R',

$$R=\frac{us+u's'}{K_2}, \quad R'=\frac{u's+us'}{K_2}; \quad \ldots \ldots \quad (132)$$

in which

$$u=\frac{h\left(1+2\frac{f^2K_2}{h^2K_1}\right)}{4\left(1+\frac{f^2K_2}{h^2K_1}\right)},\quad u'=\frac{h}{4\left(1+\frac{f^2K_2}{h^2K_1}\right)}\,;\,u+u'=\frac{h}{2}\;.\;.\;.\;(133)$$

Noting also that the deflection terms of joints B and B' respectively equal

$$\frac{hK_1}{2f}\,(R'-R)+K_2R=ts+t's',$$

and

$$\frac{hK_1}{2f}\,(R-R')+K_2R'=t's+ts',$$

in which

$$t=\frac{h\left(1+\frac{2f^2K_2}{h^2K_1}\right)-f}{4\left(1+\frac{f^2K_2}{h^2K_1}\right)},\;t'=\frac{f+h}{4\left(1+\frac{f^2K_2}{h^2K_1}\right)},\;t+t'=\frac{h}{2},\;.\;.\;(134)$$

the joint expressions at A, B and B' become:

Joint A,

$$2K_1A+\frac{K_1}{2}B+\frac{K_1}{2}B'=-FM_{AB};\;.\;.\;.\;.\;.\;.\;(135)$$

Joint B,

$$\left[K_1+K_2-\frac{t'K_1}{2f}+t\left(\frac{K_1}{f}-\frac{3K_2}{2h}\right)\right]B+\frac{(f+h)}{2f}K_1A$$

$$+\left[t'\left(\frac{K_1}{f}-\frac{3K_2}{2h}\right)-\frac{tK_1}{2f}\right]B'+\left(\frac{K_2}{2}-\frac{3tK_2}{2h}\right)C-\frac{3t'K_2}{2h}C'=-FM_{BA}$$

$$-\frac{t}{f}\left(FM_{AB}+\frac{1}{2}FM_{BA}\right)+\frac{t'}{2f}FM_{BA}-(t-t')(l-2e)\frac{P}{4f}=-Q_B;(153)$$

Joint B',

$$\left[K_1+K_2-\frac{t'K_1}{2f}+t\left(\frac{K_1}{f}-\frac{3K_2}{2h}\right)\right]B'+\frac{(f+h)}{2f}K_1A$$

$$+\left[t'\left(\frac{K_1}{f}-\frac{3K_2}{2h}\right)-\frac{tK_1}{2f}\right]B-\frac{3t'K_2}{2h}C+\left(\frac{K_2}{2}-\frac{3tK_2}{2h}\right)C'-\frac{t}{2f}FM_{BA}$$

$$-\frac{t'}{f}\left(FM_{AB}+\frac{1}{2}FM_{BA}\right)+(t-t')(l-2e)\frac{P}{4f}=-Q_{B'}\;.\;.\;.\;(154)$$

Eqs. (135), (153), and (154) are independent of the support condition at the bases, which condition affects only the joint expressions of C and C'. For fixed bases, the joint equation at C is in the form

$$M_{CB}+M_{CC'}+M_{CD}=K_2\left(C+\frac{B}{2}-R\right)+K_3\left(C+\frac{C'}{2}\right)+K_4(C-R_1)=0\;.\;(a)$$

But

$$R=\frac{us+u's'}{K_2}, \quad R_1=\frac{3}{8}(C+C').$$

Substituting these values in eq. (a), the joint expression becomes:

$$\left[K_2+K_3+\frac{5}{8}K_4-\frac{3uK_2}{2h}\right]C+\frac{hK_1}{2f}A+\left[\frac{K_2}{2}+u\left(\frac{K_1}{f}-\frac{3K_2}{2h}\right)-\frac{u'K_1}{2f}\right]B$$

$$+\left[u'\left(\frac{K_1}{f}-\frac{3K_2}{2h}\right)-\frac{uK_1}{2f}\right]B'+\left[\frac{K_3}{2}-\frac{3u'K_2}{2h}-\frac{3}{8}K_4\right]C'$$

$$=\frac{(u'-u)}{2f}FM_{BA}-\frac{u}{f}FM_{AB}+(u'-u)(l-2e)\frac{P}{4f}=-Q_C \quad . \quad . \quad (155)$$

Similarly, at C',

$$\left[K_2+K_3+\frac{5}{8}K_4-\frac{3uK_2}{2h}\right]C'+\frac{hK_1}{2f}A+\left[u'\left(\frac{K_1}{f}-\frac{3K_2}{2h}\right)-\frac{uK_1}{2f}\right]B$$

$$+\left[\frac{K_2}{2}+u\left(\frac{K_1}{f}-\frac{3K_2}{2h}\right)-\frac{u'K_1}{2f}\right]B'+\left[\frac{K_3}{2}-\frac{3u'K_2}{2h}-\frac{3}{8}K_4\right]C$$

$$=\frac{(u-u')}{2f}FM_{BA}-\frac{u'}{f}FM_{AB}+(u-u')(l-2e)\frac{P}{4f}=-Q_{C'} \quad . \quad . \quad . \quad (156)$$

In the case of hinged connections at the bases D and D', Fig. 147, the end moment M_{CD} in eq. (a) equals $K_4\left(\frac{3}{4}C-\frac{R_1}{2}\right)$, and $R_1=\frac{3}{4}(C+C')$.

Accordingly, for hinged bases, eqs. (155) and (156) are modified as follows:

Joint C,

$$\left[K_2+K_3+\frac{3}{8}K_4-\frac{3uK_2}{2h}\right]C+\frac{hK_1}{2f}A+\left[\frac{K_2}{2}+u\left(\frac{K_1}{f}-\frac{3K_2}{2h}\right)-\frac{u'K_1}{2f}\right]B$$

$$+\left[u'\left(\frac{K_1}{f}-\frac{3K_2}{2h}\right)-\frac{uK_1}{2f}\right]B'+\left[\frac{K_3}{2}-\frac{3u'K_2}{2h}-\frac{3}{8}K_4\right]C'$$

$$=\frac{(u'-u)}{2f}FM_{BA}-\frac{u}{f}FM_{AB}+(u'-u)(l-2e)\frac{P}{4f}=-Q_C \quad . \quad . \quad . \quad (155a)$$

Joint C',

$$\left[K_2+K_3+\frac{3}{8}K_4-\frac{3uK_2}{2h}\right]C'+\frac{hK_1}{2f}A+\left[u'\left(\frac{K_1}{f}-\frac{3K_2}{2h}\right)-\frac{uK_1}{2f}\right]B$$

$$+\left[\frac{K_2}{2}+u\left(\frac{K_1}{f}-\frac{3K_2}{2h}\right)-\frac{u'K_1}{2f}\right]B'+\left[\frac{K_3}{2}-\frac{3u'K_2}{2h}-\frac{3}{8}K_4\right]C$$

$$=\frac{(u-u')}{2f}FM_{BA}-\frac{u'}{f}FM_{AB}+(u-u')(l-2e)\frac{P}{4f}=-Q_{C'} \quad . \quad . \quad (156a)$$

Except for the load constants, eqs. (135), (154) to (156) are typical. Denoting the load constants in the s and s' equations—eqs. (152) and (152a)—by q and q', respectively, the corresponding joint load factors

Q for some other loadings are given below:

(1) Uniform vertical loading, w per linear feet of horizontal projection, Fig. 148:

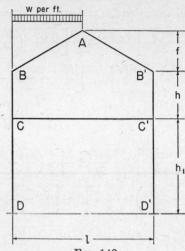

FIG. 148.

Bases fixed or hinged:

$$q=-\frac{7}{96}\cdot\frac{wl^2}{f}, \quad q'=\frac{5}{96}\cdot\frac{wl^2}{f};$$

$$-Q_B=\frac{wl^2}{48}+tq+t'q',$$

$$-Q_{B'}=t'q+tq',$$

$$-Q_C=uq+u'q',$$

$$-Q_{C'}=u'q+uq'.$$

(2) Single horizontal load, applied to the member AB, Fig. 148a:

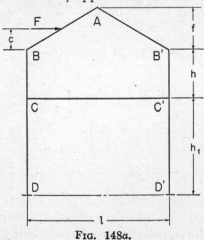

FIG. 148a.

Bases fixed or hinged:

$$q=\frac{1}{f}\left(FM_{AB}+\frac{1}{2}FM_{BA}\right)+\frac{2f-c}{2f}F,$$

$$q'=\frac{1}{2f}FM_{BA}+\frac{cF}{2f};$$

$$-Q_B=-FM_{BA}+tq+t'q',$$

$$-Q_{B'}=t'q+tq'.$$

Bases fixed:

$$-Q_C=uq+u'q'+\frac{Fh_1}{4},$$

$$-Q_{C'}=u'q+uq'+\frac{Fh_1}{4};$$

Bases hinged:

$$-Q_C=uq+u'q'+\frac{Fh_1}{2};$$

$$-Q_{C'}=u'q+uq'+\frac{Fh_1}{2}.$$

(3) Single horizontal load, applied to the member BC, Fig. 148b:

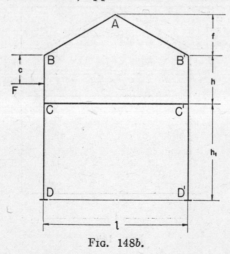

Fig. 148b.

Bases fixed or hinged:

$$q = \frac{1}{h}(FM_{BC} + FM_{CB}) + \left(1 - \frac{c}{h}\right)F,$$

$$q' = 0;$$

$$-Q_B = -FM_{BC} + tq,$$

$$-Q_{B'} = t'q.$$

Bases fixed:

$$-Q_C = -FM_{CB} + uq + \frac{Fh_1}{4},$$

$$-Q_{C'} = u'q + \frac{Fh_1}{4};$$

Bases hinged:

$$-Q_C = -FM_{CB} + uq + \frac{Fh_1}{2},$$

$$-Q_{C'} = u'q + \frac{Fh_1}{2}.$$

(4) Uniform horizontal load, w per linear foot of vertical projection, applied to the member AB, Fig. 148c:

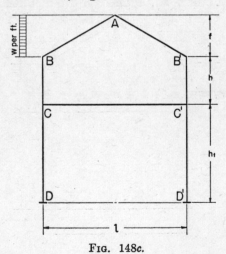

Fig. 148c.

Bases fixed or hinged:

$$q=\frac{17}{24}wf,$$

$$q'=\frac{5}{24}wf;$$

$$-Q_B=\frac{wf^2}{12}+tq+t'q',$$

$$-Q_{B'}=t'q+tq'.$$

Bases fixed:

$$-Q_C=uq+u'q'+\frac{wfh_1}{4},$$

$$-Q_{C'}=u'q+uq'+\frac{wfh_1}{4}.$$

Bases hinged:

$$-Q_C=uq+u'q'+\frac{wfh_1}{2},$$

$$-Q_{C'}=u'q+uq'+\frac{wfh_1}{2}.$$

(5) Uniform horizontal load, w per linear foot of vertical projection, applied to the member BC, Fig. 148d:

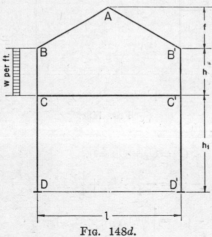

FIG. 148d.

Bases fixed or hinged:

$$q=\frac{wh}{2},$$

$$q'=0;$$

$$-Q_B=-\frac{wh^2}{12}+tq,$$

$$-Q_{B'}=t'q.$$

Bases fixed:

$$-Q_C=uq+\frac{wh^2}{12}+\frac{whh_1}{4},$$

$$-Q_{C'}=u'q+\frac{whh_1}{4}.$$

Bases hinged:

$$-Q_C=uq+\frac{wh^2}{12}+\frac{whh_1}{2},$$

$$-Q_{C'}=u'q+\frac{whh_1}{2}.$$

(6) Single horizontal load, applied to the member CD, Fig. 148e:

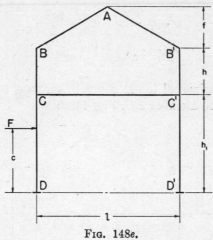

Fig. 148e.

(*a*) Bases fixed:

$$Q_A=Q_B=Q_{B'}=0,$$

$$-Q_C=-\frac{3}{4}FM_{CD}+\frac{1}{4}FM_{DC}+\frac{cF}{4},$$

$$-Q_{C'}=\frac{1}{4}(FM_{CD}+FM_{DC})+\frac{cF}{4}.$$

(*b*) Bases hinged:

$$Q_A=Q_B=Q_{B'}=0,$$

$$-Q_C=-\frac{1}{2}HM_{CD}+\frac{cF}{2},$$

$$-Q_{C'}=\frac{1}{2}HM_{CD}+\frac{cF}{2}.$$

(7) Uniform horizontal load, w per linear foot, applied to the member CD, Fig. 148f:

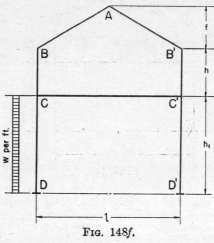

FIG. 148f.

(a) Bases fixed:

$$Q_A = Q_B = Q_{B'} = 0,$$

$$-Q_C = \frac{1}{24}wh^2, \quad -Q_{C'} = \frac{1}{8}wh^2.$$

(b) Bases hinged:

$$Q_A = Q_B = Q_{B'} = 0,$$

$$-Q_C = \frac{3}{16}wh^2, \quad -Q_{C'} = \frac{5}{16}wh^2.$$

ILLUSTRATIVE EXAMPLE

The roof member AB of the symmetrical bent shown in Fig. 149 is carrying a uniform vertical load of one kip per linear foot of horizontal projection. Assuming the legs to be fixed at the bases D and D' determine the end moments.

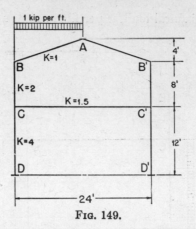

FIG. 149.

Solution: Applying eqs. (133), (134) and the load constants in (1),

$$u=\frac{8(1+1)}{4(1+0.5)}=\frac{8}{3}, \quad u'=\frac{8}{4(1+0.5)}=\frac{4}{3};$$

$$t=\frac{8(1+1)-4}{4(1+0.5)}=2, \quad t'=\frac{4+8}{4(1+0.5)}=2;$$

$$q=-\frac{7\times24^2}{4\times96}=-10.5, \quad q'=\frac{5\times24^2}{4\times96}=7.5.$$

Also, eqs. (135), (153) to (156),

$$2.0A+0.5B+0.5B'=-12,$$

$$1.5A+2.5B-0.5B'+0.25C-0.75C'=6,$$

$$1.5A-0.5B+2.5B'-0.75C+0.25C'=-6,$$

$$1.0A+0.5B-0.5B'+5.0C-1.25C'=-18,$$

$$1.0A-0.5B+0.5B'-1.25C+5.0C'=6.$$

The solution of the equations is performed in the usual tabular form, after eliminating A.   These values are:

$$A=-9.802,$$

$$B=10.390,$$

$$B'=4.820,$$

$$C=-1.354,$$

$$C'=3.382.$$

From eqs. (152) and(152a),

$$s=\frac{9.802}{4}+\frac{10.390}{8}+\frac{4.820}{8}-\frac{3\times1.354}{8}-10.5=-6.656,$$

$$s'=\frac{9.802}{4}+\frac{10.390}{8}+\frac{4.820}{8}+\frac{3\times3.382}{8}+7.5=13.120;$$

and from eqs. (132) and (130),

$$R=\frac{-8\times6.656+4\times13.120}{3\times2}=-0.129,$$

$$R'=\frac{-4\times6.656+8\times13.120}{3\times2}=13.056,$$

$$R_{AB}=-R_{AB'}=13.056+0.129=13.185,$$

$$R_{CD}=R_{C'D'}=\frac{3}{8}(3.382-1.354)-0.760.$$

With these values, the end moments become:

$$M_{AB}=-9.802+5.195-13.185+12=-5.79,$$
$$M_{AB'}=-9.802+2.410+13.185=5.79;$$

$$M_{BA}=10.390-4.901-13.185-12=-19.69,$$
$$M_{BC}=2(10.390-0.677+0.129)=19.69;$$

$$M_{B'A}=4.820-4.901+13.185=13.10,$$
$$M_{B'C'}=2(4.820+1.691-13.056)=-13.10;$$

$$M_{CB}=2(-1.354+5.195+0.129)=7.94,$$
$$M_{CC'}=1.5(-1.354+1.691)=0.51,$$
$$M_{CD}=4(-1.354-0.760)=-8.45;$$

$$M_{C'B'}=2(3.382+2.410-13.056)=-14.53,$$
$$M_{C'C}=1.5(3.382-0.677)=4.05,$$
$$M_{C'D'}=4(3.382-0.760)=10.48;$$

$$M_{DC}=4(-0.677-0.760)=-5.75;$$

$$M_{D'C'}=4(1.691-0.760)=3.72.$$

PROBLEMS

43. The lower column *CD* of the two-story symmetrical bent shown in Fig. 148*g* is subjected to a bracket load. Obtain the load constants of the joint expressions corresponding to two conditions of support at bases *D* and *D'*:

(*a*) Fixed bases;

(*b*) Hinged bases.

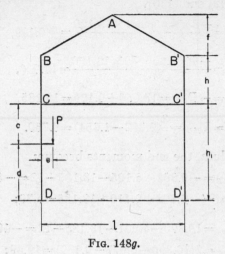

FIG. 148*g*.

Denote the fixed and hinged-end moments by their symbols.

44. The two-story symmetrical bent shown in Fig. 149a is subjected to a uniform horizontal load of one kip per linear vertical foot. Assuming the bent to be fixed at the bases *D* and *D'*, determine the end moments.

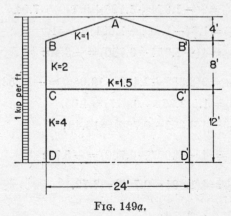

FIG. 149*a*.

51. Single-story Unsymmetrical Bent.—Fig. 150 (*a*) illustrates an

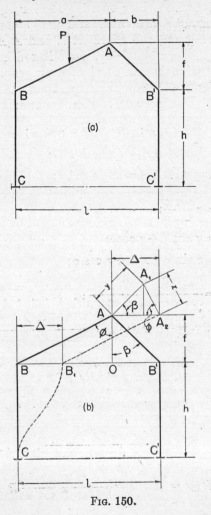

FIG. 150.

unsymmetrical gabled bent. Here, due to dissymmetry of framing, the deflections of the two legs, as well as the deflections of the top members, will differ regardless the type of loading or the stiffnesses of the members. As in the case of the symmetrical bent, the deflections of the top and leg members are interrelated. To establish this interrelation, consider the displacement diagram shown in Fig. 150 (*b*). The construction is similar to that shown in Fig. 116: first, the left leg, *BC*, is allowed to deflect, while the right leg is held in position; as a result, the joint *B* moves into B_1, and the crown joint *A* moves into A_1. The displacement BB_1 represents the deflection Δ of the member BC, and A_1 is the point of intersection of two arcs having centers at B_1 and B' and the respective radii $B_1A_2(=BA)$ and $B'A$. (Since the displacements are small, and unlike the magnified representation of the diagram, the chords A_1A and A_1A_2—drawn normal to AB' and AB, respectively—are substituted for the two arcs.) Accordingly, the triangle AA_1A_2 indicates graphically the interrelation of deflections of the top members AB and AB' and the leg BC. The derivation of the algebraic relation follows: Let

$$y=\overline{AA}y=\Delta_{AB'}; \quad x=\overline{A_1A_2}=-\Delta_{AB}; \quad R=\frac{\Delta}{h};$$

$$\beta=\text{angle } A_1AA_2=\text{angle } B'AO;$$

$$\phi=\text{angle } A_1A_2A=\text{angle } BAO;$$

then

$$y=x\frac{\sin\phi}{\sin\beta};$$

$$\Delta=y\cos\beta+x\cos\phi$$

$$=x\sin\phi\cot\beta+x\cos\phi;$$

or

$$x=\frac{\Delta}{\cos\phi+\sin\phi\cot\beta}; \quad \cdots\cdots\cdots\cdots (a)$$

$$-R_{AB}=\frac{x}{f}\cos\phi=\frac{h}{h}\cdot\frac{\Delta}{f}\cdot\frac{\cos\phi}{\cos\phi+\sin\phi\cot\beta}$$

$$=\frac{1}{1+\tan\phi\cot\beta}\frac{h}{f}R$$

$$=\frac{b}{a+b}\cdot\frac{h}{f}R=\frac{bh}{fl}R \quad \cdots\cdots\cdots\cdots (b)$$

Also,

$$y=\frac{\Delta}{\cos\beta+\sin\beta\cot\phi}; \quad \cdots\cdots\cdots (c)$$

and

$$R_{AB'}=\frac{y}{f}\cos\beta=\frac{1}{1+\tan\beta\cot\phi}\frac{h}{f}R$$

$$=\frac{h}{f}R\cdot\frac{a}{a+b}=\frac{ah}{fl}R \quad \cdots\cdots\cdots\cdots (d)$$

Similarly, if the joint B' is displaced a distance Δ', while the left leg is held in position, for R_{AB} and $R_{AB'}$ we will have:

$$R_{AB}=\frac{bh}{fl}R'; \quad R_{AB'}=-\frac{ah}{fl}R'; \quad \cdots\cdots\cdots (e)$$

in which R' is the deflection term for the leg $B'C'$, and is equal to $\frac{\Delta'}{h}$.

The interrelation of deflection terms $R_{AB}, R_{AB'}, R$ and R', when both legs of the bent are allowed to deflect, is obtained from eqs. (*b*), (*d*) and (*e*):

$$R_{AB}=\frac{bh}{fl}(R'-R); \quad R_{AB'}=\frac{ah}{fl}(R-R') \quad \ldots \quad (158)$$

(It is to be noted that when a and b equal $\frac{l}{2}$, eq. (158) becomes identical with eq. (130), as derived in Art. 47 for a symmetrical bent; and, when b is zero, R_{AB} also becomes zero.)

Having thus obtained the fundamental relation between the deflection terms of top and leg members of the bent, the joint and deflection expressions are derived as for a symmetrical bent. Consider, for example, the bent shown in Fig. 151. Assuming the legs to be

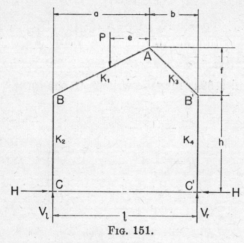

FIG. 151.

fixed at the bases C and C', we have:

$$M_{AB}+M_{BA}+V_l a-Pe-Hf=0, \quad M_{BC}+M_{CB}-Hh=0.$$

Noting that

$$V_l l=-(M_{BA}+M_{B'A})+P(b+e),$$

and eliminating H,

$$\frac{1}{f}(M_{AB}+M_{BA})-\frac{1}{h}(M_{BC}+M_{CB})-\frac{a}{lf}(M_{BA}+M_{B'A})+\frac{b}{fl}(a-e)P=0\ldots(f).$$

But

$$M_{AB}=K_1\left[A+\frac{B}{2}-\frac{bh}{fl}(R'-R)\right]+FM_{AB};$$

$$M_{BA}=K_1\left[\frac{A}{2}+B-\frac{bh}{fl}(R'-R)\right]+FM_{BA};$$

$$M_{B'A}=K_3\left[\frac{A}{2}+B'-\frac{ah}{fl}(R-R')\right];$$

$$M_{BC}=K_2(B-R);$$

$$M_{CB}=K_2\left(\frac{B}{2}-R\right).$$

Substituting these values for the end moments in eq. (f),

$$\left[\frac{h}{f^2 l}\left(2bK_1+\frac{a^2}{l}K_3-\frac{ab}{l}K_1\right)+\frac{2}{h}K_2\right]R-\frac{h}{f^2 l}\left(2bK_1+\frac{a^2}{l}K_3-\frac{ab}{l}K_1\right)R'$$

$$=\left[\frac{a}{2fl}(K_1+K_3)-\frac{3}{2f}K_1\right]A+\left[\left(\frac{a}{l}-\frac{3}{2}\right)\frac{K_1}{f}+\frac{3}{2h}K_2\right]B+\frac{a}{fl}K_3B'$$

$$+\frac{a}{fl}FM_{BA}-\frac{1}{f}(FM_{AB}+FM_{BA})-\frac{b}{fl}(a-e)P=s \ . \ . \ . \ . \ . \ (159)$$

Similarly, from the shear expressions of the members AB' and $B'C'$ we obtain:

$$\left[\frac{h}{f^2 l}\left(2aK_3+\frac{b^2}{l}K_1-\frac{ab}{l}K_3\right)+\frac{2}{h}K_4\right]R'-\frac{h}{f^2 l}\left(2aK_3+\frac{b^2}{l}K_1-\frac{ab}{l}K_3\right)R$$

$$=\left[\frac{b}{2fl}(K_1+K_3)-\frac{3}{2f}K_3\right]A+\frac{b}{fl}K_1B+\left[\left(\frac{b}{l}-\frac{3}{2}\right)\frac{K_3}{f}+\frac{3}{2h}K_4\right]B'$$

$$+\frac{b}{fl}FM_{BA}+\frac{b}{fl}(a-e)P=s' \ . \ . \ . \ . \ . \ . \ . \ . \ . \ . \ . \ . \ (159a)$$

Eqs. (159) and (159a) may be written in the form

$$\left.\begin{aligned}c_1R-c_2R'&=s,\\ -c_3R+c_4R'&=s'.\end{aligned}\right\} \ . \ . \ . \ . \ . \ . \ . \ . \ . \ (160)$$

From which

$$\left.\begin{aligned}R&=\frac{c_4 s+c_2 s'}{c_1 c_4-c_2 c_3}=u_1 s+u_2 s',\\[2mm] R'&=\frac{c_3 s+c_1 s'}{c_1 c_4-c_2 c_3}=u_3 s+u_4 s';\end{aligned}\right\} \ . \ . \ . \ . \ . \ . \ . \ (161)$$

and

$$R-R'=(u_1-u_3)s+(u_2-u_4)s'.$$

The deflection terms of the members AB and AB', forming the joint A, are given by the expression

$$-\frac{bh}{fl}(R'-R)K_1-\frac{ah}{fl}(R-R')K_3=\frac{h}{fl}(bK_1-aK_3)(R-R')$$

$$=\frac{h}{fl}(bK_1-aK_3)[(u_1-u_3)s+(u_2-u_4)s'] \ . \ . \ . \ . \ . \ (g)$$

At joint B, from the deflection terms of the members BA and BC, we have:

$$-\frac{bh}{fl}(R'-R)K_1-K_2R=\frac{bh}{fl}K_1[(u_1-u_3)s+(u_2-u_4)s']-K_2(u_1 s+u_2 s'); \ (h)$$

and at B',

$$\frac{ah}{fl}K_3[(u_3-u_1)s+(u_4-u_2)s']-K_4(u_3 s+u_4 s') \ . \ . \ . \ . \ (i)$$

Substituting the values of s and s' from eqs. (159) and (159a) in eqs. (g), (h) and (i), the joint expressions at A, B and B' become:

Joint A,

$$\left\{K_1+K_3+\frac{h}{2f^2l}(bK_1-aK_3)\left[(u_1-u_3)\left(\frac{a}{l}(K_1+K_3)-3K_1\right)\right.\right.$$
$$\left.+(u_2-u_4)\left(\frac{b}{l}(K_1+K_3)-3K_3\right)\right]\right\}A$$
$$+\left\{\frac{1}{2}K_1+\frac{h}{fl}(bK_1-aK_3)\left\{(u_1-u_3)\left[\left(\frac{a}{l}-\frac{3}{2}\right)\frac{K_1}{f}+\frac{3K_2}{2h}\right]\right.\right.$$
$$\left.\left.+(u_2-u_4)\frac{bK_1}{fl}\right\}\right\}B+\left\{\frac{1}{2}K_3+\frac{h}{fl}(bK_1-aK_3)\left\{(u_1-u_3)\frac{aK_3}{fl}\right.\right.$$
$$\left.\left.+(u_2-u_4)\left[\left(\frac{b}{l}-\frac{3}{2}\right)\frac{K_3}{f}+\frac{3K_4}{2h}\right]\right\}\right\}B'=-FM_{AB}$$
$$-\frac{h}{f^2l^2}(bK_1-aK_3)\left[\,[a(u_1-u_3)+b(u_2-u_4)]FM_{BA}\right.$$
$$\left.-b(a-e)(u_1-u_2-u_3+u_4)P\right]$$
$$+\frac{h}{f^2l}(bK_1-aK_3)(u_1-u_3)(FM_{AB}+FM_{BA});\ .\ .\ .\ .\ .\ .\ .\ .\ (162)$$

Joint B,

$$\left\{K_1+K_2+\left[\frac{bh}{fl}K_1(u_1-u_3)-u_1K_2\right]\left[\left(\frac{a}{l}-\frac{3}{2}\right)\frac{K_1}{f}+\frac{3K_2}{2h}\right]\right.$$
$$+\left[\frac{bh}{fl}K_1(u_2-u_4)-u_2K_2\right]\frac{bK_1}{fl}\right\}B+\left\{\frac{1}{2}K_1\right.$$
$$+\left[\frac{bh}{fl}K_1(u_1-u_3)-u_1K_2\right]\left[\frac{a}{2fl}(K_1+K_3)-\frac{3K_1}{2f}\right]$$
$$+\left[\frac{bh}{fl}K_1(u_2-u_4)-u_2K_2\right]\left[\frac{b}{2fl}(K_1+K_3)-\frac{3K_3}{2f}\right]\right\}A$$
$$+\left\{\frac{aK_3}{fl}\left[\frac{bh}{fl}K_1(u_1-u_3)-u_1K_2\right]\right.$$
$$\left.+\left[\frac{bh}{fl}K_1(u_2-u_4)-u_2K_2\right]\left[\left(\frac{b}{l}-\frac{3}{2}\right)\frac{K_3}{f}+\frac{3K_4}{2h}\right]\right\}B'=-FM_{BA}$$
$$-\frac{1}{f}\left[\frac{bh}{fl}K_1(u_1-u_3)-u_1K_2\right]\left[\frac{a}{l}FM_{BA}\right.$$
$$\left.-(FM_{AB}+FM_{BA})-\frac{b}{l}(a-e)P\right]$$
$$-\frac{b}{fl}\left[\frac{bh}{fl}K_1(u_2-u_4)-u_2K_2\right][FM_{BA}+(a-e)P];\ .\ .\ .\ .\ .\ (163)$$

Joint B',

$$\left\{K_3+K_4+\left[\frac{ah}{fl}K_3(u_3-u_1)-u_3K_4\right]\frac{aK_3}{fl}\right.$$

$$+\left[\frac{ah}{fl}K_3(u_4-u_2)-u_4K_4\right]\left[\left(\frac{b}{l}-\frac{3}{2}\right)\frac{K_3}{f}+\frac{3K_4}{2h}\right]\right\}B'+\left\{\frac{1}{2}K_3\right.$$

$$+\left[\frac{ah}{fl}K_3(u_3-u_1)-u_3K_4\right]\left[\frac{a}{2fl}(K_1+K_3)-\frac{3K_1}{2f}\right]$$

$$+\left[\frac{ah}{fl}K_3(u_4-u_2)-u_4K_4\right]\left[\frac{b}{2fl}(K_1+K_3)-\frac{3K_3}{2f}\right]\right\}A$$

$$+\left\{\left[\frac{ah}{fl}K_3(u_3-u_1)-u_3K_4\right]\left[\left(\frac{a}{l}-\frac{3}{2}\right)\frac{K_1}{f}+\frac{3K_2}{2h}\right]\right.$$

$$+\left[\frac{ah}{fl}K_3(u_4-u_2)-u_4K_4\right]\frac{bK_1}{fl}\right\}B=-\left[\frac{ah}{fl}K_3(u_3-u_1)\right.$$

$$\left.-u_3K_4\right]\left[\frac{a}{fl}FM_{BA}-\frac{1}{f}(FM_{AB}+FM_{BA})-\frac{b}{fl}(a-e)P\right]$$

$$-\left[\frac{ah}{fl}K_3(u_4-u_2)-u_4K_4\right]\left[\frac{b}{fl}FM_{BA}+\frac{b}{fl}(a-e)P\right]\quad\ldots\ldots(164)$$

In the case of the bent shown in Fig. 152, having hinged bases, the

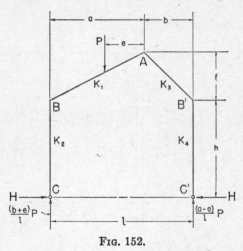

FIG. 152.

vertical reactions are determinate. From the shear expressions of the members AB and BC we have:

$$\frac{1}{f}(M_{AB}+M_{BA})+\frac{b}{fl}(a-e)P-\frac{1}{h}M_{BC}=0;$$

and, substituting the values of the end moments,

$$\left(\frac{2bhK_1}{f^2l}+\frac{K_2}{2h}\right)R-\frac{2bhK_1}{f^2l}R'=-\frac{3K_1}{2f}A+\left(\frac{3K_2}{4h}-\frac{3K_1}{2f}\right)B$$

$$-\frac{1}{f}(FM_{AB}+FM_{BA})-\frac{b}{fl}(a-e)P=s \dots \dots \dots (165)$$

Similarly, from the shear expressions of the members AB' and $B'C'$ we obtain:

$$\left(\frac{2ahK_3}{f^2l}+\frac{K_4}{2h}\right)R'-\frac{2ahK_3}{f^2l}R=-\frac{3K_3}{2f}A+\left(\frac{3K_4}{4h}-\frac{3K_3}{2f}\right)B'$$

$$+\frac{b}{fl}(a-e)P=s'. \dots \dots \dots \dots (165a)$$

Let

$$d_1=\frac{2bhK_1}{f^2l}+\frac{K_2}{2h};\ d_2=\frac{2bhK_1}{f^2l};\ d_3=\frac{2ahK_3}{f^2l};\ d_4=\frac{2ahK_3}{f^2l}+\frac{K_4}{2h}.$$

Then for eqs. (165) and (165a) we can write:

$$\left.\begin{aligned} d_1R-d_2R'&=s,\\ -d_3R+d_4R'&=s; \end{aligned}\right\} \dots \dots \dots 1(160a)$$

from which

$$\left.\begin{aligned} R&=\frac{d_4s+d_2s'}{d_1d_4-d_2d_3}=u_1s+u_2s',\\ R'&=\frac{d_3s+d_1s'}{d_1d_4-d_2d_3}=u_3s+u_4s'; \end{aligned}\right\} \dots \dots (161a)$$

and

$$R-R'=(u_1-u_3)s+(u_2-u_4)s'.$$

Substituting these values for the deflection terms, the joint equations become:

Joint A,

$$\left[K_1+K_3+\frac{3h}{2f^2l}(u_1-u_3)(aK_3-bK_1)K_1+\frac{3h}{2l^2f}(u_2-u_4)(aK_3-bK_1)K_3\right]A$$

$$+\left[\frac{1}{2}K_1+\frac{h}{fl}(u_1-u_3)(bK_1-aK_3)\left(\frac{3K_2}{4h}-\frac{3K_1}{2f}\right)\right]B$$

$$+\left[\frac{1}{2}K_3+\frac{h}{fl}(u_2-u_4)(bK_1-aK_3)\left(\frac{3K_4}{4h}-\frac{3K_3}{2f}\right)\right]B'$$

$$=-FM_{AB}+\frac{h}{lf^2}(u_1-u_3)(bK_1-aK_3)(FM_{AB}+FM_{BA})$$

$$+\frac{hb}{f^2l^2}(bK_1-aK_3)(a-e)[(u_1-u_3)-(u_2-u_4)]P \dots \dots (166)$$

Joint B,

$$\left[K_1+\frac{3}{4}K_2+\left(\frac{bh}{fl}(u_1-u_3)K_1-\frac{u_1K_2}{2}\right)\left(\frac{3K_2}{4h}-\frac{3K_1}{2f}\right)\right]B$$

$$+\left[\frac{1}{2}K_1+\frac{3K_1}{2f}\left(\frac{bh}{fl}(u_3-u_1)K_1+\frac{u_1K_2}{2}\right)\right.$$

$$+\frac{3K_3}{2f}\left(\frac{bh}{fl}(u_4-u_2)K_1+\frac{u_2K_2}{2}\right)\right]A+\left[\frac{bh}{fl}(u_2-u_4)K_1-\frac{u_2K_2}{2}\right]\left(\frac{3K_4}{4h}\right.$$

$$\left.-\frac{3K_3}{2f}\right)B'=-FM_{BA}+\left[\frac{bh}{lf^2}(u_1-u_3)K_1-\frac{u_1K_2}{2f}\right](FM_{AB}$$

$$+FM_{BA})+\frac{bP}{fl}(a-e)\left[\frac{bh}{lf}(u_1-u_3-u_2+u_4)K_1+(u_2-u_1)\frac{K_2}{2}\right].\quad(167)$$

Joint B',

$$\left[K_3+\frac{3}{4}K_4+\left(\frac{ah}{fl}(u_4-u_2)K_3-u_4\frac{K_4}{2}\right)\left(\frac{3K_4}{4h}-\frac{3K_3}{2f}\right)\right]B'$$

$$+\left[\frac{K_3}{2}+\frac{3K_1}{2f}\left(\frac{ah}{fl}(u_1-u_3)K_3+u_3\frac{K_4}{2}\right)\right.$$

$$+\frac{3K_3}{2f}\left(\frac{ah}{fl}(u_2-u_4)K_3+u_4\frac{K_4}{2}\right)\right]A+\left[\frac{ah}{fl}(u_3-u_1)K_3-u_3\frac{K_4}{2}\right]\left(\frac{3K_2}{4h}\right.$$

$$\left.-\frac{3K_1}{2f}\right)B=-\left[\frac{ah}{lf^2}(u_1-u_3)K_3+\frac{u_3K_4}{2f}\right](FM_{AB}+FM_{BA})$$

$$+\frac{bP}{fl}(a-e)\left[\frac{ah}{fl}(u_2+u_3-u_1-u_4)K_3+(u_4-u_3)\frac{K_4}{2}\right].\quad\ldots\quad(168)$$

If the loading is uniform, as is shown in Fig. 153, the load constants

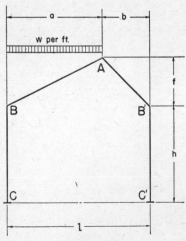

Fig. 153.

in s and s' expressions for the two conditions of support assume the following simplified forms:

(*a*) Fixed bases:

$$\left.\begin{array}{l} q=-(a+6b)\dfrac{a^2w}{12fl}, \\[2ex] q'=\dfrac{5}{12}\cdot\dfrac{a^2bw}{fl}; \end{array}\right\} \quad\ldots\ldots\ldots\ldots \quad (j)$$

(*b*) Hinged bases:

$$\left.\begin{array}{l} q=-\dfrac{a^2bw}{2fl}, \\[2ex] q'=\dfrac{a^2bw}{2fl}. \end{array}\right\} \quad\ldots\ldots\ldots\ldots \quad (k)$$

ILLUSTRATIVE EXAMPLE

The top member AB of the unsymmetrical bent shown in Fig. 154 is carrying a uniform vertical load of one kip per linear foot of horizontal projection. Assuming the legs to be fixed at the bases C and C' determine the end moments.

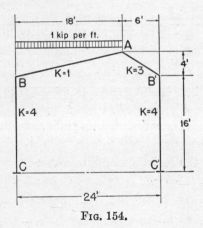

Fig. 154.

Solution: Applying equations (160), (159) and (159a) and load constants (j),

$$u_1 = \frac{18}{13}, \quad u_2 = \frac{8}{13}, \quad u_3 = \frac{16}{13}, \quad u_4 = \frac{10}{13};$$

$$q = -\frac{243}{16}, \quad q' = \frac{135}{16};$$

$$s = \frac{3}{16}B + \frac{9}{16}B' - \frac{243}{16},$$

$$s' = -A + \frac{1}{16}B - \frac{9}{16}B' + \frac{135}{16}.$$

Substituting the numerical constants in equations (162), (163) and (164), the joint equations become:

$$2.7692A + 0.3462B + 0.1154B' = -56.07,$$
$$3.1154A + 3.8269B - 1.5577B' = -32.72,$$
$$3.1923A - 1.2885B + 4.4038B' = -81.52;$$

from which

$$A = -21.30, \; B = 8.55, \; B' = -0.57.$$

Then

$$s = 1.60 - 0.32 - 15.19 = -13.91,$$
$$s' = 21.29 + 0.53 + 0.32 + 8.44 = 30.58;$$

and from equations (161) and (158),

$$R \quad = -19.26 + 18.83 = -0.43,$$
$$R' \quad = -17.11 + 23.53 = 6.42,$$
$$R_{AB} = 6.42 + 0.43 = 6.85,$$
$$R_{AB'} = -3 \times 6.85 = -20.55.$$

With these values, the end moments become:

$$M_{AB} \quad = (-21.30 + 4.27 - 6.85) + 27 = 3.12,$$
$$M_{AB'} \quad = 3(-21.30 - 0.29 + 20.55) = -3.12;$$

$$M_{BA} \quad = (8.55 - 10.65 - 6.85) - 27 = -35.95,$$
$$M_{BC} \quad = 4(8.55 + 0.43) = 35.92;$$

$$M_{B'A} \quad = 3(-0.57 - 10.65 + 20.55) = 27.99,$$
$$M_{B'C'} \quad = 4(-0.57 - 6.42) = -27.96;$$

$$M_{CB} \quad = 4(4.27 + 0.43) = 18.80;$$

$$M_{C'B'} \quad = 4(-0.28 - 6.42) = -26.80.$$

PROBLEMS

45. Determine the load factors in the s and s' expressions corresponding to (1) fixed and (2) hinged bases, for the loadings shown in Fig. 155:

(a) Single horizontal load, applied to member AB;
(b) Uniform lateral load, applied to member AB;
(c) Single horizontal load, applied to member BC;
(d) Uniform lateral load, applied to member BC.

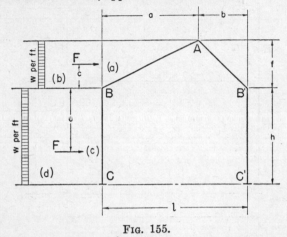

FIG. 155.

46. The single-story unsymmetrical bent shown in Fig. 154a is subjected to a uniform lateral load of one kip per linear vertical foot. Assuming the bent to be fixed at the bases C and C', obtain the end moments.

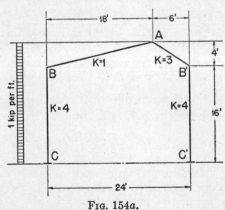

FIG. 154a.

52. Two-story Unsymmetrical Bent.—With some modifications, the solution of the single-story unsymmetrical bent, discussed in the preceding article, may also be used in obtaining the moments in an unsymmetrical bent of two stories. Consider, for example, the bent shown in Fig. 156.   In the top panel $CBAB'C'$, the interrelation of deflec-

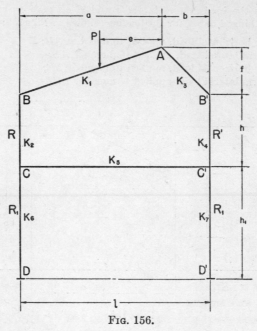

FIG. 156.

tions of the members is obtained as in a single-story bent.   Denoting
the deflection terms of the members BC and $B'C'$, respectively, by
R and R', for the deflections of the top members AB and AB' we then
have:

$$R_{AB}=\frac{bh}{fl}(R'-R),\left.\begin{array}{}\\\\\end{array}\right\}\quad\cdots\cdots\cdots\cdots\quad(158)$$
$$R_{AB'}=\frac{ah}{fl}(R-R').$$

Except for an additional term due to the deflection angles at C and
C', the s and s' expressions, eqs. (159) and (159a), remain unchanged.

The additional term in the former is $\frac{3K_2}{2h}C$, and in the latter $\frac{3K_4}{2h}C'$.
With these additions, we can write:

$$\left[\frac{h}{f^2l}\left(2bK_1+\frac{a^2}{l}K_3-\frac{ab}{l}K_1\right)+\frac{2}{h}K_2\right]R-\frac{h}{f^2l}\left(2bK_1+\frac{a^2}{l}K_3-\frac{ab}{l}K_1\right)R'$$

$$=\left[\frac{a}{2fl}(K_1+K_3)-\frac{3}{2f}K_1\right]A+\left[\left(\frac{a}{l}-\frac{3}{2}\right)\frac{K_1}{f}+\frac{3}{2h}K_2\right]B+\frac{aK_3}{fl}B'$$

$$+\frac{3K_2}{2h}C+\frac{a}{fl}FM_{BA}-\frac{1}{f}(FM_{AB}+FM_{BA})-\frac{b}{fl}(a-e)P=s\quad\cdots\quad(169)$$

$$\left[\frac{h}{f^2l}\left(2aK_3+\frac{b^2}{l}K_1-\frac{ab}{l}K_3\right)+\frac{2}{h}K_4\right]R'-\frac{h}{f^2l}\left(2aK_3+\frac{b^2}{l}K_1-\frac{ab}{l}K_3\right)R$$

$$=\left[\frac{b}{2fl}(K_1+K_3)-\frac{3}{2f}K_3\right]A+\frac{bK_1}{fl}B+\left[\left(\frac{b}{l}-\frac{3}{2}\right)\frac{K_3}{f}+\frac{3}{2h}K_4\right]B'$$

$$+\frac{3K_4}{2h}C'+\frac{b}{fl}FM_{BA}+\frac{b}{fl}(a-e)P=s'.\quad\ldots\ldots\ldots\ldots\quad (169a)$$

Written in the general form,

$$\left.\begin{aligned}c_1R-c_2R'&=s,\\-c_3R+c_4R_1&=s';\end{aligned}\right\}\quad\ldots\ldots\ldots\ldots\quad (160)$$

from which

and

$$\left.\begin{aligned}R&=\frac{c_4s+c_2s'}{c_1c_4-c_2c_3}=u_1s+u_2s',\\R'&=\frac{c_3s+c_1s'}{c_1c_4-c_2c_3}=u_3s+u_4s'.\end{aligned}\right\}\quad\ldots\ldots\ldots\quad (161)$$

The support condition at the bases D and D' will not alter the typical forms of joint expressions at A, B and B'. These expressions, corresponding to both fixed and hinged bases, are:

Joint A,

$$\left\{K_1+K_3+\frac{h}{2f^2l}(bK_1-aK_3)\left[(u_1-u_3)\left(\frac{a}{l}(K_1+K_3)-3K_1\right)\right.\right.$$

$$\left.\left.+(u_2-u_4)\left(\frac{b}{l}(K_1+K_3)-3K_3\right)\right]\right\}A+\left\{\frac{1}{2}K_1+\frac{h}{fl}(bK_1\right.$$

$$-aK_3)\left\{(u_1-u_3)\left[\left(\frac{a}{l}-\frac{3}{2}\right)\frac{K_1}{f}+\frac{3K_2}{2h}\right]+(u_2-u_4)\frac{bK_1}{fl}\right\}\bigg\}B+\left\{\frac{1}{2}K_3\right.$$

$$+\frac{h}{fl}(bK_1-aK_3)\left\{(u_1-u_3)\frac{aK_3}{fl}+(u_2-u_4)\left[\left(\frac{b}{l}-\frac{3}{2}\right)\frac{K_3}{f}+\frac{3K_4}{2h}\right]\right\}\bigg\}B'$$

$$+\frac{3K_2}{2fl}(bK_1-aK_3)(u_1-u_3)C+\frac{3K_4}{2fl}(bK_1-aK_3)(u_2-u_4)C'=-FM_{AB}$$

$$+\frac{h}{f^2l}(bK_1-aK_3)(u_1-u_3)(FM_{AB}+FM_{BA})$$

$$-\frac{h}{f^2l^2}(bK_1-aK_3)\Big([a(u_1-u_3)$$

$$+b(u_2-u_4)]FM_{BA}-b(a-e)(u_1-u_2-u_3+u_4)P\Big)\quad\ldots\quad (170)$$

Joint B,

$$\left\{K_1+K_2+\left[\frac{bh}{fl}(u_1-u_3)K_1-u_1K_2\right]\left[\left(\frac{a}{l}-\frac{3}{2}\right)\frac{K_1}{f}+\frac{3K_2}{2h}\right]\right.$$

$$\left.+\left[\frac{bh}{fl}(u_2-u_4)K_1-u_2K_2\right]\frac{bK_1}{fl}\right\}B$$

$$+\left\{\frac{1}{2}K_1+\left[\frac{bh}{fl}(u_1-u_3)K_1-u_1K_2\right]\left[\frac{a}{2fl}(K_1+K_3)-\frac{3K_1}{2f}\right]\right.$$

$$\left.+\left[\frac{bh}{fl}(u_2-u_4)K_1-u_2K_2\right]\left[\frac{b}{2fl}(K_1+K_3)-\frac{3K_3}{2f}\right]\right\}A$$

$$+\left\{\frac{aK_3}{fl}\left[\frac{bh}{fl}(u_1-u_3)K_1-u_1K_2\right]\right.$$

$$\left.+\left[\frac{bh}{fl}(u_2-u_4)K_1-u_2K_2\right]\left[\left(\frac{b}{l}-\frac{3}{2}\right)\frac{K_3}{f}+\frac{3K_4}{2h}\right]\right\}B'$$

$$+\left[\frac{K_2}{2}+\frac{3bK_1K_2}{2fl}(u_1-u_3)-\frac{3u_1K_2^2}{2h}\right]C$$

$$+\left[\frac{3bK_1K_4}{2fl}(u_2-u_4)-\frac{3u_2K_2K_4}{2h}\right]C'=-FM_{BA}$$

$$-\frac{1}{f}\left[\frac{bh}{fl}(u_1-u_3)K_1-u_1K_2\right]\left[\frac{a}{l}FM_{BA}\right.$$

$$\left.-(FM_{AB}+FM_{BA})-\frac{b}{l}(a-e)P\right]$$

$$-\frac{b}{fl}\left[\frac{bh}{fl}K_1(u_2-u_4)-u_2K_2\right][FM_{BA}+(a-e)P];\ \ .\ .\ .\ .\ .\ (171)$$

Joint B',

$$\left\{K_3+K_4+\left[\frac{ah}{fl}(u_3-u_1)K_3-u_3K_4\right]\frac{aK_3}{fl}\right.$$

$$+\left[\frac{ah}{fl}(u_4-u_2)K_3-u_4K_4\right]\left[\left(\frac{b}{l}-\frac{3}{2}\right)\frac{K_3}{f}+\frac{3K_4}{2h}\right]\right\}B'$$

$$+\left\{\frac{1}{2}K_3+\left[\frac{ah}{fl}(u_3-u_1)K_3-u_3K_4\right]\left[\frac{a}{2fl}(K_1+K_3)-\frac{3K_1}{2f}\right]\right.$$

$$+\left[\frac{ah}{fl}(u_4-u_2)K_3-u_4K_4\right]\left[\frac{b}{2fl}(K_1+K_3)-\frac{3K_3}{2f}\right]\right\}A$$

$$+\left\{\left[\frac{ah}{fl}K_3(u_3-u_1)-u_3K_4\right]\left[\left(\frac{a}{l}-\frac{3}{2}\right)\frac{K_1}{f}+\frac{3K_2}{2h}\right]\right.$$

$$+\left[\frac{ah}{fl}K_3(u_4-u_2)-u_4K_4\right]\frac{bK_1}{fl}\right\}B$$

$$+\left[\frac{3a}{2fl}(u_3-u_1)K_2K_3-\frac{3u_3}{2h}K_2K_4\right]C+\left[\frac{K_4}{2}+\frac{3aK_3K_4}{2fl}(u_4-u_2)\right.$$

$$\left.-\frac{3u_4K_4{}^2}{2h}\right]C'=-\left[\frac{ah}{fl}(u_3-u_1)K_3-u_3K_4\right]\left[\frac{a}{fl}FM_{BA}\right.$$

$$-\frac{1}{f}(FM_{AB}+FM_{BA})-\frac{b}{fl}(a-e)P\right]-\left[\frac{ah}{fl}(u_4-u_2)K_3\right.$$

$$\left.-u_4K_4\right]\left[\frac{b}{fl}FM_{BA}+\frac{b}{fl}(a-e)P\right] . \; . \; . \; . \; . \; . \; . \; . \; . \; . \; . \;(172)$$

For fixed bases at D and D', the deflection of the bottom panel $DCC'D'$ is given by

$$R_1=\frac{3(K_6C+K_7C')}{4(K_6+K_7)}; \; . \; . \; . \; . \; . \; . \; . \; . \;(a)$$

and, since the deflection term of joint C is in the form

$$-K_2R-K_6R_1, \; . \; . \; . \; . \; . \; . \; . \; . \;(b)$$

the corresponding joint expression becomes:

$$\left[K_2+K_5+K_6-\frac{3u_1}{2h}K_2{}^2-\frac{3K_6{}^2}{4(K_6+K_7)}\right]C-\frac{K_2}{2f}\left[(au_1+bu_2)\frac{K_1+K_3}{l}\right.$$

$$\left.-3(u_1K_1+u_2K_3)\right]A+\left\{\frac{1}{2}K_2-K_2\left[\frac{u_1}{f}\left(\frac{a}{l}-\frac{3}{2}\right)K_1+\frac{3u_1}{2h}K_2+\frac{bu_2}{fl}K_1\right]\right\}B$$

$$-\left[\frac{au_1}{fl}K_3+\frac{u_2}{f}\left(\frac{b}{l}-\frac{3}{2}\right)K_3+\frac{3u_2}{2h}K_4\right]K_2B'$$

$$+\left[\frac{1}{2}K_5-\frac{3u_2}{2h}K_2K_4-\frac{3K_6K_7}{4(K_6+K_7)}\right]C'=\frac{(au_1+bu_2)}{fl}K_2FM_{BA}$$

$$-\frac{u_1K_2}{f}(FM_{AB}+FM_{BA})+\frac{b}{fl}(u_2-u_1)(a-e)K_2P.\quad\ldots\quad(173)$$

Similarly, for the joint expression at C' we have:

$$\left[K_4+K_5+K_7-\frac{3u_4}{2h}K_4{}^2-\frac{3K_7{}^2}{4(K_6+K_7)}\right]C'-\frac{K_4}{2f}\left[\frac{(au_3+bu_4)}{l}K_1+K_3\right.$$

$$\left.-3(u_3K_1+u_4K_3)\right]A-K_4\left[\frac{u_3}{f}\left(\frac{a}{l}-\frac{3}{2}\right)K_1+\frac{3u_3}{2h}K_2+\frac{bu_4}{fl}K_1\right]B$$

$$+\left\{\frac{1}{2}K_4-K_4\left[\frac{u_4}{f}\left(\frac{b}{l}-\frac{3}{2}\right)K_3+\frac{3u_4}{2h}K_4+\frac{au_3}{fl}K_3\right]\right\}B'$$

$$+\left[\frac{1}{2}K_5-\frac{3u_3}{2h}K_2K_4-\frac{3K_6K_7}{4(K_6+K_7)}\right]C=\frac{(au_3+bu_4)}{fl}K_4FM_{BA}$$

$$-\frac{u_3}{f}K_4(FM_{AB}+FM_{BA})+\frac{bP}{fl}K_4(u_4-u_3)(a-e)\quad\ldots\ldots\quad(174)$$

If the connections at the bases D and D' are hinged, the deflection of the bottom panel is given by

$$R_1=\frac{3(K_6C+K_7C')}{2(K_6+K_7)};\quad\ldots\ldots\ldots\ldots\quad(c)$$

and the deflection terms of the joints C and C' are respectively given by

$$-K_?R-\frac{1}{2}K_6R_1\quad\text{and}\quad-K_4R'-\frac{1}{2}K_7R_1\quad\ldots\ldots\quad(d)$$

Accordingly, the joint expressions become:
Joint C,

$$\left[K_2+K_5+\frac{3}{4}K_6-\frac{3u_1}{2h}K_2{}^2-\frac{3K_6{}^2}{4(K_6+K_7)}\right]C$$

$$-\frac{K_2}{2f}\left[\frac{(au_1+bu_2)}{l}K_1+K_3-3(u_1K_1+u_2K_3)\right]A$$

$$+\left\{\frac{1}{2}K_2-K_2\left[\frac{u_1}{f}\left(\frac{a}{l}-\frac{3}{2}\right)K_1+\frac{3u_1}{2h}K_2+\frac{bu_2}{fl}K_1\right]\right\}B$$

$$-K_2\left[\frac{au_1}{fl}K_3+\frac{u_2}{f}\left[\frac{b}{l}-\frac{3}{2}\right)K_3+\frac{3u_2}{2h}K_4\right]B'$$

$$+\left[\frac{1}{2}K_5-\frac{3u_2}{2h}K_2K_4-\frac{3K_6K_7}{4(K_6+K_7)}\right]C'$$

$$-\frac{(au_1+bu_2)}{fl}K_2FM_{BA}-\frac{u_1}{f}K_2(FM_{AB}+FM_{BA})$$

$$+\frac{b}{fl}(u_2-u_1)(a-e)K_2P;\ \ldots\ldots\ldots\ldots\ldots \quad (173a)$$

Joint C',

$$\left[K_4+K_5+\frac{3}{4}K_7-\frac{3u_4}{2h}K_4{}^2-\frac{3K_7{}^2}{4(K_6+K_7)}\right]C'$$

$$-\frac{K_4}{2f}\left[\frac{(au_3+bu_4)}{l}K_1+K_3-3(u_3K_1+u_4K_3)\right]A$$

$$-K_4\left[\frac{u_3}{f}\left(\frac{a}{l}-\frac{3}{2}\right)K_1+\frac{3u_3}{2h}K_2+\frac{bu_4}{fl}K_1\right]B$$

$$+\left\{\frac{1}{2}K_4-K_4\left[\frac{u_4}{f}\left(\frac{b}{l}-\frac{3}{2}\right)K_3+\frac{3u_4}{2h}K_4+\frac{au_3}{fl}K_3\right]\right\}B'$$

$$+\left[\frac{1}{2}K_5-\frac{3u_3}{2h}K_2K_4-\frac{3K_6K_7}{4(K_6+K_7)}\right]C=\frac{K_4}{fl}(au_3+bu_4)FM_{BA}$$

$$-\frac{u_3}{f}K_4(FM_{AB}+FM_{BA})+\frac{b}{fl}(u_4-u_3)(a-e)K_4P\ \ldots\ldots \quad (174a)$$

As in the case of the preceding bents, the joint coefficients, that is, the terms on the left sides of the expressions, are typical and independent of the loading. The load factors q and q' of s and s' expressions—eqs. (169) and (169a)—for some other loadings follow:

(1) Single horizontal load, applied to member AB, Fig. 157:

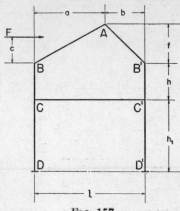

FIG. 157.

Fixed and hinged bases:

$$q = \frac{a}{fl}FM_{BA} - \frac{1}{f}(FM_{AB} + FM_{BA}) + \frac{F}{f}\left(f - \frac{bc}{l}\right),$$

$$q' = \frac{b}{fl}FM_{BA} + \frac{bcF}{fl}.$$

(2) Single horizontal load, applied to member BC, Fig. 158(a):

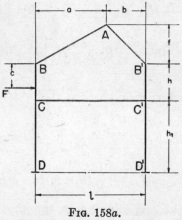

FIG. 158a.

Fixed and hinged bases:

$$q = \frac{1}{h}(FM_{BC} + FM_{CB}) + \left(1 - \frac{c}{h}\right)F,$$

$$q' = 0$$

(3) Uniform horizontal load, w per linear vertical foot, applied to member AB, Fig. 158b:

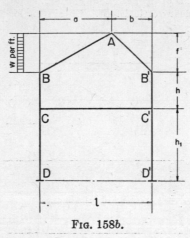

FIG. 158b.

Fixed and hinged bases:

$$q=\left[\frac{f}{2}\left(1+\frac{a}{l}\right)-\frac{af}{12l}\right]w,$$

$$q'=\frac{5}{12}\cdot\frac{bf}{l}w.$$

(4) Uniform horizontal load, w per linear vertical foot, applied to member BC, Fig. 158c:

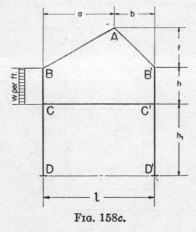

FIG. 158c.

Fixed and hinged bases:

$$q=\frac{wh}{2},\ \ q'=0.$$

47. The bottom leg *CD* of the bent shown in Fig. 158*d* is subjected to a uniform lateral load of *w* per linear vertical foot.   Obtain the load factors *q* and *Q* for:

    (*a*) Fixed bases;
    (*b*) Hinged bases.

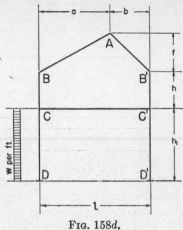

FIG. 158*d*.

48. The roof member *AB* of the two-story unsymmetrical bent shown in Fig. 159 is carrying a nuiform vertical load of one kip per linear foot of horizontal projection.   Assuming the legs to be fixed at the bases *D* and *D'*, determine the end moments.

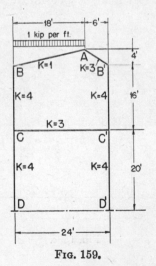

FIG. 159.

53. Two-span Symmetrical Bent with Symmetrical Loading.—The

dotted lines in Fig. 160 indicate the deformations of a two-span

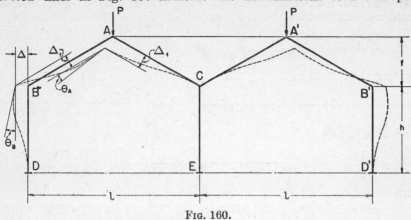

FIG. 160.

symmetrical bent under symmetrical loading. Since the loads are
placed symmetrically with respect to the center joint C, the deflection
angle at this joint, as well as the deflection of the middle column CE,
is zero. The left leg BD sways counterclockwise a distance Δ, while
the top members AB and AC each deflect a distance Δ_1 — the former
clockwise and the latter counterclockwise. As explained in Art. 47,
the deflections Δ and Δ_1 are interrelated. If the deflection term of
the leg BD, that is, the term $6E\dfrac{\Delta}{h}$ be indicated by R, then, in accordance with the derivation in Art. 47, for the corresponding terms of the
members AB and AC we will have:

$$R_{AB}=-\frac{h}{2f}R, \quad R_{AC}=\frac{h}{2f}R \quad . \quad . \quad . \quad . \quad . \quad . \quad (175)$$

The derivation of joint and deflection expressions is similar to the
preceding cases. Consider, for example, the loading in Fig. 161.

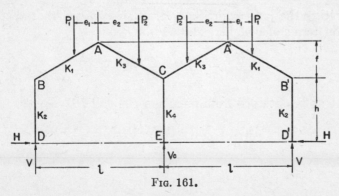

FIG. 161.

Assuming the bent to be fixed at the bases D, E and D', the shear expressions of the members AB and BD will give:

$$M_{AB}+M_{BA}+V\frac{l}{2}-P_1e_1-Hf=0; \quad \ldots \ldots \ldots \quad (a)$$

$$M_{BD}+M_{DB}-Hh=0 \quad \ldots \ldots \ldots \ldots \ldots \quad (b)$$

Noting that

$$Vl=-(M_{BA}+M_{CA})+P_1\left(\frac{l}{2}+e_1\right)+P_2\left(\frac{l}{2}-e_2\right), \quad \ldots \quad (c)$$

and eliminating H from eqs. (a) and (b),

$$\frac{1}{f}M_{AB}+\frac{1}{2f}(M_{BA}-M_{CA})-\frac{1}{h}(M_{BD}+M_{DB})+\frac{P_1}{4f}(l-2e_1)+\frac{P_2}{4f}(l-2e_2)=0. \quad (d)$$

But

$$M_{AB}=K_1\left(A+\frac{B}{2}+\frac{h}{2f}R\right)+FM_{AB},$$

$$M_{BA}=K_1\left(\frac{A}{2}+B+\frac{h}{2f}R\right)+FM_{BA},$$

$$M_{CA}=K_3\left(\frac{A}{2}-\frac{h}{2f}R\right)+FM_{CA},$$

$$M_{BD}=K_2(B-R).$$

$$M_{DB}=K_2\left(\frac{B}{2}-R\right).$$

Substituting these values for the end moments in eq. (d), and solving for R, the deflection expression becomes:

$$\left[\frac{h(3K_1+K_3)}{4f^2}+\frac{2K_2}{h}\right]R=-\left(\frac{5K_1-K_3}{4f}\right)A-\left(\frac{K_1}{f}-\frac{3K_2}{2h}\right)B$$

$$-\frac{1}{f}\left(FM_{AB}+\frac{1}{2}FM_{BA}-\frac{1}{2}FM_{CA}\right)-\frac{P_1}{4f}(l-2e_1)-\frac{P_2}{4f}(l-2e_2). \quad (176)$$

In writing the joint expression for A, it is noted that the sum of deflection terms of members AB and AC equals

$$\frac{hK_1}{2f}R-\frac{hK_3}{2f}R=\frac{h}{2f}(K_1-K_3)R \quad ; \quad \ldots \ldots \quad (e)$$

and that at B, obtained from members BA and BD, equals

$$\frac{hK_1}{2f}R-K_2R=\frac{(hK_1-2fK_2)}{2f}R \quad \ldots \ldots \ldots \quad (f)$$

With the value of R as given by eq. (176), for the respective joint expression we have:

Joint A,

$$
\left[K_1+K_3-\frac{h^2(K_1-K_3)(5K_1-K_3)}{2h^2(3K_1+K_3)+16f^2K_2}\right]A
$$

$$
+\left[\frac{K_1}{2}-\frac{h(K_1-K_3)(2hK_1-3fK_2)}{h^2(3K_1+K_3)+8f^2K_2}\right]B=-FM_{AB}-FM_{AC}
$$

$$
+\frac{2h^2(K_1-K_3)}{h^2(3K_1+K_3)+8f^2K_2}\left[FM_{AB}+\frac{1}{2}FM_{BA}-\frac{1}{2}FM_{CA}\right.
$$

$$
+\frac{P_1}{4}(l-2e_1)+\frac{P_2}{4}(l-2e_2)\Big];\ \ldots\ldots\ldots\ldots\ldots (177)
$$

Joint B,

$$
\left[\frac{K_1}{2}-\frac{h(hK_1-2fK_2)(5K_1-K_3)}{2h^2(3K_1+K_3)+16f^2K_2}\right]A
$$

$$
+\left[K_1+K_2-\frac{(hK_1-2fK_2)(2hK_1-3fK_2)}{h^2(3K_1+K_3)+8f^2K_2}\right]B=-FM_{BA}
$$

$$
+\frac{2h(hK_1-2fK_2)}{h^2(3K_1+K_3)+8f^2K_2}\left[FM_{AB}+\frac{1}{2}FM_{BA}-\frac{1}{2}FM_{CA}\right.
$$

$$
+\frac{P_1}{4}(l-2e_1)+\frac{P_2}{4}(l-2e_2)\Big]\ \ldots\ldots\ldots\ldots\ldots (178)
$$

In the case of hinged bases at D, E and D', the end moment expression for member BD at B is in the form

$$
M_{BD}=K_2\Big(\frac{3}{4}B-\frac{R}{2}\Big);
$$

and M_{DB} equals zero. With these changes, the deflection expression, eq. (176), becomes:

$$
\left[\frac{h(3K_1+K_3)}{4f^2}+\frac{K_2}{2h}\right]R=-\frac{(5K_1-K_3)}{4f}A-\Big(\frac{K_1}{f}-\frac{3K_2}{4h}\Big)B
$$

$$
-\frac{1}{f}\Big(FM_{AB}+\frac{1}{2}FM_{BA}-\frac{1}{2}FM_{CA}\Big)-\frac{P_1}{4f}(l-2e_1)-\frac{P_2}{4f}(l-2e_2);(176a)
$$

and eq. (f) assumes the form

$$
\frac{hK_1}{2f}R-\frac{K_2}{2}R=\frac{hK_1-fK_2}{2f}R\ \ldots\ldots\ldots (g)
$$

Accordingly, for joint equations at A and B we can write:
Joint A,

$$\left[K_1+K_3-\frac{h^2(K_1-K_3)(5K_1-K_3)}{2h^2(3K_1+K_3)+4f^2K_2}\right]A$$

$$+\left[\frac{K_1}{2}-\frac{h(K_1-K_3)(4hK_1-3fK_2)}{2h^2(3K_1+K_3)+4f^2K_2}\right]B=-FM_{AB}-FM_{AC}$$

$$+\frac{2h^2(K_1-K_3)}{h^2(3K_1+K_3)+2f^2K_2}\left[FM_{AB}+\frac{1}{2}FM_{BA}-\frac{1}{2}FM_{CA}\right.$$

$$\left.+\frac{P_1}{4}(l-2e_1)+\frac{P_2}{4}(l-2e_2)\right] \quad\ldots\ldots\ldots\ldots\ldots\ldots \quad (179)$$

Joint B,

$$\left[\frac{K_1}{2}-\frac{h(hK_1-fK_2)(5K_1-K_3)}{2h^2(3K_1+K_3)+4f^2K_2}\right]A$$

$$+\left[K_1+\frac{3}{4}K_2-\frac{(hK_1-fK_2)(4hK_1-3fK_2)}{2h^2(3K_1+K_3)+4f^2K_2}\right]B$$

$$=-FM_{BA}+\frac{2h(hK_1-fK_2)}{h^2(3K_1+K_3)+2f^2K_2}\left[FM_{AB}+\frac{1}{2}FM_{BA}\right.$$

$$\left.-\frac{1}{2}FM_{CA}+\frac{P_1}{4}(l-2e_1)+\frac{P_2}{4}(l-2e_2)\right] \quad\ldots\ldots\ldots\ldots\ldots \quad (180)$$

If the loading is uniform, as in Fig. 162, the load factors q in eqs.

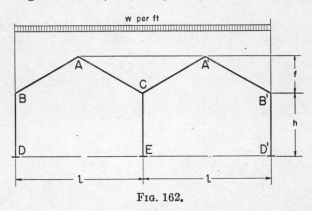

Fig. 162.

(176) and (176a), for both fixed and hinged bases, reduce to the following simplified form:

$$q=-\frac{wl^2}{8f} \quad\ldots\ldots\ldots\ldots\ldots \quad (h)$$

The loading of the symmetrical bent shown in Fig. 163 consists of a uniform vertical load of one kip per linear foot of roof projection. Assuming the three legs to be fixed at the bases, determine the end moments.

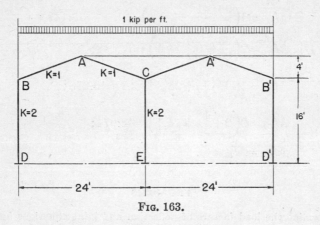

FIG. 163.

Solution: Applying eqs. (177) and (178),

$$2A + \frac{1}{2}B = 0 \quad ,$$

$$\frac{1}{2}A + 3B = 12 \quad ;$$

from which

$$A = -\frac{24}{23}, \ B = \frac{96}{23} \ .$$

Substituting these values in eq. (176), and noting that q equals $-\dfrac{24^2}{8 \times 4} = -18$,

$$\frac{5}{4}R = \frac{1}{4} \times \frac{24}{23} - \frac{1}{16} \times \frac{96}{23} - 18, \quad R = -14.4 \quad ;$$

$$R_{AB} = \frac{16}{2 \times 4} \times 14.4 = 28.8, \quad R_{AC} = -28.8$$

Accordingly, the end moments become:

$$M_{AB}=1\left(-\frac{24}{23}+\frac{48}{23}-28.8\right)+12=-15.756,$$

$$M_{AC}=1\left(-\frac{24}{23}+0+28.8\right)-12=15.756;$$

$$M_{BA}=1\left(\frac{96}{23}-\frac{12}{23}-28.8\right)-12=-37.148,$$

$$M_{BD}=2\left(\frac{96}{23}+0+14.4\right)=37.148;$$

$$M_{CA}=1\left(0-\frac{12}{23}+28.8\right)+12=40.278;$$

$$M_{DB}=2\left(0+\frac{48}{23}+14.4\right)=32.974;$$

$$M_{CE}=M_{EC}=0.$$

PROBLEMS

49. Determine the load factors of deflection and joint equations for the bent shown in Fig. 164, corresponding to:

(a) Fixed bases;
(b) Hinged bases.

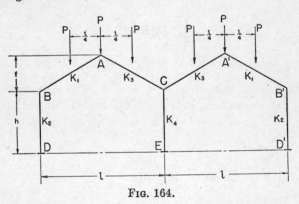

Fig. 164.

50. Assuming the legs of the bent shown in Fig. 163 to be hinged at the bases D, E and D', obtain the end moments.

54. Two-span Symmetrical Bent with Unsymmetrical Loading.— When the loading is unsymmetrical, as is shown, in Fig. 165, the deflections of the three legs will differ. The deflections of the roof members, however, may again be expressed in terms of the deflections of the legs. To obtain these relations, let the deflection terms of the legs BD, CE and $B'D'$ be indicated, respectively, by R_1, R_2 and R_3; then, for the deflection terms of the remaining members, we have:

$$R_{AB}=\frac{h}{2f}(R_2-R_1), \qquad R_{AC}=\frac{h}{2f}(R_1-R_2),$$

$$\qquad \qquad \qquad \qquad \cdots \cdots (a)$$

$$R_{A'C}=\frac{h}{2f}(R_3-R_2), \qquad R_{A'B'}=\frac{h}{2f}(R_2-R_3).$$

In developing the deflection and joint expressions for frames involving side sway, the following general procedure was consistently used in the preceding articles:

(1) From the shear equations of the members obtain the deflection expression by eliminating all the unknown reactions;

(2) Obtain the joint expressions by substituting for the deflection terms their values derived in (1).

The first step entails no difficulty, even when dealing with arched or multi-span frames. In the case of the bent shown in Fig. 165, there

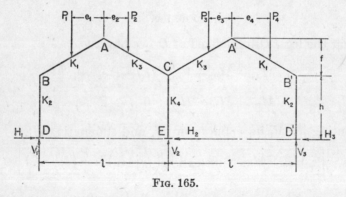

FIG. 165.

are two unknown reactions of each base. At D, for example, we have the vertical reaction V_1 and the horizontal reaction H_1. Considering the portion BAC severed from the main bent, Fig. 166 (a), the value of V_1 is obtained from the relation

$$M_{BA}+M_{CA}+V_1l-P_1\left(\frac{l}{2}+e_1\right)-P_2\left(\frac{l}{2}-e_2\right)=0; \quad \cdots \quad (b)$$

while H_1 is eliminated by subtracting the shear expression of the member BD from that of member AB. Referring to Fig. 166b, and

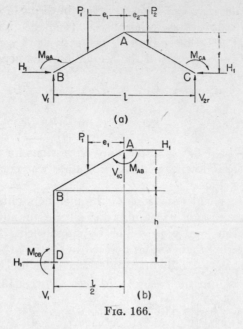

$$(a)$$

$$(b)$$

FIG. 166.

assuming the leg BD to be fixed at D, we have:

$$M_{AB}+M_{BA}+V_1\frac{l}{2}-H_1f-P_1e_1=0,$$

$$(M_{BD}+M_{DB}-H_1h)=0 \quad . \quad . \quad . \quad . \quad . \quad . \quad . \quad . \quad . \quad (c)$$

Substituting for V_1 its value from (b), and eliminating H_1,

$$\frac{1}{f}\left[\frac{3}{2}M_{BA}+M_{AB}-\frac{1}{2}M_{CA}+\frac{P_1}{2}\left(\frac{l}{2}-e_1\right)+\frac{P_2}{2}\left(\frac{l}{2}-e_2\right)\right]$$

$$-\frac{1}{h}(M_{BD}+M_{DB})=0 \quad . \quad . \quad . \quad . \quad . \quad . \quad . \quad (d)$$

The similar expression for the second bay is in the form

$$\frac{1}{f}\left[\frac{1}{2}M_{B'A'}+M_{A'B'}-\frac{1}{2}M_{CA'}-\frac{P_3}{2}\left(\frac{l}{2}-e_3\right)-\frac{P_4}{2}\left(\frac{l}{2}-e_4\right)\right]$$

$$-\frac{1}{h}(M_{B'D'}+M_{D'B'})=0 \quad . \quad . \quad . \quad . \quad . \quad . \quad . \quad (e)$$

A third expression of shear is obtained from the consideration that the sum of the three horizontal reactions at the bases must equal zero:

$$\frac{1}{h}(M_{BD}+M_{DB}+M_{CE}+M_{EC}+M_{B'D'}+M_{D'B'})=0 \quad . \quad . \quad . \quad (f)$$

Equations (d), (e) and (f) represent the general expressions for the three deflections. After substitution of values for the end moments, these expressions become:

$$\left[\frac{2K_2}{h}+\frac{h}{4f^2}(3K_1+K_3)\right]R_1-\frac{h}{4f^2}(3K_1+K_3)R_2=-\frac{1}{4f}(5K_1-K_3)A$$

$$-\left(\frac{K_1}{f}-\frac{3K_2}{2h}\right)B+\frac{K_3}{2f}C-\frac{P_1}{2f}\left(\frac{l}{2}-e_1\right)-\frac{P_2}{2f}\left(\frac{l}{2}-e_2\right)$$

$$-\frac{1}{f}(FM_{AB}+\tfrac{1}{2}FM_{BA}-\tfrac{1}{2}FM_{CA}),\ \dots\dots\dots\dots\quad(181)$$

$$\left[\frac{2K_2}{h}+\frac{h}{4f^2}(3K_1+K_3)\right]R_3-\frac{h}{4f^2}(3K_1+K_3)R_2=-\frac{1}{4f}(5K_1-K_3)A'$$

$$-\left(\frac{K_1}{f}-\frac{3K_2}{2h}\right)B'+\frac{K_3}{2f}C+\frac{P_3}{2f}\left(\frac{l}{2}-e_3\right)+\frac{P_4}{2f}\left(\frac{l}{2}-e_4\right)$$

$$-\frac{1}{f}\left(FM_{A'B'}+\tfrac{1}{2}FM_{B'A'}-\tfrac{1}{2}FM_{CA'}\right)\ \dots\dots\dots\quad(182)$$

$$2K_4R_2+2K_2(R_1+R_3)=\frac{3K_2}{2}B+\frac{3K_2}{2}B'+\frac{3K_4}{2}C\ \dots\dots\quad(183)$$

Eliminating R_2,

$$\left[\frac{2K_2}{h}+\frac{h}{4f^2}(3K_1+K_3)\left(1+\frac{K_2}{K_4}\right)\right]R_1+\frac{hK_2}{4f^2K_4}(3K_1+K_3)R_3$$

$$=-\frac{1}{4f}(5K_1-K_3)A-\left[\frac{K_1}{f}-\frac{3K_2}{2h}-\frac{3hK_2}{16f^2K_4}(3K_1+K_3)\right]B$$

$$+\frac{3hK_2}{16f^2K_4}(3K_1+K_3)B'+\left[\frac{K_3}{2f}+\frac{3h}{16f^2}(3K_1+K_3)\right]C$$

$$-\frac{1}{f}\left(FM_{AB}+\tfrac{1}{2}FM_{BA}-\tfrac{1}{2}FM_{CA}\right)-\frac{P_1}{2f}\left(\frac{l}{2}-e_1\right)$$

$$-\frac{P_2}{2f}\left(\frac{l}{2}-e_2\right);\ \dots\dots\dots\dots\dots\dots\quad(184)$$

$$\left[\frac{2K_2}{h}+\frac{h}{4f^2}(3K_1+K_3)\left(1+\frac{K_2}{K_4}\right)\right]R_3+\frac{hK_2}{4f^2K_4}(3K_1+K_3)R_1$$

$$=-\frac{1}{4f}(5K_1-K_3)A'+\frac{3hK_2}{16f^2K_4}(3K_1+K_3)B$$

$$-\left[\left(\frac{K_1}{f}-\frac{3K_2}{2h}\right)-\frac{3hK_2}{16f^2K_4}(3K_1+K_3)\right]B'$$

$$+\left[\frac{K_3}{2f}+\frac{3h}{16f^2}(3K_1+K_3)\right]C-\frac{1}{f}\left(FM_{A'B'}+\tfrac{1}{2}FM_{B'A'}-\tfrac{1}{2}FM_{CA'}\right)$$

$$+\frac{P_3}{2f}\left(\frac{l}{2}-e_3\right)+\frac{P_4}{2f}\left(\frac{l}{2}-e_4\right).\ \dots\dots\dots\dots\quad(185)$$

The second step of the solution involves substitution of R_1, R_2 and R_3 values obtained from eqs. (183), (184) and (185) into the joint expressions of the bent. For fixed bases, these expressions are as follows:

$$\left.\begin{aligned}
&(K_1+K_3)A+\frac{K_1}{2}B+\frac{K_3}{2}C+\frac{h}{2f}(K_1-K_3)(R_1-R_2)\\
&\quad=-FM_{AB}-FM_{AC},\\[4pt]
&(K_1+K_2)B+\frac{K_1}{2}A+\Big(\frac{hK_1}{2f}-K_2\Big)R_1-\frac{hK_1}{2f}R_2=-FM_{BA},\\[4pt]
&(2K_3+K_4)C+\frac{K_3}{2}A+\frac{K_3}{2}A'-\frac{hK_3}{2f}R_1+\Big(\frac{hK_3}{f}-K_4\Big)R_2-\frac{hK_3}{2f}R_3\\
&\quad=-FM_{CA}-FM_{CA'},\\[4pt]
&(K_1+K_3)A+\frac{K_1}{2}B'+\frac{K_3}{2}C+\frac{h}{2f}(K_1-K_3)(R_3-R_2)\\
&\quad=-FM_{A'C}-FM_{A'B'},\\[4pt]
&(K_1+K_2)B^1+\frac{K_1}{2}A'+\Big(\frac{hK_1}{2f}-K_2\Big)R_3-\frac{hK_1}{2f}R_2=-FM_{B'A'}.
\end{aligned}\right\} \; . \; . \; (186)$$

However, in order to obviate the use of lengthy expressions and to simplify the computations, it is more convenient to perform the substitution in the numerical solution of the problem only.

If the legs of the bent shown in Fig. 165 are hinged at the bases, the corresponding deflection and joint expressions become:

$$R_2=-\frac{K_2}{K_4}(R_1+R_3)+\frac{3K_2}{2K_4}B+\frac{3K_2}{2K_4}B'+\frac{3}{2}C; \; . \; . \; . \; (187)$$

$$\begin{aligned}
&\Big[\frac{K_2}{2h}+\frac{h}{4f^2}(3K_1+K_3)\Big(1+\frac{K_2}{K_4}\Big)\Big]R_1+\frac{hK_2}{4f^2K_4}(3K_1+K_3)R_3\\
&=-\frac{1}{4f}(5K_1-K_3)A-\Big[\Big(\frac{K_1}{f}-\frac{3K_2}{4h}\Big)-\frac{3hK_2}{8f^2K_4}(3K_1+K_3)\Big]B\\
&\quad+\frac{3hK_2}{8f^2K_4}(3K_1+K_3)B'+\Big[\frac{K_3}{2f}+\frac{3h}{8f^2}(3K_1+K_3)\Big]C\\
&\quad-\frac{1}{f}\Big(FM_{AB}+\frac{1}{2}FM_{BA}-\frac{1}{2}FM_{CA}\Big)-\frac{P_1}{2f}\Big(\frac{l}{2}-e_1\Big)\\
&\quad-\frac{P_2}{2f}\Big(\frac{l}{2}-e_2\Big), \; . \; . \; . \; . \; . \; . \; . \; . \; . \; . \; (188)
\end{aligned}$$

$$\left[\frac{K_2}{2h}+\frac{h}{4f^2}(3K_1+K_3)\left(1+\frac{K_2}{K_4}\right)\right]R_3+\frac{hK_2}{4f^2K_4}(3K_1+K_3)R_1$$

$$=-\frac{1}{4f}(5K_1-K_3)A'+\frac{3hK_2}{8f^2K_4}(3K_1+K_3)B-\left[\left(\frac{K_1}{f}-\frac{3K_2}{4h}\right)\right.$$

$$-\frac{3hK_2}{8f^2K_4}(3K_1+K_3)\Big]B'+\left[\frac{K_3}{2f}+\frac{3h}{8f^2}(3K_1+K_3)\right]C$$

$$-\frac{1}{f}\Big(FM_{A'B'}+\frac{1}{2}FM_{B'A'}-\frac{1}{2}FM_{CA'}\Big)+\frac{P_3}{2f}\Big(\frac{l}{2}-e_3\Big)$$

$$+\frac{P_4}{2f}\Big(\frac{l}{2}-e_4\Big),\quad\ldots\ldots\ldots\ldots\ldots\ldots\quad(189)$$

$$(K_1+K_3)A+\frac{K_1}{2}B+\frac{K_3}{2}C+\frac{h}{2f}(K_1-K_3)(R_1-R_2)=-FM_{AB}-FM_{AC},$$

$$\Big(K_1+\frac{3}{4}K_2\Big)B+\frac{K_1}{2}A+\Big(\frac{hK_1}{2f}-\frac{K_2}{2}\Big)R_1-\frac{hK_1}{2f}R_2=-FM_{BA},$$

$$\Big(2K_3+\frac{3}{4}K_4\Big)C+\frac{K_3}{2}A+\frac{K_3}{2}A'-\frac{hK_3}{2f}R_1+\Big(\frac{h}{f}K_3-\frac{K_4}{2}\Big)R_2-\frac{hK_3}{2f}R_3$$

$$=-FM_{CA}-FM_{CA'},$$

$$(K_1+K_3)A'+\frac{K_1}{2}B'+\frac{K_3}{2}C+\frac{h}{2f}(K_1-K_3)(R_3-R_1)$$

$$=-FM_{A'B'}-FM_{A'C},$$

$$\Big(K_1+\frac{3}{4}K_2\Big)B'+\frac{K_1}{2}A'+\Big(\frac{hK_1}{2f}-\frac{K_2}{2}\Big)R_3-\frac{hK_1}{2f}R_2=-FM_{B'A'}.$$

$$(190)$$

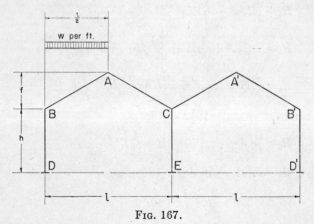

FIG. 167.

When the loading is uniform, as is shown in Fig. 167, the load factor

$$\frac{P_1}{2f}\Big(\frac{l}{2}-e_1\Big)$$

reduces to

$$\frac{wl^2}{16f}\quad\ldots\ldots\ldots\ldots\ldots\ldots\quad(g)$$

ILLUSTRATIVE EXAMPLE

The first span of the symmetrical bent shown in Fig. 168 is subjected to a uniform vertical load of 1 kip per linear foot. Assuming the legs to be fixed at the bases, determine the end moments.

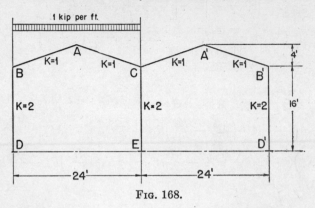

FIG. 168.

Solution: Applying eqs. (184) and (185), and solving for R_1 and R_3

$$\frac{9}{4}R_1+R_3=-\frac{1}{4}A+\frac{11}{16}B+\frac{3}{4}B'+\frac{7}{8}C-18,$$

$$R_1+\frac{9}{4}R_3=-\frac{1}{4}A'+\frac{3}{4}B+\frac{11}{16}B'+\frac{7}{8}C;$$

$$R_1=-\frac{9}{65}A+\frac{4}{65}A'+\frac{51}{260}B+\frac{16}{65}B'+\frac{7}{26}C-\frac{648}{65},$$

$$R_3=\frac{4}{65}A-\frac{9}{65}A'+\frac{16}{65}B+\frac{51}{260}B'+\frac{7}{26}C+\frac{288}{65}.$$

From eq. (183),

$$R_2=\frac{1}{13}A+\frac{1}{13}A'+\frac{4}{13}B+\frac{4}{13}B'+\frac{11}{52}C+\frac{72}{13}.$$

Substituting these values in eqs. (186),

$$2A+\frac{1}{2}B+\frac{1}{2}C=0,$$

$$\frac{9}{26}A-\frac{2}{13}A'+\frac{31}{13}B-\frac{8}{13}B'-\frac{11}{26}C=\frac{300}{13},$$

$$\frac{21}{26}A+\frac{21}{26}A'-\frac{7}{26}B-\frac{7}{26}B'+\frac{87}{26}C=\frac{444}{13},$$

$$2A'+\frac{1}{2}B'+\frac{1}{2}C=0,$$

$$-\frac{2}{13}A+\frac{9}{26}A'-\frac{8}{13}B+\frac{31}{13}B'-\frac{11}{26}C=\frac{144}{13};$$

from which

$$A = -0.060, \quad R_1 = -9.223,$$
$$A' = 0.984, \quad R_2 = 8.204,$$
$$B = 9.479, \quad R_3 = 5.177,$$
$$B' = 5.305, \quad R_{AB} = 34.854,$$
$$C = -9.240, \quad R_{A'C} = -6.054.$$

Accordingly, the end moments become:

$$M_{AB} = -0.060 + 4.740 - 34.854 + 12 = -18.174,$$
$$M_{AC} = -0.060 - 4.620 + 34.854 - 12 = 18.174;$$

$$M_{BA} = 9.479 - 0.030 - 34.854 - 12 = -37.405,$$
$$M_{BD} = 2(9.479 + 9.223) = 37.404;$$

$$M_{CA} = -9.240 - 0.030 + 34.854 + 12 = 37.584,$$
$$M_{CA'} = -9.240 + 0.492 + 6.054 = -2.694,$$
$$M_{CE} = 2(-9.24 - 8.204) = -34.888;$$

$$M_{A'C} = 0.984 - 4.620 + 6.054 = 2.418,$$
$$M_{A'B'} = 0.984 + 2.652 - 6.054 = -2.418;$$

$$M_{B'A'} = 5.305 + 0.492 - 6.054 = -0.257,$$
$$M_{B'D'} = 2(5.305 - 5.177) = 0.256;$$

$$M_{DB} = 2(4.740 + 9.223) = 27.925;$$

$$M_{EC} = 2(-4.62 - 8.204) = -25.648;$$

$$M_{D'B'} = 2(2.672 - 5.177) = -5.049.$$

PROBLEMS

51. Determine the load constants of deflection expressions for a two-span symmetrical bent corresponding to (a) fixed and, (b) hinged bases, and the following loading conditions, Fig. 169:

(1) Single horizontal load—applied to member AB;
(2) Single horizontal load—applied to member BD;
(3) Uniform horizontal load—applied to member AB;
(4) Uniform horizontal load—applied to member BD.

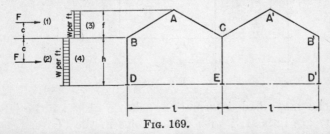

FIG. 169.

52. Assuming the bent shown in Fig. 168 to be hinged at the bases, determine the end moments.

Chapter V

LEAN-TO BENTS

55. Lean-to Bents with Rigid Connections.—A familiar bent in old-type truss-and-column framing, its modern prototype, the "streamlined" lean-to bent, retains an equally important share in rigidly framed structures. According to their outline, the discussion of lean-to bents may be confined to the following four main groups:

(1) Rectangular bent with two lean-tos;
(2) Gabled bent with two lean-tos;
(3) Rectangular bent with a single lean-to;
(4) Gabled bent with a single lean-to.

The analysis for the first two groups may be further simplified by separate treatment of symmetrical and unsymmetrical loading.

56. Symmetrical Lean-to Bent with Symmetrical Vertical Loading.— From the standpoint of analysis, the loading and arrangement of members shown in Fig. 170 constitute the simplest type of a lean-to

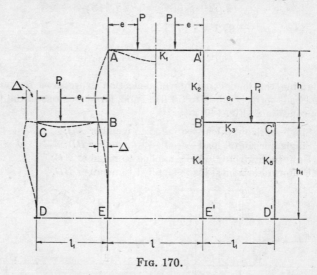

Fig. 170.

bent. The magnified deformations (shown only for the left half of the bent) are indicated with dotted lines in the figure. It is to be noted that, when the bent deflects under the symmetrical loading,

234

the upper joints A and A' rotate without displacement; while the lower joints B and C, as well as joints B' and C', rotate and displace laterally an equal distance Δ. Accordingly, Δ represents the common deflection of the members AB, BE and CD. Indicating the deflection term of the member AB by R, for the corresponding term of the members BE and CD we can write:

$$R_{BE}=R_{CD}=-\frac{h}{h_1}R=-nR \ldots \ldots \ldots (a)$$

An expression for R is easily obtained from the consideration that the horizontal thrust H just above the joint B, Fig. 170a, must equal

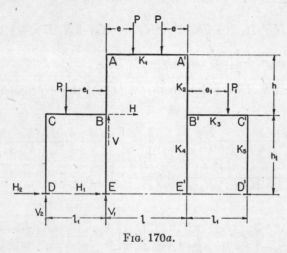

FIG. 170a.

the sum of the two horizontal reactions at the bases D and E, that is,

$$H=H_1+H_2 \ldots \ldots \ldots \ldots (b)$$

The value of each reaction, in turn, is given by the shear expression of the respective member. Thus, from the member AB, we have:

$$H=\frac{1}{h}(M_{AB}+M_{BA});$$

and from members BE and CD,

$$H_1=\frac{1}{h_1}(M_{BE}+M_{EB}),$$

$$H_2=\frac{1}{h_1}(M_{CD}+M_{DC}).$$

Then

$$\frac{1}{h}(M_{AB}+M_{BA})=\frac{1}{h_1}(M_{BE}+M_{EB}+M_{CD}+M_{DC}) \ldots \ldots (c)$$

Assuming the bent to be fixed at the bases, eq. (c) reduces to

$$\frac{1}{h}\left[\frac{3}{2}K_2(A+B)-2K_2R\right]=\frac{1}{h_1}\left[\frac{3}{2}(K_4B+K_5C)+2n(K_4+K_5)R\right] \quad . \; . \; (d)$$

from which

$$R=\frac{3}{4}\cdot\frac{K_2A+(K_2-nK_4)B-nK_5C}{K_2+n^2(K_4+K_5)}. \quad . \; . \; . \; . \; (191)$$

The joint expressions of the bent, for the same condition of base restraint, are in the following forms:

$$\left.\begin{aligned}\left(\frac{1}{2}K_1+K_2\right)A+\frac{1}{2}K_2B-K_2R&=-FM_{AA'},\\[2mm](K_2+K_3+K_4)B+\frac{1}{2}K_2A+\frac{1}{2}K_3C-(K_2-nK_4)R&=-FM_{BC},\\[2mm](K_3+K_5)C+\frac{1}{2}K_3B+nK_5R&=-FM_{CB}.\end{aligned}\right\} \quad . \; (e)$$

Substituting for R its value from eq. (191), the expressions become:

Joint A,

$$\left[\frac{1}{2}K_1+K_2-\frac{3}{4}\cdot\frac{K_2{}^2}{K_2+n^2(K_4+K_5)}\right]A+\left[\frac{1}{2}K_2-\frac{3}{4}\cdot\frac{K_2(K_2-nK_4)}{K_2+n^2(K_4+K_5)}\right]B$$

$$+\frac{3}{4}\cdot\frac{nK_2K_5}{K_2+n^2(K_4+K_5)}C=-FM_{AA'}; \quad . \; . \; . \; . \; . \; . \; (192)$$

Joint B,

$$\left[K_2+K_3+K_4-\frac{3}{4}\cdot\frac{(K_2-nK_4)^2}{K_2+n^2(K_4+K_5)}\right]B+\left[\frac{1}{2}K_2-\frac{3}{4}\cdot\frac{K_2(K_2-nK_4)}{K_2+n^2(K_4+K_5)}\right]A$$

$$+\left[\frac{1}{2}K_3+\frac{3}{4}\cdot\frac{nK_5(K_2-nK_4)}{K_2+n^2(K_4+K_5)}\right]C=-FM_{BC} \; ; \quad . \; . \; . \; . \; (193)$$

Joint C,

$$\left[K_3+K_5-\frac{3}{4}\cdot\frac{n^2K_5{}^2}{K_2+n^2(K_4+K_5)}\right]C+\frac{3}{4}\cdot\frac{nK_2K_5}{K_2+n^2(K_4+K_5)}A$$

$$+\left[\frac{1}{2}K_3+\frac{3}{4}\cdot\frac{nK_5(K_2-nK_4)}{K_2+n^2(K_4+K_5)}\right]B=-FM_{CB} \quad . \; . \; . \; (194)$$

In the case of hinged connections at the bases, eq. (c) reduces to

$$\frac{1}{h}\left[\frac{3}{2}K_2(A+B)-2K_2R\right]=\frac{1}{h_1}\left[\frac{3}{4}(K_4B+K_5C)+\frac{n}{2}(K_4+K_5)R\right] \; ; \; . \; (f)$$

from which

$$R=\frac{3}{2}\cdot\frac{2K_2A+(2K_2-nK_4)B-nK_5C}{4K_2+n^2(K_4+K_5)} \quad . \; . \; . \; . \; (191a)$$

Then for the corresponding joint expressions we have:
Joint A,

$$\left[\frac{1}{2}K_1+K_2-\frac{3K_2{}^2}{4K_2+n^2(K_4+K_5)}\right]A+\left[\frac{1}{2}K_2-\frac{3}{2}\cdot\frac{K_2(2K_2-nK_4)}{4K_2+n^2(K_4+K_5)}\right]B$$
$$+\frac{3}{2}\cdot\frac{nK_2K_5}{4K_2+n^2(K_4+K_5)}C=-FM_{AA'};\;\ldots\;(192a)$$

Joint B,

$$\left[K_2+K_3+\frac{3}{4}K_4-\frac{3}{4}\cdot\frac{(2K_2-nK_4)^2}{4K_2+n^2(K_4+K_5)}\right]B+\left[\frac{1}{2}K_2-\frac{3}{2}\cdot\frac{K_2(2K_2-nK_4)}{4K_2+n^2(K_4+K_5)}\right]A$$
$$+\left[\frac{1}{2}K_3+\frac{3}{4}\cdot\frac{nK_5(2K_2-nK_4)}{4K_2+n^2(K_4+K_5)}\right]C=-FM_{BC};\;\ldots\;(193a)$$

Joint C,

$$\left[K_3+\frac{3}{4}K_5-\frac{3}{4}\cdot\frac{n^2K_5{}^2}{4K_2+n^2(K_4+K_5)}\right]C+\frac{3}{2}\cdot\frac{nK_2K_5}{4K_2+n^2(K_4+K_5)}A$$
$$+\left[\frac{1}{2}K_3+\frac{3}{4}\cdot\frac{nK_5(2K_2-nK_4)}{4K_2+n^2(K_4+K_5)}\right]B=-FM_{CB}\;\ldots\;(194a)$$

ILLUSTRATIVE EXAMPLE

The framing and the loading of the bent shown in Fig. 171 are symmetrical. Assuming the legs to be fixed at the bases, determine the end moments.

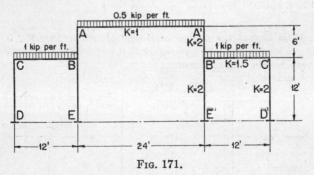

FIG. 171.

Solution: Substituting the numerical values in eqs. (192), (193) and (194), and noting that n equals $\frac{1}{2}$, the three joint expressions become:

$$1.5A+0.5B+0.5C=+24,$$
$$0.5A+5.25B+1.0C=-12,$$
$$0.5A+1.0B+3.25C=12;$$

from which

$$A=16.62, \quad B=-4.34, \quad C=2.47.$$

Substituting these values in eq. (191),

$$R=6.61, \text{ and } R_{BE}=R_{CD}=-3.30.$$

Then for the end moments we have:

$$M_{AA'}=8.31-24=-15.69,$$
$$M_{AB}=2(16.62-2.17-6.61)=15.68;$$

$$M_{BA}=2(-4.34+8.31-6.61)=-5.28,$$
$$M_{BE}=2(-4.34+3.30)=-2.08,$$
$$M_{BC}=1.5(-4.34+1.23)+12=7.34;$$

$$M_{CB}=1.5(2.47-2.17)-12=-11.55,$$
$$M_{CD}=2(2.47+3.30)=11.54;$$

$$M_{DC}=2(1.24+3.30)=9.08;$$

$$M_{EB}=2(-2.17+3.30)=2.26.$$

PROBLEMS

53. Assuming the members CB and $C'B'$ of the bent shown in Fig. 170a to be hinged at the joints B and B', derive the deflection and joint expressions for two conditions of support:

    (a) Fixed bases;
    (b) Hinged bases.

54. The middle bay of the symmetrical bent shown in Fig. 172 is carrying a uniform vertical loading of 1 kip per linear foot. Assuming the legs to be fixed at bases, determine the end moments.

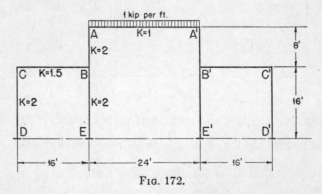

FIG. 172.

57. Symmetrical Lean-to Bent with Symmetrical Horizontal Loading.—When the lateral loading is symmetrically applied to the members, as in the case of earthquake loading, the solution of the lean-to bent becomes identical with that of a rectangular frame subjected to horizontal forces. The deformations of the bent under this particular loading are shown in Fig. 173. In deflecting, the joints

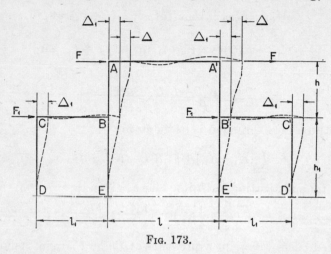

FIG. 173.

C, B, B' and C' sway the same distance Δ_1, while the upper joints A and A' displace a distance Δ with respect to the joints B and B'. Denoting the deflection term of the member AB by R and that of the members BE and CD by R_1, we proceed with the derivation of the corresponding deflection expressions in the usual manner. Referring to Fig. 173a, from the shear expression of the member AB we have:

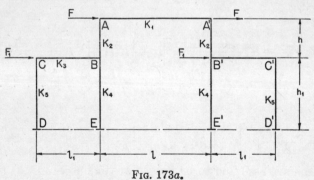

FIG. 173a.

$$M_{AB}+M_{BA}+Fh=0,$$

or

$$\frac{3}{2}K_2(A+B)-2K_2R+Fh=0;$$

from which

$$R=\frac{3}{4}(A+B)+\frac{Fh}{2K_2} \quad \cdots \cdots \cdots \quad (195)$$

Assuming the legs to be fixed at the bases, from the shear equations of the members BE and CD we obtain:

$$M_{BE}+M_{EB}+M_{CD}+M_{DC}+h_1(F+r'_1)=0, \quad \ldots \ldots \quad (a)$$

or

$$\frac{3}{2}(K_4B+K_5C)-2(K_4+K_5)R_1+h_1(F+F_1)=0;$$

from which

$$R_1=\frac{3}{4}\cdot\frac{K_4B+K_5C}{K_4+K_5}+\frac{h_1(F+F_1)}{2(K_4+K_5)} \quad \ldots \ldots \quad (196)$$

At A, the joint expression is in the form

$$\left(\frac{3}{2}K_1+K_2\right)A+\frac{1}{2}K_2B-K_2R=0;$$

which, after substituting for R its value as given by eq. (195), becomes

$$\left(\frac{3}{2}K_1+\frac{1}{4}K_2\right)A-\frac{1}{4}K_2B=\frac{Fh}{2} \quad \ldots \ldots \quad (197)$$

For fixed bases, the joint expressions at B and C are in the following forms:

$$(K_2+K_3+K_4)B+\frac{1}{2}K_2A+\frac{1}{2}K_3C-K_2R-K_4R_1=0,$$

$$(K_3+K_5)C+\frac{1}{2}K_3B-K_5R_1=0.$$

Then, with the values of R and R_1 as given by eqs. (195) and (196), we can write:

Joint B,

$$\left[\frac{1}{4}K_2+K_3+K_4-\frac{3}{4}\cdot\frac{K_4^2}{K_4+K_5}\right]B-\frac{1}{4}K_2A+\left[\frac{1}{2}K_3-\frac{3}{4}\cdot\frac{K_4K_5}{K_4+K_5}\right]C$$

$$=\frac{Fh}{2}+\frac{h_1(F+F_1)K_4}{2(K_4+K_5)}; \quad \ldots \ldots \ldots \quad (198)$$

Joint C,

$$\left[K_3+K_5-\frac{3}{4}\cdot\frac{K_5^2}{K_4+K_5}\right]C+\left[\frac{1}{2}K_3-\frac{3}{4}\cdot\frac{K_4K_5}{K_4+K_5}\right]B=\frac{h_1(F+F_1)K_5}{2(K_4+K_5)}. \quad \ldots \quad (199)$$

If the legs are assumed to be hinged at the bases, eq. (a) reduces to

$$\frac{3}{4}(K_4B+K_5C)-\frac{1}{2}(K_4+K_5)R_1+h_1(F+F_1)=0;$$

from which

$$R_1=\frac{3}{2}\cdot\frac{K_4B+K_5C}{K_4+K_5}+\frac{2h_1(F+F_1)}{K_4+K_5} \quad \ldots \ldots \quad (196a)$$

The corresponding joint expressions at B and C become:
Joint B,

$$\left[\frac{1}{4}K_2+K_3+\frac{3}{4}K_4-\frac{3}{4}\cdot\frac{K_4{}^2}{K_4+K_5}\right]B-\frac{1}{4}K_2A+\left[\frac{1}{2}K_3-\frac{3}{4}\cdot\frac{K_4K_5}{K_4+K_5}\right]C$$
$$=\frac{Fh}{2}+\frac{h_1(F+F_1)K_4}{K_4+K_5}; \quad \ldots \ldots \quad (198a)$$

Joint C,

$$\left[K_3+\frac{3}{4}K_5-\frac{3}{4}\cdot\frac{K_5{}^2}{K_4+K_5}\right]C+\left[\frac{1}{2}K_3-\frac{3}{4}\cdot\frac{K_4K_5}{K_4+K_5}\right]B=\frac{h_1(F+F_1)K_5}{K_4+K_5}. \quad (199a)$$

The joint expression at A remains the same for both fixed and hinged bases, and is given by eq. (197).

The horizontal loading and the members of the bent shown in Fig. 174 are symmetrical. Assuming the legs to be fixed at the bases, determine the end moments.

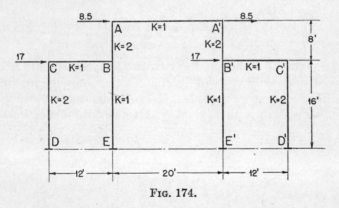

FIG. 174.

Solution: Applying eqs. (197), (198) and (199),

$$2A-0.5B=34,$$
$$-0.5A+2.25B=102,$$
$$2C=136;$$

from which

$$A=30, B=52, C=68.$$

Substituting these values in equations (195) and (196),

$$R=78.5, \quad R_1=115.$$

Accordingly, for the end moments we have:

$$M_{AA'} = 1.5 \times 30 = 45,$$
$$M_{AB} = 2(30 + 26 - 78.5) = -45;$$

$$M_{BA} = 2(52 + 15 - 78.5) = -23,$$
$$M_{BE} = 52 - 115 = -63,$$
$$M_{BC} = 52 + 34 = 86;$$

$$M_{CB} = 68 + 26 = 94,$$
$$M_{CD} = 2(68 - 115) = -94;$$

$$M_{DC} = 2(34 - 115) = -162;$$

$$M_{EB} = 26 - 115 = -89.$$

PROBLEMS

55. Assuming the members BC and $B'C'$ shown in Fig. 173a to have hinged connections at the joints B and B', respectively, derive the corresponding deflection and joint expressions of the bent for two conditions of support:

(a) Fixed bases;
(b) Hinged bases.

56. Assuming the legs of the bent shown in Fig. 174 to be hinged to the bases, determine the end moments.

58. Symmetrical Lean-to Bent with Unsymmetrical Horizontal Loading.—Under a system of lateral loading, applied to one side, or unsymmetrically to both sides, the bent deflects according to the dashed outline shown in Fig. 175. Of the four deflections Δ, Δ',

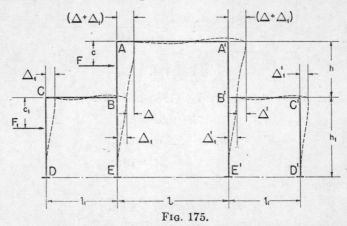

FIG. 175.

Δ_1 and Δ_1', three may be considered as independent displacements while the fourth deflection is obtained from the geometry of the displacement diagram. The simple relation is deduced from the fact that the joints A and A', B and C, and B' and C' displace the same distance, respectively. For example, if the deflection of the member AB be indicated by Δ, that of $A'B'$ by Δ', and the common deflection of members BE and CD by Δ_1, then for the deflection Δ'_1 of members $B'E'$ and $C'D'$ we can write:

$$\Delta_1' = \Delta + \Delta_1 - \Delta' \quad . \quad . \quad . \quad . \quad . \quad . \quad . \quad . \quad (a)$$

Likewise, if R, R' and R_1 denote the deflection terms—corresponding to Δ, Δ' and Δ_1, respectively, then the deflection term R_1' of members $B'E'$ and $C'D'$ becomes:

$$R_1' = \frac{\Delta_1'}{h_1} = \frac{h}{h_1}(R - R') + R_1 \quad . \quad . \quad . \quad . \quad . \quad . \quad (b)$$

Expressions for the three unknown deflections—R, R' and R_1—may be obtained from the following relations:

$$\frac{1}{h}(M_{AB} + M_{BA} + M_{A'B'} + M_{B'A'}) + \frac{F}{h}(h - c) = 0 \quad . \quad . \quad . \quad . \quad . \quad . \quad (c)$$

$$\frac{1}{h_1}(M_{CD} + M_{DC} + M_{BE} + M_{EB}) - \frac{1}{h}(M_{AB} + M_{BA}) + \frac{Fc}{h} + \frac{F_1}{h_1}(h_1 - c_1) = 0 \quad (d)$$

$$\frac{1}{h_1}(M_{C'D'} + M_{D'C'} + M_{B'E'} + M_{E'B'}) - \frac{1}{h}(M_{A'B'} + M_{B'A'}) = 0 \quad . \quad . \quad . \quad (e)$$

Eq. (c) is the shear expression of the $BAA'B'$ portion of the bent; representing the algebraic sum of the two horizontal reactions just below joints A and A'; eq. (d) indicates the sum of horizontal reactions at joint B obtained from the members CD, BE and AB; and eq. (e) is the similar expression at joint B'. Referring to the stiffnesses shown in Fig. 175a, and substituting the values of the end

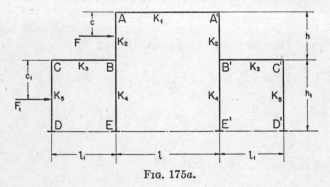

FIG. 175a.

moments, eq. (c) takes the form

$$\frac{3}{2}K_2(A + B + A' + B') - 2K_2(R + R') + (FM_{AB} + FM_{BA}) + F'(h - c) = 0. \quad (f)$$

With similar substitutions, and assuming the legs of the bent to be fixed at the bases, eqs. (d) and (e) become:

$$\frac{3h}{2h_1}(K_4B+K_5C)-\frac{3}{2}K_2(A+B)-\frac{2h}{h_1}(K_4+K_5)R_1+2K_2R$$

$$+\frac{h}{h_1}(FM_{CD}+FM_{DC})-(FM_{AB}+FM_{BA})+Fc+\frac{h}{h_1}(h_1-c_1)P_1=0; \quad (g)$$

$$\frac{3h}{2h_1}(K_4B'+K_5C')-\frac{3}{2}K_2(A'+B')+2K_2R'-\frac{2h}{h_1}(K_4+K_5)R_1$$

$$-\frac{2h^2}{h_1{}^2}(K_4+K_5)(R-R')=0. \quad \ldots \ldots \ldots \ldots \ldots \ldots (h)$$

Substituting the values of R' and R_1 from eqs. (f) and (g) into eq. (h), and solving for R,

$$R=\frac{3}{8}\Big(1+\frac{K_2}{m}\Big)A+\frac{3}{8}\Big(1+\frac{K_2}{m}-\frac{hK_4}{mh_1}\Big)B+\frac{3}{8}\Big(1-\frac{K_2}{m}\Big)A'$$

$$+\frac{3}{8}\Big(1-\frac{K_2}{m}+\frac{hK_4}{mh_1}\Big)B'-\frac{3hK_5}{8mh_1}C+\frac{3hK_5}{8mh_1}C'$$

$$+\frac{1}{4m}[(FM_{AB}+FM_{BA})-Fc]+\frac{1}{4K_2}[(h-c)F+(FM_{AB}+FM_{BA})]$$

$$-\frac{h}{4mh_1}[(h_1-c_1)F_1+(FM_{CD}+FM_{DC})]; \quad \ldots \ldots \ldots \ldots (200)$$

in which

$$m=K_2+\frac{h^2}{h_1{}^2}(K_4+K_5) \quad \ldots \ldots \ldots \ldots (k)$$

R thus determined in terms of deflection angles and load constants, R' and R_1 are then obtained from eqs. (f) and (g):

$$R'=-R+\frac{3}{4}(A+B+A'+B')+\frac{1}{2K_2}(FM_{AB}+FM_{BA})+\frac{(h-c)}{2K_2}F; \quad (201)$$

$$R_1=\frac{h_1K_2}{h(K_4+K_5)}R-\frac{3}{4}\cdot\frac{h_1K_2}{h(K_4+K_5)}A+\frac{3}{4}\cdot\frac{K_2}{K_4+K_5}\Big(\frac{K_4}{K_2}-\frac{h_1}{h}\Big)B$$

$$-\frac{3}{4}\cdot\frac{K_5}{K_4+K_5}C+\frac{h_1}{2h(K_4+K_5)}[Fc-(FM_{AB}+FM_{BA})]$$

$$+\frac{1}{2(K_4+K_5)}[(h_1-c_1)F_1+(FM_{CD}+FM_{DC})] \quad \ldots \ldots \ldots (202)$$

The joint equations of the bent, for fixed bases, are in the following forms:

$$(K_1+K_2)A+\frac{K_1}{2}A'+\frac{K_2}{2}B-K_2R+FM_{AB}=0,$$

$$(K_1+K_2)A'+\frac{K_1}{2}A+\frac{K_2}{2}B'-K_2R'=0,$$

$$(K_2+K_3+K_4)B+\frac{K_2}{2}A+\frac{K_3}{2}C-K_2R-K_4R_1+FM_{BA}=0,$$

$$(K_2+K_3+K_4)B'+\frac{K_2}{2}A'+\frac{K_3}{2}C'-K_2R'-\frac{h}{h_1}K_4(R-R')$$
$$-K_4R_1=0,$$

$$(K_3+K_5)C+\frac{K_3}{2}B-K_5R_1+FM_{CD}=0,$$

$$(K_3+K_5)C'+\frac{K_3}{2}B'-K_5R_1-\frac{h}{h_1}K_5(R-R')=0.$$

$$\left.\right\} \ . \ . \ (203)$$

As in the case of two-span gabled bents (Art. 54), to avoid rather lengthy expressions, no attempt is made to substitute values of deflection terms in the above equations, it being simpler to perform that part of the work in the numerical solution of a given problem.

If the bent has hinged connections at the bases, the deflection and joint equations become:

$$R=\frac{3}{8}\left(1+\frac{K_2}{n}\right)A+\frac{3}{8}\left(1+\frac{K_2}{n}-\frac{hK_4}{2nh_1}\right)B+\frac{3}{8}\left(1-\frac{K_2}{n}\right)A'$$
$$+\frac{3}{8}\left(1-\frac{K_2}{n}+\frac{hK_4}{2nh_1}\right)B'-\frac{3hK_5}{16nh_1}C+\frac{3hK_5}{16nh_1}C'$$
$$+\frac{1}{4n}[(FM_{AB}+FM_{BA})-Fc]+\frac{1}{4K_2}[(h-c)F+(FM_{AB}+FM_{BA})]$$
$$-\frac{h}{4nh_1}[HM_{CD}+(h_1-c_1)F_1]; \ . \ . \ . \ . \ . \ . \ . \ . \ . \ . \ . \ . \ . \ (200a)$$

$$R'=-R+\frac{3}{4}(A+B+A'+B')+\frac{1}{2K_2}(FM_{AB}+FM_{BA})+\frac{(h-c)}{2K_2}F \ ; \ . \ (201)$$

$$R_1=\frac{4h_1K_2}{h(K_4+K_5)}R-\frac{3h_1K_2}{h(K_4+K_5)}A+\frac{3K_2}{K_4+K_5}\left(\frac{K_4}{2K_2}-\frac{h_1}{h}\right)B$$
$$+\frac{3K_5}{2(K_4+K_5)}C+\frac{2h_1}{h(K_4+K_5)}[Fe-(FM_{AB}+FM_{BA})]$$
$$+\frac{2}{K_4+K_5}[(h_1-c_1)F_1+HM_{CD}]; \ . \ . \ . \ . \ . \ . \ . \ . \ . \ (202a)$$

in which

$$n = K_2 + \frac{h^2}{4h_1^2}(K_4 + K_5) \quad \cdots \cdots \cdots \cdots \cdots \quad (l)$$

$$\left.\begin{aligned}
(K_1 + K_2)A + \frac{K_1}{2}A' + \frac{K_2}{2}B - K_2R + FM_{AB} &= 0, \\[4pt]
(K_1 + K_2)A' + \frac{K_1}{2}A + \frac{K_2}{2}B' - K_2R' &= 0, \\[4pt]
\left(K_2 + K_3 + \frac{3}{4}K_4\right)B + \frac{K_2}{2}A + \frac{K_3}{2}C - K_2R - \frac{K_4}{2}R_1 + FM_{BA} &= 0, \\[4pt]
\left(K_2 + K_3 + \frac{3}{4}K_4\right)B' + \frac{K_2}{2}A' + \frac{K_3}{2}C' - K_2R' - \frac{K_4}{2}R_1 - \frac{hK_4}{2h_1}(R - R') &= 0, \\[4pt]
\left(K_3 + \frac{3}{4}K_5\right)C + \frac{K_3}{2}B - \frac{K_5}{2}R_1 + HM_{CD} &= 0, \\[4pt]
\left(K_3 + \frac{3}{4}K_5\right)C' + \frac{K_3}{2}B' - \frac{K_5}{2}R_1 - \frac{hK_5}{2h_1}(R - R') &= 0.
\end{aligned}\right\} (203a)$$

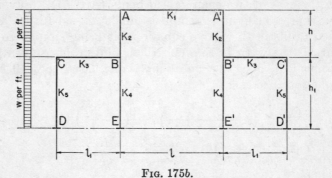

FIG. 175b.

When the loading is uniform, Fig. 175b, the resultant load factors of R, R' and R_1 expressions—denoted by Q, Q' and Q_1, respectively—assume the following simplified forms:

Fixed bases:

$$\left.\begin{aligned}
Q &= \left(\frac{1}{K_2} - \frac{1}{m}\right)\frac{wh^2}{8} - \frac{h}{8mh_1}w_1h_1^2, \\[4pt]
Q' &= \left(\frac{1}{K_2} + \frac{1}{m}\right)\frac{wh^2}{8} + \frac{h}{8mh_1}w_1h_1^2, \\[4pt]
Q_1 &= \frac{h_1}{h(K_4 + K_5)}\left(3 - \frac{K_2}{m}\right)\frac{wh^2}{8} + \frac{2m - K_2}{8m(K_4 + K_5)}w_1h_1^2
\end{aligned}\right\} \cdots (204)$$

Hinged bases:

$$Q = \left(\frac{1}{K_2} - \frac{1}{n}\right)\frac{wh^2}{8} - \frac{5}{32}\cdot\frac{h}{nh_1}w_1h_1{}^2,$$

$$Q' = \left(\frac{1}{K_2} + \frac{1}{n}\right)\frac{wh^2}{8} + \frac{5}{32}\cdot\frac{h}{nh_1}w_1h_1{}^2,$$

$$Q_1 = \frac{h_1}{h(K_4+K_5)}\left(3 - \frac{K_2}{n}\right)\frac{wh^2}{2} + \frac{5(2n-K_2)}{8n(K_4+K_5)}w_1h_1^2$$

$$\left.\begin{array}{c} \\ \\ \\ \end{array}\right\} \quad . \quad (204a)$$

59. Symmetrical Lean-to Bent with Unsymmetrical Vertical Loading.—Except for the load constants, all relations derived for horizontal loading, Art. 58, are equally applicable for vertical loading. Obviously, eq. (b) is not altered; and, in obtaining deflection expressions, the consideration is that the horizontal reaction just above joint B, Fig. 176, must equal that above B', as well as the sum of horizon-

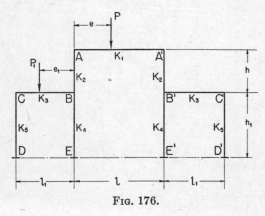

FIG. 176.

tal reactions at bases D and E. Accordingly, we have:

$$\frac{1}{h}(M_{AB}+M_{BA}+M_{A'B'}+M_{B'A'})=0,$$

$$\frac{1}{h_1}(M_{CD}+M_{DC}+M_{BE}+M_{EB}) - \frac{1}{h}(M_{AB}+M_{BA})=0,$$

$$\frac{1}{h_1}(M_{C'D'}+M_{D'C'}+M_{B'E'}+M_{E'B'}) - \frac{1}{h}(M_{A'B'}+M_{B'A'})=0.$$

$$\left.\begin{array}{c} \\ \\ \\ \end{array}\right\} \quad . \quad (i)$$

Substituting the values of the end moments, and assuming fixed bases,

$$\left.\begin{aligned}
&\frac{3}{2}K_2(A+B+A'+B')-2K_2(R+R')=0,\\[2mm]
&\frac{3h}{2h_1}(K_4B+K_5C)-\frac{3}{2}K_2(A+B)+2K_2R-\frac{2h}{h_1}(K_4+K_5)R_1=0,\\[2mm]
&\frac{3h}{2h_1}(K_4B'+K_5C')-\frac{3}{2}K_2(A'+B')-2K_2R'-\frac{2h}{h_1}(K_4+K_5)R_1\\[2mm]
&\qquad\qquad -\frac{2h^2}{h_1^2}(K_4+K_5)(R-R')=0.
\end{aligned}\right\} \quad \cdot\cdot\ (j)$$

Solving for R and R', the deflection terms of members AB and $A'B'$, respectively,

$$R=\frac{3}{8}\Big[\Big(1+\frac{K_2}{m}\Big)A+\Big(1+\frac{K_2}{m}-\frac{hK_4}{mh_1}\Big)B+\Big(1-\frac{K_2}{m}\Big)A'$$
$$+\Big(1-\frac{K_2}{m}+\frac{hK_4}{mh_1}\Big)B'-\frac{hK_5}{mh_1}C+\frac{hK_5}{mh_1}C'\Big]; \ \cdot\ \cdot\ \cdot\ \cdot \quad (205)$$

$$R'=\frac{3}{8}\Big[\Big(1-\frac{K_2}{m}\Big)A+\Big(1-\frac{K_2}{m}+\frac{hK_4}{mh_1}\Big)B+\Big(1+\frac{K_2}{m}\Big)A'$$
$$+\Big(1+\frac{K_2}{m}-\frac{hK_4}{mh_1}\Big)B'+\frac{hK_5}{mh_1}C-\frac{hK_5}{mh_1}C'\Big]; \ \cdot\ \cdot\ \cdot\ \cdot \quad (206)$$

in which

$$m=K_2+\frac{h^2}{h_1^2}(K_4+K_5) \ \cdot\ \cdot\ \cdot\ \cdot\ \cdot\ \cdot\ \cdot\ \cdot\ \cdot \quad (k)$$

The value of R_1—deflection term of members BE and CD—is obtained from the second equation of eqs. (j):

$$R_1=\frac{h_1K_2}{h(K_4+K_5)}R+\frac{3K_2}{4(K_4+K_5)}\Big[\Big(\frac{K_4}{K_2}-\frac{h_1}{h}\Big)B-\frac{h_1}{h}A+\frac{K_5}{K_2}C\Big]\cdot\cdot\ (207)$$

If the legs of the bent are assumed to be hinged at the bases, the corresponding deflection expressions become:

$$R=\frac{3}{8}\Big[\Big(1+\frac{K_2}{n}\Big)A+\Big(1+\frac{K_2}{n}-\frac{hK_4}{2nh_1}\Big)B+\Big(1-\frac{K_2}{n}\Big)A'$$
$$+\Big(1-\frac{K_2}{n}+\frac{hK_4}{2nh_1}\Big)B'-\frac{hK_5}{2nh_1}C+\frac{hK_5}{2nh_1}C'\Big], \ \cdot\ \cdot\ \cdot\ \cdot \quad (205a)$$

$$R'=\frac{3}{8}\Big[\Big(1-\frac{K_2}{n}\Big)A+\Big(1-\frac{K_2}{n}+\frac{hK_4}{2nh_1}\Big)B+\Big(1+\frac{K_2}{n}\Big)A'$$
$$+\Big(1+\frac{K_2}{n}-\frac{hK_4}{2nh_1}\Big)B'+\frac{hK_5}{2nh_1}C-\frac{hK_5}{2nh_1}C'\Big], \ \cdot\ \cdot\ \cdot\ \cdot \quad (206a)$$

$$R_1=\frac{4h_1K_2}{h(K_4+K_5)}R+\frac{3K_2}{K_4+K_5}\Big[\Big(\frac{K_4}{2K_2}-\frac{h_1}{h}\Big)B-\frac{h_1}{h}A+\frac{K_5}{2K_2}C\Big];(207a)$$

in which

$$n=K_2+\frac{h^2}{4h_1{}^2}(K_4+K_5) \dots \dots \dots (l)$$

With due allowance for the change in the fixed-end moments, the joint expressions for fixed and hinged bases are obtained from eqs. 203) and (203a).

ILLUSTRATIVE EXAMPLE

The member CB of the symmetrical bent shown in Fig. 177 is carrying a uniform load of 1 kip per linear foot. Assuming the legs to be fixed at the bases, determine the end moments.

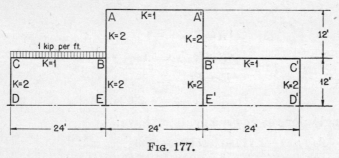

FIG. 177.

Solution: From eqs. (k), (205), (206) and (207) we have:

$$m=2+1(2+2)=6,$$

$$R=\frac{1}{2}A+\frac{1}{4}A'+\frac{3}{8}B+\frac{3}{8}B'-\frac{1}{8}C+\frac{1}{8}C',$$

$$R'=\frac{1}{4}A+\frac{1}{2}A'+\frac{3}{8}B+\frac{3}{8}B'+\frac{1}{8}C-\frac{1}{8}C',$$

$$R_1=-\frac{1}{8}A+\frac{1}{8}A'+\frac{3}{16}B+\frac{3}{16}B'+\frac{5}{16}C+\frac{1}{16}C'.$$

Substituting these values for the deflection terms in eqs. (203), and noting that FM equals zero at joints A, A', B' and C', $+48$ at B, and -48 at C, the joint equations become:

$$2A+\frac{1}{4}B-\frac{3}{4}B'+\frac{1}{4}C-\frac{1}{4}C'=0,$$

$$2A'-\frac{3}{4}B+\frac{1}{4}B'-\frac{1}{4}C+\frac{1}{4}C'=0,$$

$$\frac{1}{4}A-\frac{3}{4}A'+3\frac{7}{8}B-1\frac{1}{8}B'+\frac{1}{8}C-\frac{3}{8}C'=-48,$$

$$-\frac{3}{4}A+\frac{1}{4}A'-1\frac{1}{8}B+3\frac{7}{8}B'-\frac{3}{8}C+\frac{1}{8}C'=0,$$

$$\frac{1}{4}A-\frac{1}{4}A'+\frac{1}{8}B-\frac{3}{8}B'+2\frac{3}{8}C-\frac{1}{8}C'=48,$$

$$-\frac{1}{4}A+\frac{1}{4}A'-\frac{3}{8}B+\frac{1}{8}B-\frac{1}{8}C+2\frac{3}{8}C'=0.$$

Eliminating A and A', and obtaining values of B, B', C and C' from the usual tabular solution of simultaneous equations,

$$B = -14.143,$$
$$B' = -2.284,$$
$$C = 20.483,$$
$$C' = -0.975.$$

Then

$$A = -1.771,$$
$$A' = -2.336;$$

and

$$R = R_{AB} = -10.312,$$
$$R' = R_{A'B'} = 5.089,$$
$$R_1 = R_{BE} = 3.189,$$
$$R_1' = R_{B'E'} = -2.034.$$

Accordingly, for the end moments we have:

$$M_{AA'} = -1.771 - 1.168 = -2.939,$$
$$M_{AB} = 2(-1.771 - 7.072 + 10.312) = 2.938;$$

$$M_{A'A} = -2.336 - 0.886 = -3.222,$$
$$M_{A'B'} = 2(-2.336 - 1.142 + 5.089) = 3.222;$$

$$M_{BA} = 2(-14.143 - 0.886 + 10.312) = -9.434,$$
$$M_{BE} = 2(-14.143 - 3.189) = -34.664,$$
$$M_{BC} = -14.143 + 10.242 + 48 = 44.099;$$

$$M_{B'A'} = 2(-2.284 - 1.168 + 5.089) = 3.274,$$
$$M_{B'E'} = 2(-2.284 + 2.034) = -0.500,$$
$$M_{B'C'} = -2.284 - 0.488 = -2.772;$$

$$M_{CB} = 20.483 - 7.072 - 48 = -34.589,$$
$$M_{CD} = 2(20.483 - 3.189) = 34.588;$$

$$M_{C'B'} = -0.975 - 1.142 = -2.117,$$
$$M_{C'D'} = 2(-0.975 + 2.034) = 2.118;$$

$$M_{DC} = 2(10.242 - 3.189) = 14.106;$$

$$M_{EB} = 2(-7.072 - 3.189) = -20.522;$$

$$M_{E'B'} = 2(-1.142 + 2.034) = 1.784;$$

$$M_{D'C'} = 2(-0.488 + 2.034) = 3.092.$$

PROBLEMS

57. Derive the load factors of the deflection expressions for a symmetrical bent carrying a bracket loading. The bracket is supported on column AB (Fig. 177a). Denote the overturning moment Pe by M, and obtain the constants for

    (a) Fixed bases;
    (b) Hinged bases.

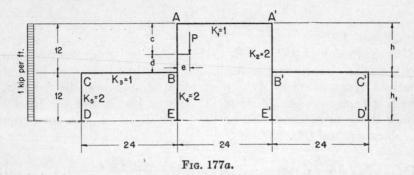

FIG. 177a.

58. The columns AB and CD of the bent shown in Fig. 177a are subjected to a uniform horizontal load of 1 kip per linear vertical foot. Assuming the legs to be fixed at the bases, determine the end moments.

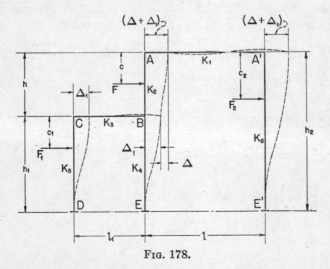

FIG. 178.

60. **Rectangular Bent with Single Lean-to.**—Fig. 178 represents an unsymmetrical rectangular lean-to bent. The deformations under a system of lateral loading are shown in dotted lines. It is noted that there are only two independent deflections for the four vertical members. Obviously, legs CD and BE have the same deflection, and the total displacement of joint A equals that of A'. Denoting

the deflection of member AB by Δ, and that of members CD and BE by Δ_1, we then have:

$$R_{AB} = \frac{\Delta}{h} = R, \quad \ldots \ldots \ldots \ldots \ldots \quad (a)$$

$$R_{CD} = R_{BE} = \frac{\Delta_1}{h_1} = R_1, \quad \ldots \ldots \ldots \ldots \quad (b)$$

$$R_{A'E'} = \frac{\Delta + \Delta_1}{h_2} = \frac{h}{h_2}R + \frac{h_1}{h_2}R_1 \quad \ldots \ldots \ldots \quad (c)$$

The expressions for R and R_1 may be obtained from the following two considerations: (1) The horizontal shear just below the joint A, obtained from member AB, must equal that below the joint A' resulting from member $A'E'$; (2) The shear just above the joint B equals the sum of shears below the joints B and C, obtained from members BE and CD. Thus

$$\frac{1}{h}(M_{AB} + M_{BA}) + \frac{F}{h}(h-c) = -\frac{1}{h_2}(M_{A'E'} + M_{E'A'}) - \frac{F_2}{h_2}(h_2 - c_2); \ldots \quad (d)$$

$$\frac{1}{h}(M_{AB} + M_{BA}) - \frac{Fc}{h} = \frac{1}{h_1}(M_{BE} + M_{EB} + M_{CD} + M_{DC}) + \frac{F_1}{h_1}(h_1 - c_1) \ldots \quad (e)$$

Substituting the values of the end moments in eqs. (d) and (e), and assuming the legs of the bent to be fixed at the bases,

$$\frac{3}{2}K_2(A+B) - 2K_2R + (FM_{AB} + FM_{BA}) + (h-c)F = -\frac{3h}{2h_2}K_6A'$$
$$+ \frac{2h^2}{h_2{}^2}K_6R + \frac{2hh_1}{h_2{}^2}K_6R_1 - \frac{h}{h_2}(FM_{A'E'} + FM_{E'A'}) - \frac{h}{h_2}(h_2 - c_2)F_2,$$

$$\frac{3}{2}K_2(A+B) - 2K_2R + (FM_{AB} + FM_{BA}) - Fc = \frac{3h}{2h_1}(K_4B + K_5C)$$
$$- \frac{2h}{h_1}(K_4 + K_5)R_1 + \frac{h}{h_1}(FM_{CD} + FM_{DC}) + \frac{h}{h_1}(h_1 - c_1)F_1;$$

or

$$\left(K_2 + \frac{h^2}{h_2{}^2}K_6\right)R + \frac{hh_1}{h_2{}^2}K_6R_1 = \frac{3}{4}K_2(A+B) + \frac{3h}{4h_2}K_6A'$$
$$+ \frac{1}{2}[(FM_{AB} + FM_{BA}) + (h-c)F$$
$$+ \frac{h}{h_2}(FM_{A'E'} + FM_{E'A'}) + \frac{h}{h_2}(h_2 - c_2)F_2], \quad \ldots \ldots \quad (f)$$

$$-K_2R + \frac{h}{h_1}(K_4 + K_5)R_1 = -\frac{3}{4}K_2(A+B) + \frac{3h}{4h_1}(K_4B + K_5C)$$
$$- \frac{1}{2}[(FM_{AB} + FM_{BA}) - Fc - \frac{h}{h_1}(FM_{CD} + FM_{DC})$$
$$- \frac{h}{h_1}(h_1 - c_1)F_1]; \quad \ldots \ldots \ldots \ldots \ldots \ldots \quad (g)$$

from which

$$R = \frac{3}{4}\left(\frac{1}{d}+\frac{1}{e}\right)K_2 A + \frac{3}{4}\frac{hK_6}{dh_2}A' + \frac{3}{4}\left[\frac{1}{d}+\frac{1}{e}\left(1-\frac{h}{h_1}\frac{K_4}{K_2}\right)\right]K_2 B$$
$$-\frac{3hK_5}{4eh_1}C + \frac{1}{2}\left[\left(\frac{1}{d}+\frac{1}{e}\right)(FM_{AB}+FM_{BA}) + \frac{h}{dh_2}(FM_{A'E'}+FM_{E'A'})\right.$$
$$-\frac{h}{eh_1}(FM_{CD}+FM_{DC}) + \left(\frac{h-c}{d}-\frac{c}{e}\right)F + \frac{h}{dh_2}(h_2-c_2)F_2$$
$$\left. -\frac{h}{eh_1}(h_1-c_1)F_1\right], \quad \ldots \ldots \ldots \ldots \ldots \ldots \quad (208)$$

$$R_1 = \frac{3}{4}\left(\frac{1}{d_1}-\frac{1}{e_1}\right)K_2 A + \frac{3hK_6}{4d_1h_2}A' + \frac{3}{4}\left[\frac{1}{d_1}-\frac{1}{e_1}\left(1-\frac{h}{h_1}\cdot\frac{K_4}{K_2}\right)\right]K_2 B$$
$$+\frac{3hK_5}{4e_1h_1}C + \frac{1}{2}\left[\left(\frac{1}{d_1}-\frac{1}{e_1}\right)(FM_{AB}+FM_{BA}) + \frac{h}{d_1h_2}(FM_{A'E'}+FM_{E'A'})\right.$$
$$+\frac{h}{e_1h_1}(FM_{CD}+FM_{DC}) + \left(\frac{h-c}{d_1}+\frac{c}{e_1}\right)F + \frac{h}{d_1h_2}(h_2-c_2)F_2$$
$$\left. +\frac{h}{e_1h_1}(h_1-c_1)F_1\right]; \quad \ldots \ldots \ldots \ldots \ldots \ldots \quad (208a)$$

which

$$\left.\begin{aligned}
d &= K_2 + \frac{h^2}{h_2^2}\left(1+\frac{h_1^2}{h^2}\cdot\frac{K_2}{K_4+K_5}\right)K_6, \\
e &= \frac{h_2^2}{h_1^2}(K_4+K_5)\left(\frac{K_2}{K_6}+\frac{h^2}{h_2^2}\right)+K_2, \\
d_1 &= \frac{h}{h_1}\left[(K_4+K_5)\left(1+\frac{h^2}{h_2^2}\cdot\frac{K_6}{K_2}\right)+\frac{h_1^2}{h_2^2}K_6\right], \\
e_1 &= \frac{h}{h_1}\left[K_4+K_5+\frac{h_1^2}{h_2^2}\cdot\frac{K_2}{\left(\frac{K_2}{K_6}+\frac{h^2}{h_2^2}\right)}\right].
\end{aligned}\right\} \quad \ldots \ldots \quad (210)$$

The joint equations are in the following forms:

$$\left.\begin{aligned}
(K_1+K_2)A + \frac{K_1}{2}A' + \frac{K_2}{2}B - K_2 R + FM_{AB} &= 0, \\[4pt]
(K_1+K_6)A' + \frac{K_1}{2}A - K_6\left(\frac{h}{h_2}R+\frac{h_1}{h_2}R_1\right) + FM_{A'E'} &= 0, \\[4pt]
(K_2+K_3+K_4)B + \frac{K_2}{2}A + \frac{K_3}{2}C - K_2 R - K_4 R_1 + FM_{BA} &= 0, \\[4pt]
(K_3+K_5)C + \frac{K_3}{2}B - K_5 R_1 + FM_{CD} &= 0.
\end{aligned}\right\} \quad \ldots \quad (h)$$

Substituting the values of R and R_1 from eqs. (208) in eqs. (h), we have:

Joint A,

$$\left[K_1+K_2-\frac{3}{4}\left(\frac{1}{d}+\frac{1}{e}\right)K_2{}^2\right]A+\left(\frac{K_1}{2}-\frac{3}{4}\cdot\frac{h}{dh_2}K_2K_6\right)A')$$

$$+\left\{\frac{1}{2}-\frac{3}{4}\left[\frac{1}{d}+\frac{1}{e}\left(1-\frac{hK_4}{h_1K_2}\right)\right]K_2\right\}K_2B+\frac{3}{4}\cdot\frac{h}{eh_1}K_2K_5C+Q_{Af}=0 \; ; \; (211)$$

Joint A',

$$\left[K_1+K_6-\frac{3h}{4h_2}\left(\frac{h}{dh_2}+\frac{h_1}{d_1h_2}\right)K_6{}^2\right]A'$$

$$+\left\{\frac{K_1}{2}-\frac{3h}{4h_2}\left[\frac{1}{d}+\frac{1}{e}+\frac{h_1}{h}\left(\frac{1}{d_1}-\frac{1}{e_1}\right)\right]K_2K_6\right\}A$$

$$-\frac{3h}{4h_2}\left\{\frac{1}{d}+\frac{1}{e}\left(1-\frac{hK_4}{h_1K_2}\right)+\frac{h_1}{h}\left[\frac{1}{d_1}-\frac{1}{e_1}\left(1-\frac{hK_4}{h_1K_2}\right)\right]\right\}K_2K_6B$$

$$+\frac{3h}{4h_1h_2}\left(\frac{h}{e}-\frac{h_1}{e_1}\right)K_5K_6C+Q_{A'f}=0; \quad \ldots \ldots \ldots \ldots \quad (211a)$$

Joint B,

$$\left\{K_2+K_3+K_4-\frac{3}{4}\left[\frac{1}{d}+\frac{1}{e}\left(1-\frac{hK_4}{h_1K_2}\right)\right]K_2{}^2-\frac{3}{4}\left[-\frac{1}{d_1}-\frac{1}{e_1}\left(1-\frac{hK_4}{h_1K_2}\right)\right]K_2K_4\right\}B$$

$$+\left[\frac{K_2}{2}-\frac{3}{4}\left(\frac{1}{d}+\frac{1}{e}\right)K_2{}^2-\frac{3}{4}\left(\frac{1}{d_1}-\frac{1}{e_1}\right)K_2K_4\right]A-\frac{3h}{4h_2}\left(\frac{K_2}{d}+\frac{K_4}{d_1}\right)K_6A'$$

$$+\left[\frac{K_3}{2}+\frac{3h}{4h_1}\left(\frac{K_2}{e}-\frac{K_4}{e_1}\right)K_5\right]C+Q_{Bf}=0; \quad \ldots \ldots \ldots \ldots \quad (211b)$$

Joint C,

$$\left[K_3+\left(1-\cdot\frac{3}{4}\frac{hK_5}{h_1e_1}\right)K_5\right]C-\frac{3}{4}\left(\frac{1}{d_1}-\frac{1}{e_1}\right)K_2K_5A-\frac{3hK_5}{4h_2d_1}K_6A'$$

$$+\left\{\frac{K_3}{2}-\frac{3}{4}\left[\frac{1}{d_1}-\frac{1}{e_1}\left(1-\frac{hK_4}{h_1K_2}\right)\right]K_2K_5\right\}B+Q_{Cf}=0; \quad \ldots \quad (211c)$$

in which the load constants Q denote the following values:

$$Q_{Af}=FM_{AB}-\frac{K_2}{2}\left[\left(\frac{1}{d}+\frac{1}{e}\right)\left(FM_{AB}+FM_{BA}\right)\right.$$

$$+\frac{h}{dh_2}\left(FM_{A'E'}+FM_{E'A'}\right)-\frac{h}{eh_1}\left(FM_{CD}+FM_{DC}\right)$$

$$\left.-\left(\frac{h-c}{d}-\frac{c}{e}\right)F+\frac{h}{dh_2}\left(h_2-c_2\right)F_2-\frac{h}{eh_1}\left(h_1-c_1\right)F_1\right], \quad \ldots \quad (212)$$

$$Q_{A'f} = FM_{A'E'} - \frac{K_6}{2}\left\{\frac{h}{h_2}\left[\left(\frac{1}{d}+\frac{1}{e}\right)(FM_{AB}+FM_{BA})\right.\right.$$

$$+\frac{h}{dh_2}(FM_{A'E'}+FM_{E'A'}) - \frac{h}{eh_1}(FM_{CD}+FM_{DC}) + \left(\frac{h-c}{d}-\frac{c}{e}\right)F$$

$$-\frac{h}{dh_1}(h_1-c_1)F_1 + \frac{h}{dh_2}(h_2-c_2)F_2\right] + \frac{h_1}{h_2}\left[\left(\frac{1}{d_1}-\frac{1}{e_1}\right)(FM_{AB}+FM_{BA})\right.$$

$$+\frac{h}{d_1h_2}(FM_{A'E'}+FM_{E'A'}) + \left(\frac{h-c}{d_1}+\frac{c}{e_1}\right)F + \frac{h}{e_1h_1}(h_1-c_1)F_1$$

$$\left.\left.+\frac{h}{d_1h_2}(h_2-c_2)F_2\right]\right\}, \quad \ldots \ldots \ldots \ldots \quad (212a)$$

$$Q_{Bf} = FM_{BA} - \frac{K_2}{2}\left[\left(\frac{1}{d}+\frac{1}{e}\right)(FM_{AB}+FM_{BA}) + \frac{h}{dh_2}(FM_{A'E'}+FM_{E'A'})\right.$$

$$-\frac{h}{eh_1}(FM_{CD}+FM_{DC}) + \left(\frac{h-c}{d}-\frac{c}{e}\right)F - \frac{h}{eh_1}(h_1-c_1)F_1$$

$$+\frac{h}{dh_2}(h_2-c_2)F_2\right] - \frac{K_4}{2}\left(\frac{1}{d_1}-\frac{1}{e_1}\right)(FM_{AB}+FM_{BA})$$

$$+\frac{h}{e_1h_1}(FM_{CD}+FM_{DC}) + \frac{h}{d_1h_2}(FM_{A'E'}+FM_{E'A'}) + \left(\frac{h-c}{d_1}+\frac{c}{e_1}\right)F$$

$$+\frac{h}{e_1h_1}(h_1-c_1)F_1 + \frac{h}{d_1h_2}(h_2-c_2)F_2\right], \quad \ldots \ldots \ldots \quad (212b)$$

$$Q_{Cf} = FM_{CD} - \frac{K_5}{2}\left[\left(\frac{1}{d_1}-\frac{1}{e_1}\right)(FM_{AB}+FM_{BA}) + \frac{h}{e_1h_1}(FM_{CD}+FM_{DC})\right.$$

$$+\frac{h}{d_1h_2}(FM_{A'E'}+FM_{E'A'}) + \left(\frac{h-c}{d_1}+\frac{c}{e_1}\right)F + \frac{h}{e_1h_1}(h_1-c_1)F_1$$

$$+\frac{h}{d_1h_2}(h_2-c_2)F_2 \quad \ldots \ldots \ldots \ldots \ldots \quad (212c)$$

If the legs of the bent are assumed to be hinged to the bases, equations (f) and (g) become:

$$\left(2K_2+\frac{h^2K_6}{2h_2^2}\right)R + \frac{hh_1}{2h_2^2}K_6R_1 = \frac{3}{2}K_2(A+B) + \frac{3h}{4h_2}K_6A'$$

$$+ (FM_{AB}+FM_{BA}) + \frac{h}{h_2}HM_{A'E'} + (h-c)F + \frac{h}{h_2}(h_2-c_2)F_2, \quad . \quad (i)$$

$$-2K_2+\frac{h}{2h_1}(K_4+K_5)R_1 = -\frac{3}{2}K_2(A+B) + \frac{3h}{4h_1}(K_4B+K_5C)$$

$$- (FM_{AB}+FM_{BA}) + \frac{h}{h_1}HM_{CD} + Fc + \frac{h}{h_1}(h_1-c_1)F_1, \quad \ldots \ldots \quad (j)$$

from which

$$R = \frac{3}{2}\left(\frac{1}{a}+\frac{1}{b}\right)K_2A + \frac{3hK_6}{4ah_2}A' + \frac{3}{2}\left[\frac{1}{a}+\frac{1}{b}\left(1-\frac{hK_4}{2h_1K_2}\right)\right]K_2B$$

$$- \frac{3hK_5}{4bh_1}C + q_{Rh}, \quad \ldots \ldots \ldots \ldots \quad (213)$$

$$R_1 = \frac{3}{2}\left(\frac{1}{a_1}-\frac{1}{b_1}\right)K_2A + \frac{3hK_6}{4a_1h_2}A'$$

$$+ \frac{3}{2}\left[\frac{1}{a_1}-\frac{1}{b_1}\left(1-\frac{hK_4}{2h_1K_2}\right)\right]K_2B + \frac{3hK_5}{4b_1h_1}C + q_{R1h}; \quad . \quad (213a)$$

where

$$a=2K_2+\frac{h^2}{h_2{}^2}\Big[\frac{1}{2}+\frac{4h_1{}^2}{h^2}\cdot\frac{K_2}{K_4+K_5}\Big]K_6,$$

$$b=2K_2+\frac{h_2{}^2}{h_1{}^2}(K_4+K_5)\Big(\frac{2K_2}{K_6}+\frac{h^2}{2h_2{}^2}\Big),$$

$$a_1=\frac{h}{2h_1}\Big[\frac{h_1{}^2}{h_2{}^2}K_6+(K_4+K_5)\Big(1+\frac{h^2K_6}{4h_2{}^2K_2}\Big)\Big],$$

$$b_1=\frac{h}{2h_1}(K_4+K_5)+\frac{h_1}{l\Big(\dfrac{4h_2{}^2}{h^2}+\dfrac{K_6}{K_2}\Big)};$$

$$\quad\cdots\quad (214)$$

$$q_{Rh}=\Big(\frac{1}{a}+\frac{1}{b}\Big)(FM_{AB}+FM_{BA})+\frac{h}{ah_2}HM_{A'E'}-\frac{h}{bh_1}HM_{CD}$$

$$+\Big(\frac{h-c}{a}-\frac{c}{b}\Big)F-\frac{h}{bh_1}(h_1-c_1)F_1+\frac{h}{ah_2}(h_2-c_2)F_2,\;\ldots\;(215)$$

$$q_{R1h}=\Big(\frac{1}{a_1}-\frac{1}{b_1}\Big)(FM_{AB}+FM_{BA})+\frac{h}{a_1h_2}HM_{A'E'}+\frac{h}{b_1h_1}HM_{CD}$$

$$+\Big(\frac{h-c}{a_1}+\frac{c}{b_1}\Big)F+\frac{h}{b_1h_1}(h_1-c_1)F_1+\frac{h}{a_1h_2}(h_2-c_2)F_2\;\ldots\;(215a)$$

The joint equations for hinged bases are as follows:

$$(K_1+K_2)A+\frac{K_1}{2}A'+\frac{K_2}{2}B-K_2R+FM_{AB}=0,$$

$$\Big(K_1+\frac{3}{4}K_6\Big)A'+\frac{K_1}{2}A-\frac{K_6}{2}\Big(\frac{h}{h_2}R+\frac{h_1}{h_2}R_1\Big)+HM_{A'E'}=0,$$

$$\Big(K_2+K_3+\frac{3}{4}K_4\Big)B+\frac{K_2}{2}A+\frac{K_3}{2}C-K_2R-\frac{K_4}{2}R_1+FM_{BA}=0,$$

$$\Big(K_3+\frac{3}{4}K_5\Big)C+\frac{K_3}{2}B-\frac{K_5}{2}R_1+HM_{CD}=0.$$

$$\quad\cdots\;(k)$$

Substituting the values of R and R_1 from eqs. (213), the expressions become:

Joint A,

$$\Big[K_1+K_2-\frac{3}{2}\Big(\frac{1}{a}+\frac{1}{b}\Big)K_2{}^2\Big]A+\Big(\frac{K_1}{2}-\frac{3h}{4ah_2}K_2K_6\Big)A'$$

$$+\Big\{\frac{1}{2}-\frac{3}{2}\Big[\frac{1}{a}+\frac{1}{b}\Big(1-\frac{hK_4}{2h_1K_2}\Big)\Big]K_2\Big\}K_2B+\frac{3h}{4bh_1}K_2K_5C$$

$$+FM_{AB}-K_2q_{Rh}=0;\;\ldots\ldots\ldots\ldots\ldots\ldots\;(216)$$

Joint A',

$$\left[K_1+\frac{3}{4}K_6-\frac{3h}{8h_2}\left(\frac{h}{ah_2}+\frac{h_1}{a_1h_2}\right)K_6{}^2\right]A'$$

$$+\left\{\frac{K_1}{2}-\frac{3h}{4h_2}\left[\frac{1}{a}+\frac{1}{b}+\frac{h_1}{h}\left(\frac{1}{a_1}-\frac{1}{b_1}\right)\right]K_2K_6\right\}A$$

$$-\frac{3h}{4h_2}\left\{\frac{1}{a}+\frac{1}{b}\left(1-\frac{hK_4}{2h_1K_2}\right)+\frac{h_1}{h}\left[\frac{1}{a_1}-\frac{1}{b_1}\left(1-\frac{hK_4}{2h_1K_2}\right)\right]\right\}K_2K_6B$$

$$+\frac{3h}{8h_2}\left(\frac{h}{bh_1}-\frac{1}{b_1}\right)K_5K_6C+HM_{A'E'}-\frac{h}{2h_2}K_6q_{Rh}-\frac{h_1}{2h_2}K_6q_{R1h}=0\ ;$$

$$\cdots\cdots (216a)$$

Joint B,

$$\left\{K_2+K_3+\frac{3}{4}K_4-\frac{3}{2}\left[\frac{1}{a}+\frac{1}{b}\left(1-\frac{hK_4}{2h_1K_2}\right)\right]K_2{}^2\right.$$

$$\left.-\frac{3}{4}\left[\frac{1}{a_1}-\frac{1}{b_1}\left(1-\frac{hK_4}{2h_1K_2}\right)\right]K_2K_4\right\}B$$

$$+\left[\frac{K_2}{2}-\frac{3}{2}\left(\frac{1}{a}+\frac{1}{b}\right)K_2{}^2-\frac{3}{4}\left(\frac{1}{a_1}-\frac{1}{b_1}\right)K_2K_4\right]A-\frac{3h}{4h_2}\left(\frac{K_2}{a}+\frac{K_4}{2a_1}\right)K_6A'$$

$$+\left[\frac{K_3}{2}+\frac{3h}{4h_1}\left(\frac{K_2}{b}-\frac{K_4}{b_1}\right)K_5\right]C+FM_{BA}-K_2q_{Rh}-\frac{K_4}{2}q_{R1h}=0\ ;. (216b)$$

Joint C,

$$\left[K_3+\left(\frac{3}{4}-\frac{3hK_5}{8b_1h_1}\right)K_5\right]C-\frac{3}{8}\left(\frac{1}{a_1}-\frac{1}{b_1}\right)K_2K_5A-\frac{3h}{8a_1h_2}K_5K_6A'$$

$$+\left\{\frac{K_3}{2}-\frac{3}{4}\left[\frac{1}{a_1}-\frac{1}{b_1}\left(1-\frac{hK_4}{2h_1K_2}\right)\right]K_2K_5\right\}B+HM_{CD}-\frac{K_5}{2}q_{R1h}=0\,. (216c)$$

The load factors q and Q for some other loading conditions **are** given below:

(1) Concentrated vertical loading, Fig. 179a:

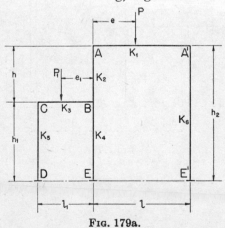

Fig. 179a.

$$q_{Rf}=q_{R1f}=q_{Rh}=q_{R1h}=0,$$

$$Q_{Af}=Q_{Ah}=-\frac{e}{l^2}(l-e)^2P,$$

$$Q_{Bf}=Q_{Bh}=\frac{e_1^2}{l_1^2}(l_1-e_1)P_1.$$

$\quad\quad\cdots\cdots\cdots\quad (m)$

(2) Uniform vertical loading, Fig. 179*b*:

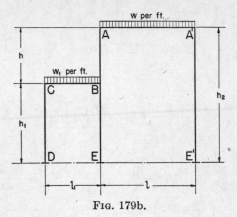

Fig. 179b.

$$q_{Rf}=q_{R1f}=q_{Rh}=q_{R1h}=0,$$

$$Q_{Af}=Q_{Ah}=-\frac{wl_2}{12},$$

$$Q_{Bf}=Q_{Bh}=\frac{w_1l_1^2}{12}.$$

$\quad\quad\cdots\cdots\cdots\quad (n)$

(3) Uniform horizontal loading, Fig. 179*c*:

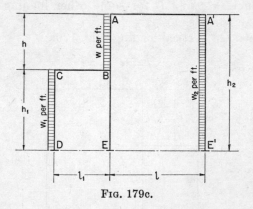

Fig. 179c.

$$q_{Rf} = \frac{h^2}{4}\left(\frac{1}{d} - \frac{1}{e}\right)w - \frac{h}{4eh_1}h_1^2w_1 + \frac{h}{4dh_2}h_2^2w_2,$$

$$q_{R1f} = \frac{h^2}{4}\left(\frac{1}{d_1} + \frac{1}{e_1}\right)w + \frac{h}{4e_1h_1}h_1^2w_1 + \frac{h}{4d_1h_2}h_2^2w_2\ ;$$

$$q_{Rh} = \frac{h^2}{2}\left(\frac{1}{a} - \frac{1}{b}\right)w - \frac{5h}{8bh_1}h_1^2w_1 + \frac{5h_2^2h}{8ah_2}w_2,$$

$$q_{R1h} = \frac{h^2}{2}\left(\frac{1}{a_1} + \frac{1}{b_1}\right)w + \frac{5h}{8b_1h_1}h_1^2w_1 + \frac{5h}{8a_1h_2}h_2^2w_2\ ;$$

$$\left. \right\} \quad . \quad . \quad . \quad (217)$$

$$Q_{Af} = \frac{h^2}{12}w - \frac{K_2}{4}\left[h^2\left(\frac{1}{d} - \frac{1}{e}\right)w - \frac{hh_1^2}{eh_2}w_1 + \frac{h_2^2}{d}\cdot\frac{h}{h_2}w_2\right],$$

$$Q_{Ah} = \frac{h^2}{12}w - \frac{K_2}{2}\left[h^2\left(\frac{1}{a} - \frac{1}{b}\right)w - \frac{5}{4}\left(\frac{hh_1^2}{bh_1}w_1 - \frac{hh_2^2}{ah_2}w_2\right)\right];$$

$$Q_{A'f} = \frac{h_2^2}{12}w_2 - \frac{K_6}{4}\left\{\left[\frac{h}{h_2}\left(\frac{1}{d} - \frac{1}{e}\right) + \frac{h_1}{h_2}\left(\frac{1}{d_1} + \frac{1}{e_1}\right)\right]h^2w\right.$$
$$\left. + \frac{h}{h_2}\left(\frac{1}{e_1} - \frac{h}{eh_1}\right)h_1^2w_1 + h\left(\frac{h}{d} + \frac{h_1}{d_1}\right)w_2\right\},$$

$$Q_{A'h} = \frac{h_2^2}{8}w_2 - \frac{K_6}{2}\left\{\left[\frac{h}{h_2}\left(\frac{1}{a} - \frac{1}{b}\right) + \frac{h_1}{h_2}\left(\frac{1}{a_1} + \frac{1}{b_1}\right)\right]\frac{h^2}{2}w\right.$$
$$\left. + \frac{5}{8}\cdot\frac{h}{h_2}\left(\frac{1}{b_1} - \frac{h}{bh_1}\right)h_1^2w_1 + \frac{5}{8}h\left(\frac{h}{a} + \frac{h_1}{a_1}\right)w_2\right\};$$

$$Q_{Bf} = -\frac{h^2}{12}w - \left[\frac{K_2}{4}\left(\frac{1}{d} - \frac{1}{e}\right) + \frac{K_4}{4}\left(\frac{1}{d_1} + \frac{1}{e_1}\right)\right]h^2w$$
$$+ \frac{h}{4h_1}\left(\frac{K_2}{e} - \frac{K_4}{e_1}\right)h_1^2w_1 - \frac{h}{4h_2}\left(\frac{K_2}{d} + \frac{K_4}{d_1}\right)h_2^2w_2,$$

$$Q_{Bh} = -\frac{h^2}{12}w - \left[\frac{K_2}{2}\left(\frac{1}{a} - \frac{1}{b}\right) + \frac{K_4}{4}\left(\frac{1}{a_1} + \frac{1}{b_1}\right)\right]h^2w$$
$$+ \frac{5h}{8h_1}\left(\frac{K_2}{b} - \frac{K_4}{2b_1}\right)h_1^2w_1 - \frac{5h}{8h_2}\left(\frac{K_2}{a} + \frac{K_4}{2a_1}\right)h_2^2w_2\ ;$$

$$Q_{Cf} = \left(\frac{1}{12} - \frac{hK_5}{4e_1h_1}\right)h_1^2w_1 - \frac{K_5}{4}\left(\frac{1}{d_1} + \frac{1}{e_1}\right)h^2w + \frac{h}{4d_1h_2}K_5 h_2^2w_2,$$

$$Q_{Ch} = \left(\frac{1}{8} - \frac{5h}{16h_1}\cdot\frac{K_5}{b_1}\right)h_1^2w_1 - \frac{K_5}{4}\left(\frac{1}{a_1} + \frac{1}{b_1}\right)h^2w - \frac{5}{16a_1}\frac{hK_5}{h_2}h_2^2w_2.$$

$$\left. \right\} (218)$$

ILLUSTRATIVE EXAMPLE

The vertical members AB and CD of the bent shown in Fig. 180 are subjected to a uniform horizontal load of 1 kip per vertical foot. Assuming the legs to be fixed at the bases, determine the end moments]

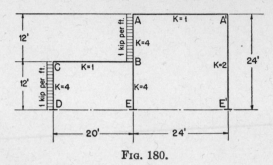

FIG. 180.

Solution: From eqs. (210) we have:

$$d = \frac{19}{4}, \ e = 76,$$

$$d_1 = \frac{19}{2}, \ e_1 = \frac{76}{9}.$$

Also, applying eqs. (211) and (218),

$$\frac{44}{19}A - \frac{5}{38}A' - \frac{10}{19}B + \frac{3}{19}C = \frac{276}{19},$$

$$-\frac{5}{38}A + \frac{105}{38}A' - \frac{18}{19}B - \frac{6}{19}C = \frac{360}{19},$$

$$-\frac{10}{19}A - \frac{18}{19}A' + \frac{99}{19}B - \frac{29}{38}C = \frac{1668}{19},$$

$$\frac{3}{19}A - \frac{6}{19}A' - \frac{29}{38}B + \frac{68}{19}C = \frac{708}{19}.$$

Obtaining the values of the unknown deflection angles by the tabular solution,

$$A = 11.496, \ A' = 17.371,$$
$$B = 23.580, \ C = 16.465;$$

and from eqs. (208) and (c),

$$R = 31.331, \ R_1 = 26.529, \ R_{A'E'} = 28.930.$$

Accordingly, the end moments become:

$$M_{AA'} = 11.496 + 8.686 = 20.182,$$
$$M_{AB} = 4(11.496 + 11.790 - 31.331) + 12 = -20.180;$$

$$M_{A'A}=17.371+5.748=23.119,$$
$$M_{A'E'}=2(17.371-28.930)=-23.118;$$

$$M_{BA}=4(23.580+5.748-31.331)-12=-20.012,$$
$$M_{BE}=4(23.580-26.529)=-11.796,$$
$$M_{BC}=23.580+8.233=31.813;$$

$$M_{CB}=16.465+11.790=28.255,$$
$$M_{CD}=4(16.465-26.529)+12=-28.256;$$

$$M_{DC}=4(8.233-26.529)-12=-85.184;$$

$$M_{EB}=4(11.790-26.529)=-58.956;$$

$$M_{E'A'}=2(8.686-28.930)=-40.488.$$

PROBLEMS

59. Assuming the member CB in Fig. 178 to be hinged at joint B, derive the deflection and joint expressions of the bent for two conditions of support, corresponding to eqs. (208), (211), (213) and (216).

60. Determine the end moments for the bent shown in Fig. 180, assuming fixed bases and the uniform horizontal loading to be applied to member $A'E'$.

61. Symmetrical, Gabled Lean-to Bent with Symmetrical Vertical Loading.—In discussing single-span gabled bents in Arts. 46 and 47, it was shown that a definite relation exists between the deflections of the sloping roof members and the legs. That interrelation is equally true for the type of lean-to bent illustrated in Fig. 181. Here, if

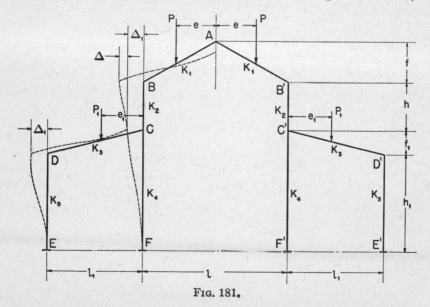

FIG. 181.

we assume the joints B and C to displace laterally a distance Δ and Δ_1, respectively, then corresponding displacements of the joints A and D can easily be obtained. Thus, neglecting the deflections due to axial deformations, it is at once seen that the joint D will displace the same distance as joint C, i. e., Δ_1; while the vertical displacement of the crown joint A equals $\frac{l}{2f}$ $(\Delta+\Delta_1)$. Denoting the deflection term of member BC by R, and that of DE by R_1, then for the similar terms of members CF and AB we have:

$$R_{CF}=\frac{h_1}{h_1+f_1}R_1; \quad R_{AB}=-\left(\frac{h}{f}R+\frac{h_1}{f}R_1\right) \quad . \quad . \quad . \quad . \quad (220)$$

As in the preceding cases, expressions for deflections R and R_1 are derived from shear equations above and below joints B and C. At B, from members AB and BC, we have:

$$\frac{1}{f}(M_{AB}+M_{BA})+\frac{P}{f}\left(\frac{l}{2}-e\right)=\frac{1}{h}(M_{BC}+M_{CB}) \quad ; \quad . \quad . \quad . \quad (a)$$

and at C, members BC, DE and CF give:

$$\frac{1}{h}(M_{BC}+M_{CB})=\frac{1}{h_1}(M_{DE}+M_{CF})+\frac{1}{h_1+f_1}(M_{CE}+M_{FC}) \quad . \quad . \quad (b)$$

Substituting values of end moments in eq. (a),

$$\frac{3h}{2f}K_1B+2K_1\left(\frac{h^2}{f^2}R+\frac{hh_1}{f^2}R_1\right)+\frac{h}{f}(FM_{AB}+FM_{BA})+\frac{h}{f}\left(\frac{l}{2}-e\right)P$$

$$=\frac{3}{2}K_2(B+C)-2K_2R \quad . \quad . \quad . \quad . \quad . \quad . \quad . \quad . \quad (c)$$

For fixed bases, with similar substitutions in eq. (b), we will have:

$$\frac{3}{2}K_2(B+C)-2K_2R=\frac{3}{2}\left(\frac{h}{h_1}K_5D+\frac{h}{h_1+f_1}K_4C\right)-2\left[\frac{h}{h_1}K_5+\frac{hh_1K_4}{(h_1+f_1)^2}\right]R_1 \; ; (d)$$

and for hinged bases,

$$\frac{3}{2}K_2(B+C)-2K_2R=\frac{3}{4}\left(\frac{h}{h_1}K_5D+\frac{h}{h_1+f_1}K_4C\right)-\frac{1}{2}\left[\frac{h}{h_1}K_5+\frac{hh_1K_4}{(h_1+f_1)^2}\right]R_1 \; ; (e)$$

or, rewritten in a simplified form,

$$\left(K_2+\frac{h^2}{f^2}K_1\right)R+\frac{hh_1}{f^2}K_1R_1=\frac{3}{4}\left(K_2-\frac{h}{f}K_1\right)B+\frac{3}{4}K_2C$$

$$-\frac{h}{2f}\left[(FM_{AB}+FM_{BA})+\left(\frac{l}{2}-e\right)P\right]\;.\;\;.\;\;.\;\;.\;\;(c1)$$

$$K_2R-\left[\frac{h}{h_1}K_5+\frac{hh_1K_4}{(h_1+f_1)^2}\right]R_1=\frac{3}{4}K_2B+\frac{3}{4}\left(K_2-\frac{h}{h_1+f_1}K_4\right)C-\frac{3h}{4h_1}K_5D,\;(d1)$$

$$K_2R-\frac{1}{4}\left[\frac{h}{h_1}K_5+\frac{hh_1K_4}{(h_1+f_1)^2}\right]R_1=\frac{3}{4}K_2B+\frac{3}{4}\left(K_2-\frac{hK_4}{2(h_1+f_1)}\right)C-\frac{3h}{8h_1}K_5D.(e1)$$

Solving for R and R_1, the deflection expressions for the two conditions of support become:

(a) Fixed bases,

$$(ac+bK_2)R=\frac{3}{4}\left[c\left(K_2-\frac{h}{f}K_1\right)+bK_2\right]B+\frac{3}{4}\left[cK_2+b\left(K_2-\frac{hK_4}{h_1+f_1}\right)\right]C$$

$$-\frac{3bh}{4h_1}K_5D-\frac{ch}{2f}\left[(FM_{AB}+FM_{BA})+\left(\frac{l}{2}-e\right)P\right]\;.\;\;.\;\;.\;\;.\;\;(221)$$

$$(ac+bK_2)R_1=\frac{3}{4}\left[K_2\left(K_2-\frac{h}{f}K_1\right)-aK_2\right]B+\frac{3}{4}\left[K_2{}^2-a\left(K_2-\frac{hK_4}{h_1+f_1}\right)\right]C$$

$$+\frac{3}{4}\frac{h}{h_1}aK_5D-\frac{hK_2}{2f}\left[(FM_{AB}+FM_{BA})+\left(\frac{l}{2}-e\right)P\right].\;\;.\;\;(221a)$$

(b) Hinged bases,

$$\left(\frac{ac}{4}+bK_2\right)R=\frac{3}{4}\left[\frac{c}{4}\left(K_2-\frac{h}{f}K_1\right)+bK_2\right]B+\frac{3}{4}\left\{\frac{c}{4}K_2+b\left[K_2-\frac{hK_4}{2(h_1+f_1)}\right]\right\}C$$

$$-\frac{3}{8}\frac{h}{h_1}bK_5D-\frac{ch}{8f}\left[(FM_{AB}+FM_{BA})+\left(\frac{l}{2}-e\right)P\right]\;.\;\;.\;\;.\;\;(222)$$

$$\left(\frac{ac}{4}+bK_2\right)R_1=\frac{3}{4}\left[K_2\left(K_2-\frac{h}{f}K_1\right)-aK_2\right]B+\frac{3}{4}\left\{K_2{}^2-a\left[K_2-\frac{hK_4}{2(h_1+f_1)}\right]\right\}C$$

$$+\frac{3}{8}\frac{h}{h_1}aK_5D-\frac{hK_2}{2f}\left[(FM_{AB}+FM_{BA})+\left(\frac{l}{2}-e\right)P\right].\;\;.\;\;(222a)$$

in which

$$a=K_2+\frac{h^2}{f^2}K_1,\quad b=\frac{hh_1}{f^2}K_1,\quad c=\frac{h}{h_1}K_5+\frac{hh_1K_4}{(h_1+f_1)^2}\;.\;\;.\;\;.\;\;(223)$$

The joint expressions at B, C and D are as follows:

(a) Fixed bases,

$$
\left.
\begin{aligned}
(K_1+K_2)B+\frac{K_2}{2}C+\left(\frac{h}{f}K_1-K_2\right)R+\frac{h_1}{f}K_1R_1+FM_{BA}&=0, \\
(K_2+K_3+K_4)C+\frac{K_2}{2}B+\frac{K_3}{2}D-K_2R-\frac{h_1K_4}{h_1+f_1}R_1+FM_{CD}&=0, \\
(K_3+K_5)D+\frac{K_3}{2}C-K_5R_1+FM_{DC}&=0.
\end{aligned}
\right\} \quad (224)
$$

(b) Hinged bases,

$$
\left.
\begin{aligned}
(K_1+K_2)B+\frac{K_2}{2}C+\left(\frac{h}{f}K_1-K_2\right)R+\frac{h_1}{f}K_1R_1+FM_{BA}&=0, \\
\left(K_2+K_3+\frac{3}{4}K_4\right)C+\frac{K_2}{2}B+\frac{K_3}{2}D-K_2R-\frac{h_1K_4}{2(h_1+f_1)}R_1+FM_{CD}&=0, \\
\left(K_3+\frac{3}{4}K_5\right)D+\frac{K_3}{2}C-\frac{K_5}{2}R_1+FM_{DC}&=0.
\end{aligned}
\right\} \quad (224a)
$$

For simplicity, here, again, elimination of R and R_1 from eqs. (224) will be confined to the numerical solution of a given problem—as illustrated in the following example.

ILLUSTRATIVE EXAMPLE

The middle span of the symmetrical lean-to bent shown in Fig. 182 is loaded with a uniform load of 1 kip per linear foot. Assuming the bent fixed at the bases, determine the end moments.

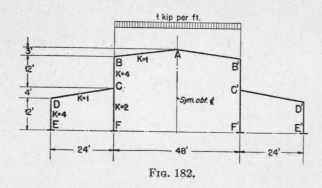

FIG. 182.

Solution: Applying eqs. (223) and (221), and noting that the load constant in the latter expressions reduces to $-\dfrac{ch}{2f}\dfrac{l^2}{8}w$, we have:

$$a=20, \quad b=16, \quad c=5\frac{1}{8};$$

$$R=0.288B+0.273C+0.288D-17.73,$$

$$R_1=-0.360B-0.153C+0.360D-13.84.$$

Substituting in eqs. (224),

$$3.558B+1.387C+1.442D=103.35,$$

$$1.387B+6.140C+1.113D=-91.68,$$

$$1.442B+1.113C+3.558D=55.35;$$

from which

$$B=48.81, \; C=-20.73, \; D=-28.85;$$

and

$$R=-0.99, \; R_1=-38.65, \; R_{AB}=158.56, \; R_{CF}=-28.99.$$

Accordingly, the end moments become:

$$M_{AB}=1(24.40-158.56)+48=-86.16;$$

$$M_{BA}=1(48.81-158.56)-48=-157.75,$$
$$M_{BC}=4(48.81-10.36+0.99)=157.76;$$

$$M_{CB}=4(-20.73+24.40+0.99)=18.64,$$
$$M_{CF}=2(-20.73+28.99)=16.52,$$
$$M_{CD}=1(-20.73-14.42)=-35.15;$$

$$M_{DC}=1(-28.85-10.36)=-39.21,$$
$$M_{DE}=4(-28.85+38.65)=39.20;$$

$$M_{ED}=4(-14.42+38.65)=96.92;$$

$$M_{FC}=2(-10.36+28.99)=37.26.$$

PROBLEMS

61. The symmetrical gabled bent shown in Fig. 183 has two rectangular lean-to panels. Derive the deflection expressions, eqs. (221) and (222), corresponding to two conditions of support:

    (*a*) Fixed bases;

    (*b*) Hinged bases.

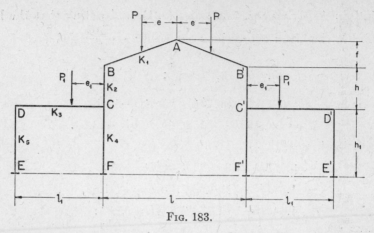

FIG. 183.

62. Assuming that a uniform load of 1 kip is applied to the roof members DC and $D'C'$ of the symmetrical bent shown in Fig. 182, determine the end moments for fixed bases.

62. Symmetrical, Gabled Lean-to Bent with Unsymmetrical Vertical Loading.—When the loading is applied unsymmetrically, as is shown in Fig. 184, the deflections of the members for the two halves

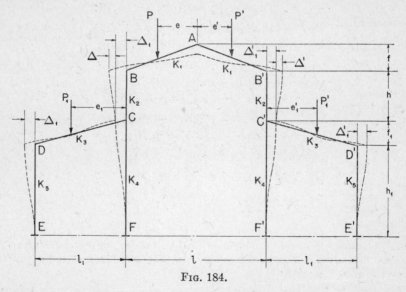

FIG. 184.

of the bent will differ. As indicated by the dotted lines outlining the exaggerated deformations, there are four independent deflections: Δ and Δ' of the members BC and $B'C'$, respectively, the common deflection Δ_1 of the members DE and CF, and the deflection Δ_1' of the members $D'E'$ and $C'F'$. The deflections of the roof members

AB and AB' are dependent upon the relative spread of joints B and B', and, therefore, may be expressed in terms of the other four deflections. With the usual notations of the deflection terms R, corresponding to Δ, Δ', Δ_1 and Δ_1', for simplicity assumed as positive quantities, we can write:

$$\left.\begin{aligned} R_{BC}&=\frac{\Delta}{h}=R, \quad R_{B'C'}=\frac{\Delta'}{h}=R'; \\ R_{DE}&=\frac{\Delta_1}{h_1}=R_1, \quad R_{D'E'}=\frac{\Delta_1'}{h_1}=R_1'; \\ R_{CF}&=\frac{\Delta_1}{f_1+h_1}=\frac{h_1}{f_1+h_1}R_1, \; R_{C'F'}=\frac{\Delta_1'}{f_1+h_1}=\frac{h_1}{f_1+h_1}R_1'; \end{aligned}\right\} \quad \ldots\ldots (a)$$

$$R_{AB}=-R_{AB'}=\frac{\Delta'+\Delta_1'}{2f}+\frac{\Delta+\Delta_1}{2f}=\frac{1}{2f}[h(R'-R)+h_1(R_1'-R_1)] \quad (225)$$

The four expressions for deflections R are derived in a manner similar to that of other gabled bents. First, considering the portion $CBAB'C'$, it is noted that the horizontal shears or reactions of members AB and BC must balance at joint B, as must those of members AB' and $B'C'$ at joint B'.

Thus

$$\left.\begin{aligned} \frac{1}{h}(M_{BC}+M_{CB})&=\frac{1}{f}\Big(M_{AB}+M_{BA}+\frac{Vl}{2}-Pe\Big), \\ \frac{1}{h}(M_{B'C'}+M_{C'B'})&=\frac{1}{f}\Big(M_{AB'}+M_{B'A}-V'\frac{l}{2}+P'e'\Big); \end{aligned}\right\} \quad \ldots (b)$$

in which V and V' indicate the vertical reactions at joints B and B', respectively, and their values are obtained from the relations

$$\left.\begin{aligned} Vl+(M_{BA}+M_{B'A})-P\Big(\frac{l}{2}+e\Big)-P'\Big(\frac{l}{2}-e'\Big)&=0, \\ -V'l+(M_{BA}+M_{B'A})+P\Big(\frac{l}{2}-e\Big)+P'\Big(\frac{l}{2}+e'\Big)&=0. \end{aligned}\right\} \quad \ldots (c)$$

Substituting in eqs. (b),

$$\left.\begin{aligned} M_{BC}+M_{CB}&=\frac{h}{f}\Big[M_{AB}+\frac{1}{2}M_{BA}-\frac{1}{2}M_{B'A}+\frac{P}{2}\Big(\frac{l}{2}-e\Big)+\frac{P'}{2}\Big(\frac{l}{2}-e'\Big)\Big], \\ M_{B'C'}+M_{C'B'}&=\frac{h}{f}\Big[M_{AB'}-\frac{1}{2}M_{BA}+\frac{1}{2}M_{B'A}-\frac{P}{2}\Big(\frac{l}{2}-e\Big)-\frac{P'}{2}\Big(\frac{l}{2}-e'\Big)\Big]. \end{aligned}\right\} (d)$$

Also, substituting values of the end moments,

$$-\Big(2K_2+\frac{h^2}{f^2}K_1\Big)R+\frac{h^2}{f^2}K_1R'-\frac{hh_1}{f^2}K_1(R_1-R_1')=-\frac{3}{2}K_2(B+C)$$

$$+\frac{h}{f}\Big[K_1A+K_1B-\frac{K_1}{2}B'+FM_{AB}+\frac{1}{2}FM_{BA}-\frac{1}{2}FM_{B'A}$$

$$+\frac{P}{2}\Big(\frac{l}{2}-e\Big)+\frac{P'}{2}\Big(\frac{l}{2}-e'\Big)\Big], \quad \ldots\ldots\ldots (e)$$

$$-\left(2K_2+\frac{h^2}{f^2}K_1\right)R'+\frac{h^2}{f^2}K_1R+\frac{hh_1}{f^2}K_1(R_1-R_1')=-\frac{3}{2}K_2(B'+C')$$

$$+\frac{h}{f}\Big[K_1A-\frac{K_1}{2}B+K_1B'+FM_{AB'}-\frac{1}{2}FM_{BA}+\frac{1}{2}FM_{B'A}$$

$$-\frac{P}{2}\Big(\frac{l}{2}-e\Big)-\frac{P'}{2}\Big(\frac{l}{2}-e'\Big)\Big], \quad \cdots \cdots \cdots \cdots \quad (f)$$

The other two expressions, obtained from shear equations above and below joints C and C', are given by eqs. $(d1)$ and $(e1)$, Art. 61:

(a) Fixed bases,

$$\left.\begin{array}{l} R=\left[\dfrac{h}{h_1}\dfrac{K_5}{K_2}+\dfrac{hh_1}{(f_1+h_1)^2}\dfrac{K_4}{K_2}\right]R_1+\dfrac{3}{4}B \\[2mm] +\dfrac{3}{4}\left[1-\dfrac{h}{(f_1+h_1)}\dfrac{K_4}{K_2}\right]C-\dfrac{3}{4}\dfrac{hK_5}{h_1K_2}D, \\[3mm] R'=\left[\dfrac{h}{h_1}\dfrac{K_5}{K_2}+\dfrac{hh_1}{(f_1+h_1)^2}\dfrac{K_4}{K_2}\right]R_1'+\dfrac{3}{4}B' \\[2mm] +\dfrac{3}{4}\left[1-\dfrac{h}{(f_1+h_1)}\dfrac{K_4}{K_2}\right]C'-\dfrac{3}{4}\dfrac{hK_5}{h_1K_2}D'. \end{array}\right\} \quad \cdots \quad (226)$$

(b) Hinged bases,

$$\left.\begin{array}{l} R=\dfrac{1}{4}\left[\dfrac{h}{h_1}\dfrac{K_5}{K_2}+\dfrac{hh_1}{(f_1+h_1)^2}\dfrac{K_4}{K_2}\right]R_1+\dfrac{3}{4}B \\[2mm] +\dfrac{3}{4}\left[1-\dfrac{h}{2(f_1+h_1)}\dfrac{K_4}{K_2}\right]C-\dfrac{3}{8}\dfrac{hK_5}{h_1K_2}D, \\[3mm] R'=\dfrac{1}{4}\left[\dfrac{h}{h_1}\dfrac{K_5}{K_2}+\dfrac{hh_1}{(f_1+h_1)^2}\dfrac{K_4}{K_2}\right]R_1'+\dfrac{3}{4}B' \\[2mm] +\dfrac{3}{4}\left[1-\dfrac{h}{2(f_1+h_1)}\dfrac{K_4}{K_2}\right]C'-\dfrac{3}{8h_1}\dfrac{hK_5}{K_2}D'. \end{array}\right\} \quad \cdots \quad (227)$$

Expressions for R_1 and R_1' may be had from eqs. (e) and (f) by substituting the values of R and R' from eqs. (226) and (227):

(a) Fixed bases,

$$-\Big\{\Big(\frac{K_2}{K_1}+\frac{h^2}{f^2}\Big)\Big[\frac{h}{h_1}\frac{K_5}{K_2}+\frac{hh_1}{(f_1+h_1)^2}\frac{K_4}{K_2}\Big]+\frac{hh_1}{f^2}\Big\}K_1R_1$$

$$+\Big\{\frac{h^2}{f^2}\Big[\frac{h}{h_1}\frac{K_5}{K_2}+\frac{hh_1}{(f_1+h_1)^2}\frac{K_4}{K_2}\Big]+\frac{hh_1}{f^2}\Big\}K_1R_1'=\frac{h}{f}K_1A+\Big(\frac{h}{f}+\frac{3}{4}\frac{h^2}{f^2}\Big)K_1B$$

$$-\Big(\frac{h}{2f}+\frac{3}{4}\frac{h^2}{f^2}\Big)K_1B'+\frac{3}{4}\Big[\frac{h^2}{f^2}K_1-\frac{hK_4}{f_1+h_1}\Big(2+\frac{h_2}{f^2}\frac{K_1}{K_2}\Big)\Big]C$$

$$-\frac{3}{4}\frac{h^2}{f^2}K_1\Big[1-\frac{h}{f_1+h_1}\frac{K_4}{K_2}\Big]C'-\frac{3}{4}\frac{h}{h_1}K_5\Big(2+\frac{h^2}{f^2}\frac{K_1}{K_2}\Big)D+\frac{3}{4}\frac{h^2}{f^2}\frac{hK_5}{h_1K_2}K_1D'$$

$$+\frac{h}{f}\Big[FM_{AB}+\frac{1}{2}FM_{BA}-\frac{1}{2}FM_{B'A}+\frac{P}{2}\Big(\frac{l}{2}-e\Big)+\frac{P'}{2}\Big(\frac{l}{2}-e'\Big)\Big], \quad (228)$$

$$-\left\{\left(2\frac{K_2}{K_1}+\frac{h^2}{f^2}\right)\left[\frac{h}{h_1}\frac{K_5}{K_2}+\frac{hh_1}{(f_1+h_1)^2}\frac{K_4}{K_2}\right]+\frac{hh_1}{f^2}\right\}K_1R_1'$$

$$+\left\{\frac{h^2}{f^2}\left[\frac{h}{h_1}\frac{K_5}{K_2}+\frac{hh_1}{(f_1+h_1)^2}\frac{K_4}{K_2}\right]+\frac{hh_1}{f^2}\right\}K_1R_1=\frac{h}{f}K_1A$$

$$-\left(\frac{h}{2f}+\frac{3}{4}\frac{h^2}{f^2}\right)K_1B+\left(\frac{h}{f}+\frac{3}{4}\frac{h^2}{f^2}\right)K_1B'-\frac{3}{4}\frac{h^2}{f^2}K_1\left[1-\frac{h}{f_1+h_1}\cdot\frac{K_4}{K_2}\right]C$$

$$+\frac{3}{4}\left[\frac{h^2}{f^2}K_1-\frac{hK_4}{f_1+h_1}\left(2+\frac{h^2}{f^2}\frac{K_1}{K_2}\right)\right]C'+\frac{3}{4}\frac{h^2}{f^2h_1}\frac{K_5}{K_2}K_1D$$

$$-\frac{3}{4}\frac{h}{h_1}K_5\left(2+\frac{h^2}{f^2}\frac{K_1}{K_2}\right)D'+\frac{h}{f}\left[FM_{AB'}-\frac{1}{2}FM_{BA}+\frac{1}{2}FM_{B'A}\right.$$

$$\left.-\frac{P}{2}\left(\frac{l}{2}-e\right)-\frac{P}{2}\left(\frac{l}{2}-e'\right)\right]; \quad \dots \dots \dots \dots \quad (228a)$$

(b) Hinged bases,

$$-\left\{\frac{1}{4}\left(\frac{2K_2}{K_1}+\frac{h^2}{f^2}\right)\left[\frac{h}{h_1}\frac{K_5}{K_2}+\frac{hh_1}{(f_1+h_1)^2}\frac{K_4}{K_2}\right]+\frac{hh_1}{f^2}\right\}K_1R_1+\left\{\frac{h^2}{4f^2}\left[\frac{h}{h_1}\frac{K_5}{K_2}\right.\right.$$

$$\left.\left.+\frac{hh_1}{(f_1+h_1)^2}\right]\frac{K_4}{K_2}+\frac{hh_1}{f^2}\right\}K_1R_1'=\frac{h}{f}K_1A+\left(\frac{h}{f}+\frac{3h^2}{4f^2}\right)K_1B-\left(\frac{h}{2f}\right.$$

$$\left.+\frac{3}{4}\frac{h^2}{f^2}\right)K_1B'+\frac{3}{4}\left[\frac{h^2}{f^2}K_1-\frac{hK_4}{2(f_1+h_1)}\left(2+\frac{h^2K_1}{f^2K_2}\right)\right]C-\frac{3}{4}\cdot\frac{h^2}{f^2}K_1\left[1\right.$$

$$\left.-\frac{h}{2(f_1+h_1)}\cdot\frac{K_4}{K_2}\right]C'-\frac{3}{8}\frac{h}{h_1}\frac{K_5}{K_2}\left(2K_2+\frac{h^2}{f^2}K_1\right)D+\frac{3}{8}\frac{h^2h}{f^2h_1}\frac{K_5}{K_2}K_1D'$$

$$+\frac{h}{f}\left[FM_{AB}+\frac{1}{2}FM_{BA}-\frac{1}{2}FM_{B'A}+\frac{P}{2}\left(\frac{l}{2}-e\right)+\frac{P'}{2}\left(\frac{l}{2}-e'\right)\right], \quad (229)$$

$$-\left\{\frac{1}{4}\left(\frac{2K_2}{K_1}+\frac{h^2}{f^2}\right)\left[\frac{h}{h_1}\frac{K_5}{K_2}+\frac{hh_1}{(f_1+h_1)^2}\frac{K_4}{K_2}\right]+\frac{hh_1}{f^2}\right\}K_1R_1'$$

$$+\left\{\frac{h^2}{4f^2}\left[\frac{h}{h_1}\frac{K_5}{K_2}+\frac{hh_1}{(f_1+h_1)^2}\frac{K_4}{K_2}\right]+\frac{hh_1}{f^2}\right\}K_1R_1=\frac{h}{f}K_1A-\left(\frac{h}{2f}+\frac{3h^2}{4f^2}\right)K_1B$$

$$+\left(\frac{h}{f}+\frac{3h^2}{4f^2}\right)K_1B'-\frac{3h^2}{4f^2}K_1\left[1-\frac{h}{2(f_1+h_1)}\frac{K_4}{K_2}\right]C$$

$$+\frac{3}{4}\left[\frac{h^2}{f^2}K_1-\frac{hK_4}{2(f_1+h_1)}\left(2+\frac{h^2K_1}{f^2K_2}\right)\right]C'+\frac{3h^2h}{8f^2h_1}\frac{K_5}{K_2}K_1D$$

$$-\frac{3}{8}\frac{h}{h_1}\frac{K_5}{K_2}\left(2K_2+\frac{h^2}{f^2}K_1\right)D'+\frac{h}{f}\left[FM_{AB'}-\frac{1}{2}FM_{BA}+\frac{1}{2}FM_{B'A}\right.$$

$$\left.-\frac{P}{2}\left(\frac{l}{2}-e\right)-\frac{P'}{2}\left(\frac{l}{2}-e'\right)\right] \quad \dots \dots \dots \dots \quad (229a)$$

If the concentrated loads P and P' be replaced by uniform loads of intensity w and w' per horizontal linear foot, respectively, the corresponding load factors in eqs. (228) and (229) become

$$\frac{h}{f}\left[\frac{7}{96}wl^2+\frac{5}{96}w_1l^2\right] \quad \dots \dots \dots \dots \quad (g)$$

and in eqs. (228a) and (229a),

$$-\frac{h}{f}\left[\frac{5}{96}wl^2+\frac{7}{96}w_1l^2\right] \quad \dots \dots \dots \dots \quad (h)$$

The joint expressions are in the following forms:

(a) Fixed bases,

$$2K_1A+\frac{K_1}{2}B+\frac{K_1}{2}B'+FM_{AB}+FM_{AB'}=0,$$

$$(K_1+K_2)B+\frac{K_1}{2}A+\frac{K_2}{2}C+\left(\frac{h}{2f}K_1-K_2\right)R-\frac{h}{2f}K_1R'$$
$$+\frac{h_1}{2f}K_1(R_1-R_1')+FM_{BA}=0,$$

$$(K_1+K_2)B'+\frac{K_1}{2}A+\frac{K_2}{2}C'+\left(\frac{h}{2f}K_1-K_2\right)R'-\frac{h}{2f}K_1R$$
$$-\frac{h_1}{2f}K_1(R_1-R_1')+FM_{B'A}=0,$$

$$(K_2+K_3+K_4)C+\frac{K_2}{2}B+\frac{K_3}{2}D-K_2R-\frac{h_1}{f_1+h_1}K_4R_1+FM_{CD}=0,$$

$$(K_2+K_3+K_4)C'+\frac{K_2}{2}B'+\frac{K_3}{2}D'-K_2R'-\frac{h_1}{f_1+h_1}K_4R_1'$$
$$+FM_{C'D'}=0,$$

$$(K_3+K_5)D+\frac{K_3}{2}C-K_5R_1+FM_{DC}=0,$$

$$(K_3+K_5)D'+\frac{K_3}{2}C'-K_5R_1'+FM_{D'C'}=0;$$

$$(230)$$

(b) Hinged bases,

$$2K_1A+\frac{K_1}{2}B+\frac{K_1}{2}B'+FM_{AB}+FM_{AB'}=0,$$

$$(K_1+K_2)B+\frac{K_1}{2}A+\frac{K_2}{2}C+\left(\frac{h}{2f}K_1-K_2\right)R-\frac{h}{2f}K_1R'$$
$$+\frac{h_1}{2f}K_1(R_1-R_1')+FM_{BA}=0,$$

$$(K_1+K_2)B'+\frac{K_1}{2}A+\frac{K_2}{2}C'+\left(\frac{h}{2f}K_1-K_2\right)R'-\frac{h}{2f}K_1R$$
$$-\frac{h_1}{2f}K_1(R_1-R_1')+FM_{B'A}=0,$$

$$\left(K_2+K_3+\frac{3}{4}K_4\right)C+\frac{K_2}{2}B+\frac{K_3}{2}D-K_2R-\frac{h_1}{2(f_1+h_1)}K_4R_1$$
$$+FM_{CD}=0,$$

$$\left(K_2+K_3+\frac{3}{4}K_4\right)C'+\frac{K_2}{2}B'+\frac{K_3}{2}D'-K_2R'-\frac{h_1}{2(f_1+h_1)}K_4R_1'$$
$$+FM_{C'D'}=0,$$

$$\left(K_3+\frac{3}{4}K_5\right)D+\frac{K_3}{2}C-\frac{K_5R_1}{2}+FM_{DC}=0,$$

$$\left(K_3+\frac{3}{4}K_5\right)D'+\frac{K_3}{2}C'-\frac{K_5R_1'}{2}+FM_{D'C'}=0.$$

$$(230a)$$

As illustrated in the following example, elimination of deflection terms R, R', R_1 and R_1' from joint expressions is more conveniently made in the numerical solution of a given problem.

ILLUSTRATIVE EXAMPLE

The symmetrical bent shown in Fig. 185 carries an unsymmetrical uniform load, applied to roof member AB. Assuming the legs to be fixed at the bases, determine the end moments.

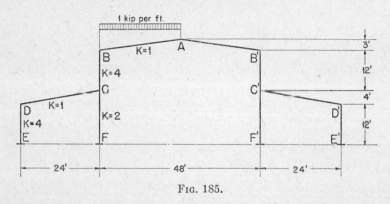

Fig. 185.

Solution: From eqs. (228) we have:

$$-46.75R_1+36.50R_1'=4A+16B-14B'+5.25C-7.50C'-18D+12D'+672,$$

$$36.50R_1-46.75R_1'=4A-14B+16B'-7.50C+5.25C'+12D-18D'-480;$$

or

$$R_1=-0.390A-0.278B+0.083B'+0.033C+0.186C'+0.473D+0.112D'-16.285,$$

$$R_1'=-0.390A+0.083B-0.278B'+0.186C+0.033C'+0.112D+0.473D'-2.447.$$

Applying eqs. (226),

$$R=-0.500A+0.394B+0.106B'+0.511C+0.238C'-0.144D+0.144D'-20.865,$$

$$R_1=-0.500A+0.106B+0.394B'+0.238C+0.511C'+0.144D-0.144D'-3.135.$$

Substituting these values for the deflection terms in the joint expressions, eqs. (230),

$$2.0A + 0.5B + 0.5B' = -48.000,$$

$$2.5A + 3.278B - 0.278B' + 0.194C - 1.194C' + 0.722D - 0.722D' = 27.676,$$

$$2.5A - 0.278B + 3.278B' - 1.194C + 0.194C' - 0.722D + 0.722D'$$
$$= -75.676,$$

$$2.585A + 0.841B - 0.548B' + 4.907C - 1.231C' + 0.368D - 0.744D'$$
$$= -107.887,$$

$$2.585A - 0.548B + 0.841B' - 1.231C + 4.907C' - 0.744D + 0.368D'$$
$$= -16.210,$$

$$1.56A + 1.112B - 0.332B' + 0.368C - 0.744C' + 3.108D - 0.448D'$$
$$= -65.140,$$

$$1.56A - 0.332B + 1.112B' - 0.744C + 0.368C' - 0.448D + 3.108D'$$
$$= -9.788;$$

from which, by tabular solution of the unknowns, we find:

$$A = -36.211, \quad B = 48.829, \quad C = -3.628, \quad D = -13.481,$$
$$B' = 0.015, \quad C' = 17.105, \quad D' = 15.367;$$

and

$$R = 22.874, \quad R_1 = -17.294, \quad R_{CF} = -12.970,$$
$$R_{AB} = 79.290, \quad R' = 23.868, \quad R_1' = 21.357, \quad R_{C'F'} = 16.018.$$

With these values, the end moments of the members become:

$$M_{AB} = -36.211 + 24.414 - 79.290 + 48 = -43.087,$$
$$M_{AB'} = -36.211 + 0.008 + 79.290 = 43.087;$$

$$M_{BA} = 48.829 - 18.105 - 79.290 - 48 = -96.566,$$
$$M_{BC} = 4(48.829 - 1.814 - 22.874) = 96.564;$$

$$M_{B'A} = 0.015 - 18.105 + 79.290 = 61.200,$$
$$M_{B'C'} = 4(0.015 + 8.553 - 23.868) = -61.200;$$

$$M_{CB} = 4(-3.628 + 24.415 - 22.874) = -8.348,$$
$$M_{CF} = 2(-3.628 + 0 + 12.970) = 18.684,$$
$$M_{CD} = -3.628 - 6.740 = -10.368;$$

$$M_{C'B'} = 4(17.105 + 0.008 - 23.868) = -27.020,$$
$$M_{C'F'} = 2(17.105 + 0 - 16.018) = 2.174,$$
$$M_{C'D'} = 17.105 + 7.684 = 24.789;$$

$$M_{DC} = -13.481 - 1.814 = -15.295,$$
$$M_{DE} = 4(-13.481 + 0 + 17.294) = 15.252;$$

$$M_{D'C'} = 15.367 + 8.553 = 23.920,$$
$$M_{D'E'} = 4(15.367 + 0 - 21.357) = -23.960;$$

$$M_{ED} = 4(0 - 6.740 + 17.294) = 42.216;$$

$$M_{FC} = 2(0 - 1.814 + 12.970) = 22.312;$$

$$M_{F'C'} = 2(0 + 8.553 - 16.018) = -14.930;$$

$$M_{E'D'} = 4(0 + 7.684 - 21.357) = -54.692.$$

PROBLEMS

63. Assuming the lower roof members CD and $C'D'$ of the bent shown in **Fig.** 184 to be horizontal, that is, $f_1 = 0$, obtain deflection expressions corresponding to eqs. (228) and (229).

64. Determine the end moment of the bent shown in Fig. 185 for a uniform load of 1 kip per linear foot applied to lower roof member CD. The legs of the bent are assumed to be fixed at the bases.

63. Symmetrical, Gabled Lean-to Bent with Unsymmetrical Lateral Loading.—Fig. 186 illustrates the case of a bent carrying unsym-

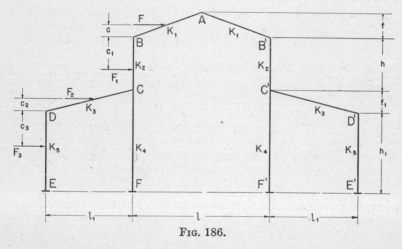

FIG. 186.

metrically applied lateral loading. Except for the load constants, the expressions derived in the preceding article are equally applicable in this instance. In obtaining these constants, the usual procedure is followed. First, considering the horizontal shear just above and below the joint B, from members AB and BC we have:

$$\frac{1}{f}\left[M_{AB} + M_{BA} - V\frac{l}{2} - F(f - c)\right] = \frac{1}{h}[M_{BC} + M_{CB} + F_1(h - c_1)] \quad . \quad (a)$$

and at B', from members AB' and $B'C'$,

$$\frac{1}{f}\left(M_{AB'} + M_{B'A} - V\frac{l}{2}\right) = \frac{1}{h}(M_{B'C'} + M_{C'B'}) \quad . \quad . \quad . \quad . \quad (b)$$

in which V indicates the vertical shear couple at B and B', and its value is given by the relation

$$-Vl+(M_{BA}+M_{B'A})+Fc=0 \quad\ldots\ldots\ldots \quad (c)$$

Substituting in eqs. (a) and (b),

$$\left.\begin{aligned} M_{BC}+M_{CB}&=\frac{h}{f}\left[M_{AB}+\frac{1}{2}M_{BA}-\frac{1}{2}M_{B'A}-F\left(f-\frac{c}{2}\right)\right]-F_1(h-c_1),\\ M_{B'C'}+M_{C'B'}&=\frac{h}{f}\left[M_{AB'}-\frac{1}{2}M_{BA}+\frac{1}{2}M_{B'A}-F\frac{c}{2}\right]. \end{aligned}\right\} \cdot (d)$$

Similarly, at joints C and C', from the shear equations of members BC, CF and DE, and $B'C'$, $C'F'$ and $D'E'$ we obtain:

$$\left.\begin{aligned} \frac{1}{h}(M_{BC}+M_{CB}-F_1c_1)&=\frac{1}{f_1+h_1}(M_{CF}+M_{FC})\\ &+\frac{1}{h_1}[M_{DE}+M_{ED}+F_3(h_1-c_3)]+F_2,\\ \frac{1}{h}(M_{B'C'}+M_{C'B'})&=\frac{1}{f_1+h_1}(M_{C'F'}+M_{F'C'})+\frac{1}{h_1}(M_{D'E'}+M_{E'D'}). \end{aligned}\right\} \cdot (e)$$

Denoting the deflection terms of members BC, $B'C'$, DE and $D'E'$ respectively by R, R', R_1 and R_1', and those of members CF, $C'F'$ and AB as given by eqs. (a) and (225) of Art. 62, for eqs. (d) we can write:

$$-\left(2K_2+\frac{h^2}{f^2}K_1\right)R+\frac{h^2}{f^2}K_1R'-\frac{hh_1}{f^2}K_1(R_1-R_1')=-\frac{3}{2}K_2(B+C)$$
$$+\frac{h}{f}\left[K_1A+K_1B-\frac{K_1}{2}B'+FM_{AB}+\frac{1}{2}FM_{BA}-F\left(f-\frac{c}{2}\right)\right]$$
$$-F_1(h-c_1)-(FM_{BC}+FM_{CB}),\ldots\ldots\ldots\ldots \quad (f)$$

$$-\left(2K_2+\frac{h^2}{f^2}K_1\right)R'+\frac{h^2}{f^2}K_1R+\frac{hh_1}{f^2}K_1(R_1-R_1')=-\frac{3}{2}K_2(B'+C')$$
$$+\frac{h}{f}\left[K_1A-\frac{K_1}{2}B+K_1B'-\frac{1}{2}FM_{BA}-F\frac{c}{2}\right]\ldots\ldots\ldots \quad (g)$$

Similar substitutions of the values of end moments in eqs. (e), corresponding to two conditions of support, will give:

(a) Fixed bases,

$$R=\left[\frac{h}{h_1}\frac{K_5}{K_2}+\frac{hh_1}{(f_1+h_1)^2}\cdot\frac{K_4}{K_2}\right]R_1+\frac{3}{4}B+\frac{3}{4}\left[1-\frac{h}{(f_1+h_1)}\cdot\frac{K_4}{K_2}\right]C$$
$$-\frac{3}{4}\frac{h}{h_1}\frac{K_5}{K_2}D+\frac{1}{2K_2}\left[(FM_{BC}+FM_{CB})-F_1c_1-\frac{h}{h_1}(FM_{DE}+FM_{ED})\right.$$
$$\left.-\frac{h}{h_1}(h_1-c_3)F_3-hF_2\right],\quad\ldots\ldots\ldots\ldots \quad (231)$$

$$R' = \left[\frac{h}{h}\frac{K_5}{K_2} + \frac{hh_1}{(f_1+h_1)^2}\cdot\frac{K_4}{K_2}\right]R_1' + \frac{3}{4}B' + \frac{3}{4}\left[1 - \frac{h}{(f_1+h_1)}\cdot\frac{K_4}{K_2}\right]C'$$
$$- \frac{3hK_5}{4h_1K_2}D' \quad \ldots \ldots \ldots \quad (231a)$$

(b) Hinged bases,

$$R = \frac{1}{4}\left[\frac{h}{h_1}\frac{K_5}{K_2} + \frac{hh_1}{(f_1+h_1)^2}\cdot\frac{K_4}{K_2}\right]R_1 + \frac{3}{4}B + \frac{3}{4}\left[1 - \frac{h}{2(f_1+h_1)}\cdot\frac{K_4}{K_2}\right]C$$
$$- \frac{3}{8}\frac{h}{h_1}\frac{K_5}{K_2}D + \frac{1}{2K_2}\left[(FM_{BC}+FM_{CB}) - F_1c_1 - \frac{h}{h_1}(HM_{DE})\right.$$
$$\left. - \frac{h}{h_1}(h_1-c_3)F_3 - hF_2\right], \quad \ldots \ldots \ldots \ldots \ldots \quad (232)$$

$$R' = \frac{1}{4}\left[\frac{h}{h_1}\frac{K_5}{K_1} + \frac{hh_1}{(f_1+h_1)^2}\cdot\frac{K_4}{K_2}\right]R_1' + \frac{3}{4}B' + \frac{3}{4}\left[1 - \frac{h}{2(f_1+h_1)}\cdot\frac{K_4}{K_2}\right]C'$$
$$- \frac{3}{8}\frac{h}{h_1}\frac{K_5}{K_2}D'. \quad \ldots \ldots \ldots \ldots \quad (232a)$$

The two expressions for R_1 and R_1' may be obtained by substituting the values of R and R' from eqs. (231) and (232) in eqs. (f) and (g):

(a) Fixed bases,

$$-\left\{\left(2\frac{K_2}{K_1} + \frac{h^2}{f^2}\right)\left[\frac{h}{h_1}\frac{K_5}{K_2} + \frac{hh_1}{(f_1+h_1)^2}\frac{K_4}{K_2}\right] + \frac{hh_1}{f^2}\right\}K_1R_1$$
$$+\left\{\frac{h^2}{f^2}\left[\frac{h}{h_1}\frac{K_5}{K_2} + \frac{hh_1}{(f_1+h_1)^2}\frac{K_4}{K_2}\right] + \frac{hh_1}{f^2}\right\}K_1R_1' = \frac{h}{f}K_1A$$
$$+\left(\frac{h}{f} + \frac{3}{4}\cdot\frac{h^2}{f^2}\right)K_1B - \left(\frac{h}{2f} + \frac{3}{4}\frac{h^2}{f^2}\right)K_1B' + \frac{3}{4}\left[\frac{h^2}{f^2}K_1\right.$$
$$- \frac{hK_4}{(f_1+h_1)}\left(2 + \frac{h^2}{f^2}\frac{K_1}{K_2}\right)\right]C - \frac{3}{4}\frac{h^2}{f^2}K_1\left[1 - \frac{h}{(f_1+h_1)}\frac{K_4}{K_2}\right]C'$$
$$- \frac{h}{h_1}K_5\left(2 + \frac{h^2}{f^2}\frac{K_1}{K_2}\right)D + \frac{3}{4}\frac{h^2h}{f^2h_1}\frac{K_5}{K_2}K_1D'$$
$$+\frac{h}{f}\left[FM_{AB} + \frac{1}{2}FM_{BA} - F\left(f - \frac{c}{2}\right)\right] - F_1(h-c_1) - (FM_{BC}+FM_{CB})$$
$$+\left(1 + \frac{h^2}{2f^2}\frac{K_1}{K_2}\right)\left[(FM_{BC}+FM_{CB}) - P_1e_1 - \frac{h}{h_1}(FM_{DE}+FM_{ED})\right.$$
$$\left. - \frac{h}{h_1}(h_1-c_3)F_3 - hF_2\right], \quad \ldots \ldots \ldots \ldots \quad (233)$$

$$-\left\{\left(2\frac{K_2}{K_1}+\frac{h^2}{f^2}\right)\left[\frac{h}{h_1}\frac{K_5}{K_2}+\frac{hh_1}{(f_1+h_1)^2}\cdot\frac{K_4}{K_2}\right]+\frac{hh_1}{f^2}\right\}K_1R_1{}'$$

$$+\left\{\frac{h^2}{f^2}\left(\frac{h}{h_1}\frac{K_5}{K_2}+\frac{hh_1}{(f_1+h_1)^2}\cdot\frac{K_4}{K_2}\right)\frac{hh_1}{f^2}\right\}K_1R_1=\frac{h}{f}K_1A-\left(\frac{h}{2f}+\frac{3}{4}\frac{h^2}{f^2}\right)K_1B$$

$$+\left(\frac{h}{f}+\frac{3h^2}{4f^2}\right)K_1B'-\frac{3}{4}\frac{h^2}{f^2}K_1\left(1-\frac{h}{(f_1+h_1)}\cdot\frac{K_4}{K_2}\right)C$$

$$+\frac{3}{4}\left[\frac{h^2}{f^2}K_1-\frac{hK_4}{(f_1+h_1)}\left(2+\frac{h^2K_1}{f^2K_2}\right)\right]C'+\frac{3}{4}\cdot\frac{h^2}{f^2}\frac{h}{h_1}\cdot\frac{K_5}{K_2}K_1D$$

$$-\frac{3}{4}\frac{h}{h_1}K_5\left(2+\frac{h^2}{f^2}\cdot\frac{K_1}{K_2}\right)D'-\frac{h}{2f}(FM_{BA}+Fc)-$$

$$\frac{h^2}{2f^2}\cdot\frac{K_1}{K_2}\Big[(FM_{BC}+FM_{CB})-F_1c_1-\frac{h}{h_1}(FM_{DE}+FM_{ED})$$

$$-\frac{h}{h_1}(h_1-c_3)F_3-hF_2\Big]; \quad\ldots\ldots\ldots\ldots\ldots\ldots\quad (233a)$$

(b) Hinged cases,

$$-\left\{\frac{1}{4}\left(\frac{2K_2}{K_1}+\frac{h^2}{f^2}\right)\left[\frac{h}{h_1}\frac{K_5}{K_2}+\frac{hh_1}{(f_1+h_1)^2}\cdot\frac{K_4}{K_2}\right]+\frac{hh_1}{f^2}\right\}K_1R_1$$

$$+\left\{\frac{h^2}{4f^2}\left[\frac{h}{h_1}\frac{K_5}{K_2}+\frac{hh_1}{(f_1+h_1)^2}\cdot\frac{K_4}{K_2}\right]+\frac{hh_1}{f^2}\right\}K_1R_1{}'$$

$$=\frac{h}{f}K_1A+\left(\frac{h}{f}+\frac{3h^2}{4f^2}\right)K_1B-\left(\frac{h}{2f}+\frac{3}{4}\frac{h^2}{f^2}\right)K_1B'$$

$$+\frac{3}{4}\left[\frac{h^2}{f^2}K_1-\frac{hK_4}{(f_1+h_1)}\left(2+\frac{h^2}{f^2}\frac{K_1}{K_2}\right)\right]C$$

$$-\frac{3}{4}\frac{h^2}{f^2}K_1\left[1-\frac{h}{2(f_1+h_1)}\cdot\frac{K_4}{K_2}\right]C'-\frac{3}{8}\frac{h}{h_1}\frac{K_5}{K_2}\left(2K_2+\frac{h^2}{f^2}K_1\right)D$$

$$+\frac{3}{8}\frac{h^2}{f^2}\frac{h}{h_1}\frac{K_5}{K_2}K_1D'+\frac{h}{f}\left(FM_{AB}+\frac{1}{2}FM_{BA}-F\left(f-\frac{c}{2}\right)\right]$$

$$-F_1(h-c_1)-(FM_{BC}+FM_{CB})+\left[1+\frac{h^2}{2f^2}\cdot\frac{K_1}{K_2}\left[\left((FM_{BC}\right.\right.\right.$$

$$+FM_{CB})-F_1c_1-\frac{h}{h_1}(HM_{DE})-\frac{h}{h_1}(h_1-c_3)F_3-hF_2\Big], \quad (234)$$

$$-\left\{\frac{1}{4}\left(\frac{2K_2}{K_1}+\frac{h^2}{f^2}\right)\left[\frac{h}{h_1}\frac{K_5}{K_2}+\frac{hh_1}{(f_1+h_1)^2}\cdot\frac{K_4}{K_2}\right]+\frac{hh_1}{f^2}\right\}K_1R_1{}'$$

$$+\frac{h^2}{4f^2}\left[\frac{hK_5}{h_1K_2}+\frac{hh_1}{(f_1+h_1)^2}\cdot\frac{K_4}{K_2}\right]+\frac{hh_1}{f^2}\Big\}K_1R_1=\frac{h}{f}K_1A-\left(\frac{h}{2f}+\frac{3h^2}{4f^2}\right)K_1B$$

$$+\left(\frac{h}{f}+\frac{3h^2}{4f^2}\right)K_1B'-\frac{3}{4}\frac{h^2}{f^2}K_1\left[1-\frac{h}{2(f_1+h_1)}\frac{K_4}{K_2}\right]C$$

$$+\frac{3}{4}\left[\frac{h^2}{f^2}K_1-\frac{hK_4}{(f_1+h_1)}\left(2+\frac{h^2K_1}{f^2K_2}\right)\right]C'+\frac{3}{8}\frac{h^2}{f^2}\frac{h}{h_1}\frac{K_5}{K_2}K_1D$$

$$-\frac{3}{8}\frac{h}{h_1}\frac{K_5}{K_2}\left(2K_2+\frac{h^2}{f^2}K_1\right)D'-\frac{h}{2f}(FM_{BA}+Fc)$$

$$-\frac{h^2K_1}{2f^2K_2}\Big[(FM_{BC}+FM_{CB})-F_1c_1-\frac{h}{h_1}(HM_{DE})$$

$$-\frac{h}{h_1}(h_1-c_3)F_3-hF_2)\Big] \quad\ldots\ldots\ldots\ldots\ldots\ldots\quad (234a)$$

When the loading is uniform, of intensity w per vertical foot, the load factors q in the foregoing equations assume the following simplified forms:

q in equation:

$$
\left.\begin{aligned}
(231) &= -\frac{wh}{2K_2}\left(\frac{h}{2}+\frac{h_1}{2}+f_1\right), \\[2mm]
(232) &= -\frac{wh}{2K_2}\left(\frac{h}{2}+\frac{5}{8}h_1+f_1\right), \\[2mm]
(233) &= -\frac{wh}{2}\left(\frac{17}{12}f+h\right)-wh\left(1+\frac{h^2K_1}{2f^2K_2}\right)\left(\frac{h}{2}+\frac{h_1}{2}+f_1\right), \\[2mm]
(233a) &= -\frac{5}{24}whf+\frac{wh^3K_1}{2f^2K_2}\left(\frac{h}{2}+\frac{h_1}{2}+f_1\right), \\[2mm]
(234) &= -\frac{wh}{2}\left(\frac{17}{12}f+h\right)-wh\left(1+\frac{h^2K_1}{2f^2K_2}\right)\left(\frac{h}{2}+\frac{5}{8}h_1+f_1\right), \\[2mm]
(234a) &= -\frac{5}{24}whf+\frac{wh^3K_1}{2f^2K_2}\left(\frac{h}{2}+\frac{5}{8}h_1+f_1\right).
\end{aligned}\right\} \quad (235)
$$

As in the preceding case, for the joint expressions we have:

(a) Fixed bases,

$$
\left.\begin{aligned}
& 2K_1A+\frac{K_1}{2}B+\frac{K_1}{2}B'+FM_{AB}=0, \\[2mm]
& (K_1+K_2)B+\frac{K_1}{2}A+\frac{K_2}{2}C+\left(\frac{h}{2f}K_1-K_2\right)R-\frac{h}{2f}K_1R' \\[1mm]
& \quad +\frac{h_1}{2f}K_1(R_1-R_1')+FM_{BA}+FM_{BC}=0, \\[2mm]
& (K_1+K_2)B'+\frac{K_1}{2}A+\frac{K_2}{2}C'+\left(\frac{h}{2f}K_1-K_2\right)R'-\frac{h}{2f}K_1R \\[1mm]
& \quad -\frac{h_1}{2f}K_1(R_1-R_1')=0, \\[2mm]
& (K_2+K_3+K_4)C+\frac{K_2}{2}B+\frac{K_3}{2}D-K_2R-\frac{h_1}{(f_1+h_1)}K_4R_1 \\[1mm]
& \quad +FM_{CB}+FM_{CD}=0, \\[2mm]
& (K_2+K_3+K_4)C'+\frac{K_2}{2}B'+\frac{K_3}{2}D'-K_2R' \\[1mm]
& \quad -\frac{h_1}{(f_1+h_1)}K_4R_1'=0, \\[2mm]
& (K_3+K_5)D+\frac{K_3}{2}C-K_5R_1+FM_{DC}+FM_{DE}=0, \\[2mm]
& (K_3+K_5)D'+\frac{K_3}{2}C'-K_5R_1'=0;
\end{aligned}\right\} \quad (230b)
$$

(b) Hinged bases,

$$2K_1A+\frac{K_1}{2}B+\frac{K_1}{2}B'+FM_{AB}=0,$$

$$(K_1+K_2)B+\frac{K_1}{2}A+\frac{K_2}{2}C+\left(\frac{h}{2f}K_1-K_2\right)R-\frac{h}{2f}K_1R'$$

$$+\frac{h_1}{2f}K_1(R_1-R_1')+FM_{BA}+FM_{BC}=0,$$

$$(K_1+K_2)B'+\frac{K_1}{2}A+\frac{K_2}{2}C'+\left(\frac{h}{2f}K_1-K_2\right)R'$$

$$-\frac{h}{2f}K_1R-\frac{h_1}{2f}K_1(R_1-R_1')=0,$$

$$\left(K_2+K_3+\frac{3}{4}K_4\right)C+\frac{K_2}{2}B+\frac{K_3}{2}D-K_2R$$

$$-\frac{h_1}{2(f_1+h_1)}\cdot K_4R_1+FM_{CB}+FM_{CD}=0,$$

$$\left(K_2+K_3+\frac{3}{4}K_4\right)C'+\frac{K_2}{2}B'+\frac{K_3}{2}D'-K_2R'$$

$$-\frac{h_1}{2(f_1+h_1)}K_4R_1'=0,$$

$$\left(K_3+\frac{3}{4}K_5\right)D+\frac{K_3}{2}C-\frac{K_5}{2}R_1+FM_{DC}+HM_{DE}=0,$$

$$\left(K_3+\frac{3}{4}K_5\right)D'+\frac{K_3}{2}C'-\frac{K_5}{2}R_1'=0.$$

$$. \quad (230c)$$

ILLUSTRATIVE EXAMPLE

The symmetrical bent in Fig. 185a is subjected to a uniform lateral load of 1 kip per vertical foot. Assuming the legs to be fixed at the bases, determine the end moments.

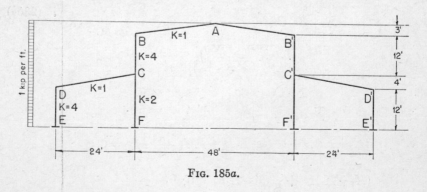

Fig. 185a.

Solution: From eqs. (233) and (235) we have:
$$-46.75R_1+36.50R_1'=4A+16B-14B'+5.25C-7.50C'-18D+12D'$$
$$-673.5,$$

$$36.50R_1-46.75R_1'=4A-14B+16B'-7.50C+5.25C'+12D-18D'$$
$$+376.5;$$

solving for R_1 and R_1',
$$R_1=-0.390A-0.278B+0.083B'+0.033C+0.186C'+0.473D$$
$$+0.112D'+20.794,$$

$$R_1'=-0.390A+0.083B-0.278B'+0.186C+0.033C'+0.112D$$
$$+0.473D'+8.182;$$

Applying eqs. 231,
$$R=-0.5A+0.394B+0.106B'+0.511C+0.238C'-0.144D+0.144D'$$
$$+2.643,$$

$$R_1=-0.5A+0.106B+0.394B'+0.238C+0.511C'+0.144D-0.144D'$$
$$+10.483;$$

Substituting in eqs. (230b),
$$2.0A+0.5B+0.5B'=0.750,$$

$$2.5A+3.278B-0.278B'+0.194C-1.194C'+0.722D-0.722D'$$
$$=-10.255,$$

$$2.5A-0.278B+3.278B'-1.194C+0.194C'-0.722D+0.722D'$$
$$=51.477,$$

$$2.585A+0.841B-0.548B'+4.907C-1.231C'+0.368D-0.744D'$$
$$=52.430,$$

$$2.585A-0.548B+0.841B'-1.231C+4.907C'-0.744D+0.368D'$$
$$=54.203,$$

$$1.560A+1.112B-0.332B'+0.368C-0.744C'+3.108D-0.448D'$$
$$=72.511,$$

$$1.560A-0.332B+1.112B'-0.744C+0.368C'-0.448D+3.108D'$$
$$=32.726;$$

from which
$$A=-13.477,\quad B=12.798,\quad C=25.234,\quad D=34.181,$$
$$B'=39.610,\quad C'=23.353,\quad D'=12.690,$$

and
$$R=33.981,\quad R'=48.546,\quad R_{CF}=36.409,$$
$$R_{AB}=-17.050,\quad R'=55.218,\quad R_1'=18.783,\quad R_{C'F'}=14.087,$$

The end moments become:

$$M_{AB} = -13.477 + 6.399 + 17.050 + 0.750 = 10.722,$$
$$M_{AB'} = -13.477 + 19.805 - 17.050 = -10.722;$$

$$M_{BA} = 12.798 - 6.739 + 17.050 - 0.750 = 22.359,$$
$$M_{BC} = 4(12.798 + 12.617 - 33.981) + 12 = -22.264;$$

$$M_{B'A} = 39.610 - 6.739 - 17.050 = 15.821,$$
$$M_{B'C'} = 4(39.610 + 11.676 - 55.218) = -15.728;$$

$$M_{CB} = 4(25.234 + 6.399 - 33.981) - 12 = -21.392,$$
$$M_{CF} = 2(25.234 + 0 - 36.409) = -22.350,$$
$$M_{CD} = 25.234 + 17.091 + 1.333 = 43.658;$$

$$M_{C'B'} = 4(23.353 + 19.805 - 55.218) = -48.240,$$
$$M_{C'F'} = 2(23.353 + 0 - 14.087) = 18.532,$$
$$M_{C'D'} = 23.353 + 6.345 = 29.698;$$

$$M_{DC} = 34.181 + 12.617 - 1.333 = 45.465,$$
$$M_{DE} = 4(34.181 + 0 - 48.546) + 12 = -45.460;$$

$$M_{D'C'} = 12.690 + 11.676 = 24.366,$$
$$M_{D'E'} = 4(12.690 + 0 - 18.783) = -24.372;$$

$$M_{ED} = 4(0 + 17.091 - 48.546) - 12 = -137.820;$$

$$M_{FC} = 2(0 + 12.617 - 36.409) = -47.584;$$

$$M_{F'C'} = 2(0 + 11.676 - 14.087) = -4.822;$$

$$M_{E'D'} = 4(0 + 6.345 - 18.783) = -49.752.$$

PROBLEMS

65. Assuming the members DC and $D'C'$ of the bent shown in Fig. 186 to be hinged at joints C and C', respectively, determine the corresponding changes in eqs. (231) to (234).

66. Determine the end moments of the bent shown in Fig. 185a, assuming the legs to be hinged at the bases.

64. Unsymmetrical, Gabled Lean-to Bent.—The loading of the bent shown in Fig. 187 consists of a system of vertical and horizontal forces. Under this loading, the bent will deflect in a manner similar to that shown in Fig. 184, resulting in three independent deflections; namely, deflections of members BC, $B'G'$ and DE or CG. Indicating

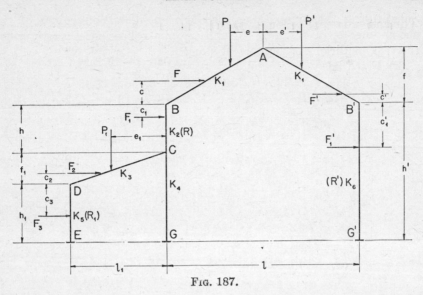

Fig. 187.

the deflection terms of the first three by R, R' and R_1, respectively, for the corresponding terms of the other members we have:

$$R_{CG} = \frac{h_1}{f_1 + h_1} R_1; \quad R_{AB} = \frac{1}{2f}(h'R' - hR - h_1 R_1) = -R_{AB'} \quad . \quad . \quad (236)$$

The three deflection expressions are obtained from the shear equations of joints B, B' and C:

$$\frac{1}{f}\left[(M_{AB} + M_{BA}) - F(f - c) - Pe + V_B \frac{l}{2}\right]$$
$$= \frac{1}{h}[(M_{BC} + M_{CB}) + F_1(h - c_1)], \quad \ldots \ldots \ldots \quad (a)$$

$$\frac{1}{f}\left[(M_{AB'} + M_{B'A}) - F'(f - c') + P'e' - V_{B'} \frac{l}{2}\right]$$
$$= \frac{1}{h'}[(M_{B'G'} + M_{G'B'}) + F'_1(h' - c'_1)], \quad \ldots \ldots \quad (b)$$

$$\frac{1}{h}[(M_{BC} + M_{CB}) - F_1 c_1] = \frac{1}{f_1 + h_1}(M_{CG} + M_{GC})$$
$$+ \frac{1}{h_1}[(M_{DE} + M_{ED}) + F_3(h_1 - c_3)] + F_2; \quad \ldots \ldots \quad (c)$$

in which V_B and $V_{B'}$ indicate the vertical shears at joints B and B', respectively; their values being obtained from the relations

$$-V_B l = M_{BA} + M_{B'A} + Fc + F'c' - P\left(\frac{l}{2} + e\right) - P'\left(\frac{l}{2} - e'\right), \Big\rbrace$$
$$V_{B'} l = M_{BA} + M_{B'A} + Fc + F'c' + P\left(\frac{l}{2} - e\right) + P'\left(\frac{l}{2} + e'\right). \Big\rbrace \quad . \quad (d)$$

Substituting these values, as well as slope-deflection values of the end moments, in eqs. (a), (b) and (c), the deflection expressions for the two conditions of support become:

(a) Fixed bases,

$$
\left(2K_2+\frac{h^2}{f^2}K_1\right)R-\frac{hh'}{f^2}K_1R'+\frac{hh_1}{f^2}K_1R_1=-\frac{h}{f}K_1A+\left(\frac{3}{2}K_2-\frac{h}{f}K_1\right)B
$$

$$
+\frac{h}{2f}K_1B'+\frac{3}{2}K_2C+\frac{h}{2f}\left[F(2f-c)+F'c'-P\left(\frac{l}{2}-e\right)-P'\left(\frac{l}{2}-e'\right)\right.
$$

$$
\left.+FM_{B'A}-FM_{BA}-2FM_{AB}\right]+F_1(h-c_1)+FM_{BC}+FM_{CB}, \quad (237)
$$

$$
\left[2K_6+\frac{(h')^2}{f^2}K_1\right]R'-\frac{hh'}{f^2}K_1R-\frac{h'h_1}{f^2}K_1R_1=-\frac{h'}{f}K_1A
$$

$$
+\frac{h'}{2f}K_1B+\left(\frac{3}{2}K_6-\frac{h'}{f}K_1\right)B'+\frac{h'}{2f}\left[Fc+F'(2f-)c'+P\left(\frac{l}{2}-e\right)\right.
$$

$$
\left.+P'\left(\frac{l}{2}-e'\right)+FM_{BA}-FM_{B'A}-2FM_{AB'}\right]+F_1'(h'-c_1')
$$

$$
+FM_{B'G'}+FM_{G'B'}, \quad \ldots \quad (237a)
$$

$$
2h\left[\frac{h_1K_4}{(f_1+h_1)^2}+\frac{K_5}{h_1}\right]R_1-2K_2R=-\frac{3}{2}K_2B+\left[\frac{3}{2}\frac{hK_4}{(f_1+h_1)}-\frac{3}{2}K_2\right]C
$$

$$
+\frac{3}{2}\frac{h}{h_1}K_5D+F_1c_1+hF_2+\left(h-c_3\frac{h}{h_1}\right)F_3
$$

$$
-(FM_{BC}+FM_{CB})+\frac{h}{h_1}(FM_{DE}+FM_{ED}); \quad \ldots \ldots \ldots (237b)
$$

(b) Hinged bases (the expression of R, eq. (237), remains the same),

$$
\left[\frac{K_6}{2}+\frac{(h')^2}{f^2}K_1\right]R'-\frac{hh'}{f^2}K_1R-\frac{h'h_1}{f^2}R_1=-\frac{h'}{f}K_1A+\frac{h'}{2f}K_1B
$$

$$
+\left(\frac{3}{4}K_6-\frac{h'}{f}K_1\right)B'+\frac{3}{2}K_2C+\frac{h'}{2f}\left[Fc+F'(2f-c')+P\left(\frac{l}{2}-e\right)\right.
$$

$$
\left.+P'\left(\frac{l}{2}-e'\right)+FM_{BA}-FM_{B'A}-2FM_{AB'}\right]
$$

$$
+F_1'(h'-c_1')+HM_{B'G'}, \quad \ldots \ldots \ldots \ldots \ldots \ldots (237c)
$$

$$
\frac{h}{2}\left[\frac{h_1K_4}{(f_1+h_1)^2}+\frac{K_5}{h_1}\right]R_1-2K_2R=-\frac{3}{2}K_2B+\left[\frac{3hK_4}{4(f_1+h_1)}-\frac{3}{2}K_2\right]C
$$

$$
+\frac{3h}{4h_1}K_5D+F_1c_1+hF_2+\left(h-c_3\frac{h}{h_1}\right)F_3-(FM_{BC}
$$

$$
+FM_{CB})+\frac{h}{h_1}HM_{DE} \quad \ldots \ldots \ldots \ldots \ldots \ldots (237d)
$$

If the loading is uniform, the intensity per horizontal and vertical foot being given by p and w, respectively, the load constants of eqs. (237) assume the following simplified forms:

q in equations:

$$(237) = \frac{h}{24f}\left[(17w+5w')f^2 - (7p+5p')\frac{l^2}{4}\right] + w_1\frac{h^2}{2},$$

$$(237a) = \frac{h'}{24f}\left[(5w+17w')f^2 + (5p+7p')\frac{l^2}{4}\right] + w_1'\frac{(h')^2}{2},$$

$$(237b) = w_1\frac{h^2}{2} + w_2 f_1 h + w_3\frac{hh_1}{2},$$

$$(237c) = \frac{h'}{24f}\left[(5w+17w')f^2 + (5p+7p')\frac{l^2}{4}\right] + \frac{5}{8}w_1'(h')^2,$$

$$(237d) = w_1\frac{h^2}{2} + w_2 f_1 h + \frac{5}{8}w_3 hh_1$$

$$\left.\right\} . \quad (238)$$

For the joint expressions we have:

(a) Fixed bases,

$$2K_1 A + \frac{K_1}{2}B + \frac{K_1}{2}B' + FM_{AB} + F'M_{AB'} = 0,$$

$$(K_1+K_2)B + \frac{K_1}{2}A + \frac{K_2}{2}C + \left(\frac{hK_1}{2f} - K_2\right)R - \frac{K_1}{2f}(h'R' - h_1 R_1)$$
$$+ FM_{BA} + FM_{BC} = 0,$$

$$(K_1+K_6)B' + \frac{K_1}{2}A + \left(\frac{h'K_1}{2f} - K_6\right)R' - \frac{K_1}{2f}(hR + h_1 R_1)$$
$$+ FM_{B'A} + FM_{B'G'} = 0,$$

$$(K_2+K_3+K_4)C + \frac{K_2}{2}B + \frac{K_3}{2}D - K_2 R - \frac{h_1 K_4}{f_1+h_1}R_1$$
$$+ FM_{CB} + FM_{CD} = 0,$$

$$(K_3+K_5)D + \frac{K_3}{2}C - K_5 R_1 + FM_{DC} + FM_{DE} = 0;$$

$$\left.\right\} . \quad (239)$$

(b) Hinged bases,

$$2K_1 A + \frac{K_1}{2}B + \frac{K_1}{2}B' + FM_{AB} + FM_{AB'} = 0,$$

$$(K_1+K_2)B + \frac{K_1}{2}A + \frac{K_2}{2}C + \left(\frac{hK_1}{2f} - K_2\right)R - \frac{K_1}{2f}(h'R' - h_1 R_1)$$
$$+ FM_{BA} + FM_{BC} = 0,$$

$$\left(K_1 + \frac{3}{4}K_6\right)B' + \frac{K_1}{2}A + \left(\frac{h'K_1}{2f} - \frac{K_6}{2}\right)R' - \frac{K_1}{2f}(hR + h_1 R_1)$$
$$+ FM_{B'A} + HM_{B'G'} = 0,$$

$$\left(K_2+K_3+\frac{3}{4}K_4\right)C + \frac{K_2}{2}B + \frac{K_3}{2}D - K_2 R - \frac{h_1 K_4}{2(f_1+h_1)}R_1$$
$$+ FM_{CB} + FM_{CD} = 0,$$

$$\left(K_3+\frac{3}{4}K_5\right)D + \frac{K_3}{2}C - \frac{1}{2}K_5 R_1 + FM_{DC} + HM_{DE} = 0.$$

$$\left.\right\} (239a)$$

In solving for the values of the unknowns, the following procedure of solution will be found convenient:

1. Obtain the values of the deflections R, R' and R_1, in terms of the deflection angles, from eqs. (237), and
2. Substitute in the joint expressions (239).
3. Determine the values of the deflection angles by either successive eliminations or tabular solution.

ILLUSTRATIVE EXAMPLE

The main roof of the bent shown in Fig. 188 is carrying a uniform load of 1 kip per linear foot of horizontal roof projection. Assuming the legs to be fixed at the bases, determine the end moments.

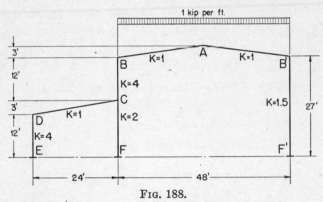

FIG. 188.

Solution: Applying eqs. (237) and (238),

$$24R - 36R' + 16R_1 = -4A + 2B + 2B' + 6.0C - 1152,$$
$$-36R + 84R' - 36R_1 = -9A + 4.5B - 6.75B' + 2592,$$
$$-8R + 10.56R_1 = -6B - 3.6C + 6D;$$

from which

$$R = -0.873A + 0.473B - 0.099B' + 0.688C - 0.036D - 4.570,$$
$$R' = -0.764A + 0.166B - 0.155B' + 0.372C + 0.217D + 27.415,$$
$$R_1 = -0.661A - 0.210B - 0.075B' + 0.180C + 0.541D - 3.462.$$

Substituting in eqs. (239),

$$2A \qquad + 0.5 \quad B + 0.5 \quad B' = 0,$$
$$4.362A + 2.887B + 0.746B' - 0.690C + 0.177D = 169.152,$$
$$1.276A - 0.028B + 2.383B' - 0.620C - 0.359D = -146.309,$$
$$4.550A + 0.444B + 0.516B' + 3.960C - 0.222D = -23.819,$$
$$2.644A + 0.840B + 0.300B' - 0.220C + 2.836D = -13.848.$$

Eliminating A, and obtaining the values of the other unknowns by tabular solution,

$$A = -5.72,$$
$$B = 83.51, \quad B' = -60.65,$$
$$C = -1.96, \quad D = -17.98;$$

and

$$R = 45.23,$$
$$R' = 50.42, \quad R_{AB} = 181.92,$$
$$R_1 = -22.75, \quad R_{CG} = -18.20.$$

The end moments become:

$$M_{AB} = -5.72 + 41.76 - 181.92 + 48 = -97.88,$$
$$M_{AB'} = -5.72 - 30.32 + 181.92 - 48 = 97.88;$$

$$M_{BA} = 83.51 - 2.86 - 181.92 - 48 \quad = -149.27,$$
$$M_{BC} = 4(83.51 - 0.98 - 45.23) \quad = 149.20;$$

$$M_{B'A} = -60.65 - 2.86 + 181.92 + 48 = 166.41,$$
$$M_{B'F'} = 1.5(-60.65 - 50.42) \quad = -166.61;$$

$$M_{CB} = 4(-1.96 + 41.76 - 45.23) \quad = -21.72,$$
$$M_{CF} = 2(-1.96 + 18.20) \quad = 32.48,$$
$$M_{CD} = -1.96 - 8.99 \quad = -10.95;$$

$$M_{DC} = -17.98 - 0.98 \quad = -18.96,$$
$$M_{DE} = 4(-17.98 + 22.75) \quad = 19.08;$$

$$M_{ED} = 4(-8.99 + 22.75) \quad = 55.04;$$

$$M_{FC} = 2(-0.98 + 18.20) \quad = 34.44;$$

$$M_{F'B'} = 1.5(-30.32 - 50.42) \quad = -121.11.$$

67. The bent shown in Fig. 187a carries two bracket loads. Determine the load constants of the deflection expressions for two conditions of support:

    (a) Fixed bases,
    (b) Hinged bases.

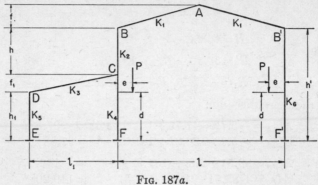

FIG. 187a.

68. Replace the vertical loading shown in Fig. 188 with a uniform lateral loading of 1 kip per vertical foot, applied to the members AB' and $B'F'$ in a counterclockwise direction, and, assuming the legs to be fixed at the bases, obtain the end moments.

Chapter VI

HIP BENTS

65. Hip-type Bent Framing.—In the framing of industrial buildings, an outline equaling the popularity of the gabled bent is presented by the so-called *hip bent*. Of the many known forms, the most familiar lines are shown in Fig. 189. That shown in (*a*) may be considered as

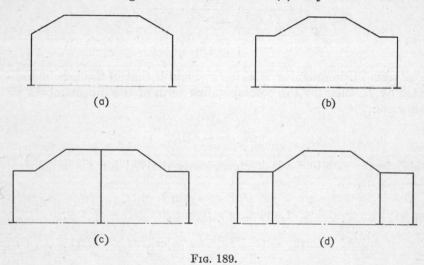

Fig. 189.

the simplest type, while the one in (*b*), often referred to as the *monitor* bent, in addition to this two-leg outline, has the further variations of three- and four-leg outlines, as shown in (*c*) and (*d*). In order to simplify the discussion, the analysis of each type will be made separately.

66. Symmetrical Hip Bent with Symmetrical Vertical Loading.— The deformations of a hip bent, under symmetrical loading, is shown in Fig. 190. In deflecting, it is noted that the top joints A and A' move downward the same distance Δ_1, while the tops of the legs, joints B and B', move outward a distance Δ. The deflection of the sloping members AB and $A'B'$ is obtained from Δ or Δ_1; that is, denoting the angle of slope of the hip by ϕ, it equals $\dfrac{\Delta}{\sin \phi}$. Obviously, the deflec-

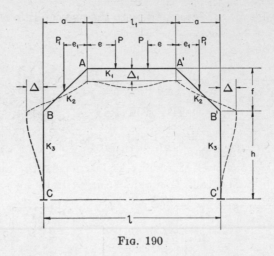

FIG. 190

tions term of the member AA' is zero; and if that of the legs be indicated by R, then for the corresponding term of the hip members we can write:

$$R_{AB} = -\frac{h}{f}R,$$

which is the familiar relation previously derived for a symmetrical gabled bent.

The deflection expression, R, here again is obtained from the horizontal shear equation of members AB and BC at the joint B:

$$\frac{1}{f}[(M_{AB}+M_{BA})+(P+P_1)a-P_1e_1]=\frac{1}{h}(M_{BC}+M_{CB}) \quad . \quad . \quad . \quad (a)$$

Substituting the values of end moments, and assuming fixed connections at the bases C and C',

$$-2\left(\frac{h^2}{f^2}K_2+K_3\right)R=\frac{3}{2}\frac{h}{f}K_2A+\frac{3}{2}\left(\frac{h}{f}K_2-K_3\right)B$$

$$+\frac{h}{f}[(FM_{AB}+FM_{BA})+(P+P_1)a-P_1e_1] \quad . \quad . \quad . \quad (240)$$

Similarly, in the case of hinged bases,

$$-\left(2\frac{h^2}{f^2}K_2+\frac{K_3}{2}\right)R=\frac{3h}{2f}K_2A+\frac{3}{2}\left(\frac{h}{f}K_2-\frac{K_3}{2}\right)B$$

$$+\frac{h}{f}[(FM_{AB}+FM_{BA})+(P+P_1)a-P_1e_1] \quad . \quad . \quad . \quad (240a)$$

The joint expressions corresponding to the two conditions of support, after eliminating R, become:

(a) Fixed bases,

$$\left[\frac{K_1}{2}+K_2-\frac{3K_2}{4\left(1+\frac{f^2K_3}{h^2K_2}\right)}\right]A+\left[\frac{K_2}{2}-\frac{3}{4}\frac{\left(K_2-\frac{f}{h}K_3\right)}{\left(1+\frac{f^2K_3}{h^2K_2}\right)}\right]B$$

$$=+-\frac{1}{2\left(1+\frac{f^2K_3}{h^2K_2}\right)}[(FM_{AB}+FM_{BA})+(P+P_1)a-P_1e_1]$$

$$-FM_{AA'}-FM_{AB}\ldots\ldots\ldots\ldots\ldots\ldots\ldots\ldots (241)$$

$$\left[\frac{K_2}{2}-\frac{3}{4}\frac{\left(K_2-\frac{f}{h}K_3\right)}{\left(1+\frac{f^2K_3}{h^2K_2}\right)}\right]A+\left[K_2+K_3-\frac{3}{4}\frac{K_2\left(1-\frac{fK_3}{hK_2}\right)}{\left(1+\frac{f^2K_3}{h^2K_2}\right)}\right]B$$

$$=+\frac{\left(1-\frac{f}{h}\cdot\frac{K_3}{K_2}\right)}{2\left(1+\frac{f^2}{h^2}\cdot\frac{K_3}{K_2}\right)}\cdot[(FM_{AB}+FM_{BA})+(P+P_1)a-P_1e_1]$$

$$-FM_{BA}\ldots\ldots\ldots\ldots\ldots\ldots\ldots\ldots\ldots (241a)$$

(b) Hinged bases,

$$\left[\frac{K_1}{2}+K_2-\frac{3K_2}{\left(4+\frac{f^2K_3}{h^2K_2}\right)}\right]A+\left[\frac{K_2}{2}-\frac{3\left(K_2-\frac{fK^3}{2h}\right)}{\left(4+\frac{f^2K_3}{h^2K_2}\right)}\right]B$$

$$=+\frac{2}{\left(4+\frac{f^2K_3}{h^2K_2}\right)}[(FM_{AB}+FM_{BA})+(P+P_1)a-P_1e_1]$$

$$-FM_{AA'}-FM_{AB}\ldots\ldots\ldots\ldots\ldots\ldots\ldots (242)$$

$$\left[\frac{K_2}{2}-\frac{3\left(K_2-\frac{K_3f}{2h}\right)}{\left(4+\frac{f^2K_3}{h^2K_2}\right)}\right]A+\left[K_2+\frac{3}{4}K_3-\frac{3K_2\left(1-\frac{fK_3}{2hK_2}\right)^2}{\left(4+\frac{f^2K_3}{h^2K_2}\right)}\right]B$$

$$=+\frac{\left(2-\frac{fK_3}{hK_2}\right)}{\left(4+\frac{f^2K_3}{h^2K_2}\right)}[(FM_{AB}+FM_{BA})+(P+P_1)a-P_1e_1]$$

$$-FM_{BA}\ldots\ldots\ldots\ldots\ldots\ldots\ldots\ldots\ldots (242a)$$

If the loading is uniform, with an intensity of w per lin. ft., the load constants in the above expressions may be simplified as follows:

q in equations:

$$(240) = \frac{a}{2}\frac{h}{f}(l-a)w,$$

$$(241) = \frac{w}{12}(l_1{}^2 - a^2) + \frac{1}{2\left(1 + \frac{f^2 K_3}{h^2 K_2}\right)}\frac{a}{2}(l-a)w,$$

$$(241a) = \frac{wa^2}{12} + \frac{1 - \frac{fK_3}{hK_2}}{2\left(1 + \frac{f^2 K_3}{h^2 K_2}\right)}\frac{a}{2}(l-a)w,$$

$$(242) = \frac{w}{12}(l_1{}^2 - a^2) + \frac{2}{\left(4 + \frac{f^2 K_3}{h^2 K_2}\right)}\frac{a}{2}(l-a)w,$$

$$(242a) = \frac{wa^2}{12} + \frac{\left(2 - \frac{fK_3}{hK_2}\right)}{\left(4 + \frac{f^2 K_3}{h^2 K_2}\right)}\frac{a}{2}(l-a)w.$$

$$\left. \right\} \quad \cdots \cdots \quad (243)$$

ILLUSTRATIVE EXAMPLE

The symmetrical bent shown in Fig. 190a is carrying a uniform vertical load of 1 kip per linear foot. Assuming the legs to be fixed at the bases, determine the end moments.

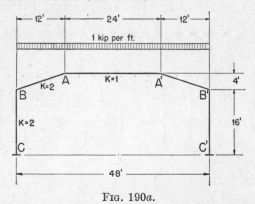

Fig. 190a.

Solution: Applying eqs. (241) and (243),

$$18.5A-1.0B=2340,$$
$$-1.0A+54.5B=1500;$$

from which

$$A=128.10, \quad B=29.87.$$

Substituting in eq. (240),

$$R=-39.26; R_{AB}=157.06.$$

With these values, the end moments become:

$$M_{AA'}=64.05-48=16.05,$$
$$M_{AB}=2(128.10+14.93-157.06)+12=-16.06;$$

$$M_{BA}=2(29.87+64.05-157.06)-12=-138.28,$$
$$M_{BC}=2(29.87+0+39.26)=138.26;$$

$$M_{CB}=2(14.94+39.26)=108.4.$$

PROBLEMS

69. The bent show is in Feb. 190b is carrying a symmetrically placed bracket loading. Obtain the load constants corresponding to the values in eqs. (243).

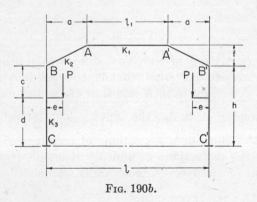

Fig. 190b.

70. Determine the end moments for the bent shown in Feb. 190a, assuming the legs to be hinged at the bases.

67. Unsymmetrical Hip Bent.—In the case of the unsymmetrical bent, subjected to any system of loading, there are three independent deflections, namely: the deflections of the two legs and one of the two bent rafters. As shown in Fig. 191(a), the deformation of the

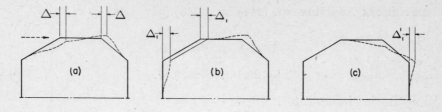

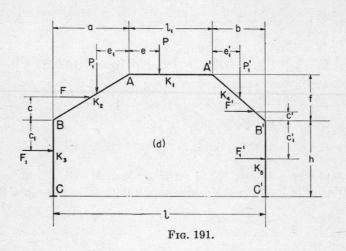

Fig. 191.

upper portion $(BAA'B')$ of the bent, due to a lateral deflection Δ, is similar to a trapezoidal panel; that is, the members AB and $A'B'$ have the same deflection term R and that of the member AA' equals $-\dfrac{a+b}{l_1}R$. Assuming Δ to be the independent lateral deflection of member AB, the additional deflections of members AA' and $A'B'$, resulting from the deflections Δ_1 and Δ_1' of members BC and $B'C'$, are sketched in (b) and (c). Accordingly, for the deflection terms we have:

$$\left.\begin{aligned}
R_{AB} &= R, \\
R_{A'B'} &= R + \frac{h}{f}(R_1 - R_1'), \\
R_{AA'} &= -\frac{a+b}{l_1}R - \frac{b}{l_1}\frac{h}{f}(R_1 - R_1'), \\
R_{BC} &= R_1, \\
R_{B'C'} &= R_1'.
\end{aligned}\right\} \quad \ldots \ldots (a)$$

Under a system of loading involving vertical and horizontal forces, shown in Fig. 191 (d), expressions for the three unknown deflections may be obtained from the following shear equations:

$$\left.\begin{aligned}
M_{BC}+M_{CB}&=\frac{h}{f}[M_{AB}+M_{BA}+V_C a-P_1 e_1-F(f-c)]-F_1(h-c_1),\\
M_{B'C'}+M_{C'B'}&=\frac{h}{f}[M_{A'B'}+M_{B'A'}-V_{C'}b+P_1'e_1'-F'(f-c')]\\
&\qquad -F_1'(h-c_1'),\\
M_{BC}+M_{CB}&+M_{B'C'}+M_{C'B'}=F_1 c_1+F_1'c_1'-h(F+F_1+F'+F_1');
\end{aligned}\right\} \quad . \quad (b)$$

in which the vertical reactions V_C and $V_{C'}$ are expressed as follows:

$$\left.\begin{aligned}
V_C l&=P(l_1+b-e)+P_1(l_1+b+e_1)+P_1'(b-e_1')\\
&\quad -[F(h+c)+F'(h+c')+F_1(h-c_1)+F_1'(h-c_1')+M_{CB}+M_{C'B'}],\\
V_{C'}l&=P(a+e)+P_1(a-e_1)+P_1'(a+l_1+e_1')+F(h+c)\\
&\quad +F'(h+c')+F_1(h-c_1)+F_1'(h-c_1')+M_{CB}+M_{C'B'}.
\end{aligned}\right\} \quad . \quad (c)$$

Substituting the values of the end moments and the vertical reactions in eqs. (b), the deflection expressions for the two conditions of support become:

(a) Fixed bases,

$$2\frac{h}{f}K_2 R-\left(2+\frac{a}{l}\frac{h}{f}\right)K_3 R_1-\frac{a}{l}\frac{h}{f}K_5 R_1'$$

$$=\frac{h}{f}\left[\frac{3}{2}K_2 A+\frac{1}{2}\left(3K_2-3K_3\frac{f}{h}-K_3\frac{a}{l}\right)B-\frac{aK_5}{2l}B'\right]$$

$$+\frac{h}{f}\left[FM_{AB}+FM_{BA}-\frac{a}{l}(FM_{CB}+FM_{C'B'})\right]-(FM_{BC}+FM_{CB})$$

$$-F_1(h-c_1)-\frac{h}{f}[P_1 e_1+F(f-c)]+\frac{ah}{lf}[P(l_1+b-e)+P_1(l_1+b+e_1)$$

$$+P_1'(b-e_1')-F(h+c)-F'(h+c')$$
$$-F_1(h-c_1)-F_1'(h-c_1')] \quad \ldots \ldots \ldots \ldots \ldots \ldots \ldots \quad (244)$$

$$2\frac{h}{f}K_4 R-\left[\left(2+\frac{b}{l}\frac{h}{f}\right)K_5+2\frac{h^2}{f^2}K_4\right]R_1'-\left(\frac{b}{l}\frac{h}{f}K_3-2\frac{h^2}{f^2}K_4\right)R_1$$

$$=\frac{h}{f}\left[\frac{3}{2}K_4 A'+\frac{1}{2}\left(3K_4-3K_5\frac{f}{h}-K_5\frac{b}{l}\right)B'-\frac{bK_3}{2l}B\right]$$

$$+\frac{h}{f}\left[FM_{A'B'}+FM_{B'A'}-\frac{b}{l}(FM_{CB}+FM_{C'B'})\right]$$

$$-(FM_{B'C'}+FM_{C'B'})-F_1'(h-c_1')+\frac{h}{f}[P_1'e_1'-F'(f-c')]$$

$$-\frac{bh}{lf}[P(a+e)+P_1(a-e_1)+P_1'(a+l_1+e_1')+F(h+c)$$

$$+F'(h+c')+F_1(h-c_1)+F'(h-c_1')] \quad \ldots \ldots \ldots \ldots \ldots \quad (244a)$$

$$2K_3R_1 + 2K_5R_1' = \frac{3}{2}(K_3B + K_5B') - F_1c_1 - F_1'c_1' + FM_{BC}$$

$$+ FM_{CB} + FM_{B'C'} + FM_{C'B'} + h(F + F_1 + F' + F_1') \; . \; . \; . \; (244b)$$

(b) Hinged bases,

$$2\frac{h}{f}K_2R - \frac{K_3}{2}R_1 = \frac{h}{f}\left[\frac{3}{2}K_2A + \frac{3}{4}\left(2K_2 - \frac{f}{h}K_3\right)B\right] + \frac{h}{f}(FM_{AB} + FM_{BA})$$

$$- HM_{BC} - F_1(h - c_1) - \frac{h}{f}[P_1e_1 + F(f - c)] + \frac{ah}{lf}[P(l_1 + b - e)$$

$$+ P_1(l_1 + b + e_1) + P_1'(b - e_1') - F(h + c) - F'(h + c')$$

$$- F_1(h - c_1) - F_1'(h - c_1')] \; . \; . \; . \; . \; . \; . \; . \; . \; . \; . \; (245)$$

$$2\frac{h}{f}K_4R - \left(\frac{K_5}{2} + 2\frac{h^2}{f^2}K_4\right)R_1' + 2K_4\frac{h^2}{f^2}R_1 = \frac{h}{f}\left[\frac{3}{2}K_4A' + \frac{3}{4}\left(2K_4 - \frac{f}{h}K_5\right)B'\right]$$

$$+ \frac{h}{f}(FM_{A'B'} + FM_{B'A'}) - HM_{B'C'} - F_1'(h - c_1')$$

$$+ \frac{h}{f}[P_1'e_1' - F'(f - c')] - \frac{bh}{lf}[P(a + e) + P_1(a - e_1) + P_1'(a + l_1 + e_1')$$

$$+ F(h + c) + F'(h + c') + F_1(h - c_1) + F_1'(h - c_1')] . \; . \; . \; . \; (245a)$$

$$\frac{K_3}{2}R_1 + \frac{K_5}{2}R_1' = \frac{3}{4}(K_3B + K_5B') + HM_{BC} + HM_{B'C'} - F_1c_1 - F_1'c_1'$$

$$+ h(F + F_1 + F' + F_1') \; . \; . \; . \; . \; . \; . \; . \; . \; . \; . \; . \; . \; (245b)$$

If the loading is uniform—intensities per foot of vertical loading on members AA', AB and $A'B'$ being indicated by p, p_1 and p_1', respectively, and the horizontal loading on members AB, BC, $A'B'$ and $B'C'$ by w, w_1, w' and w_1'—the load factors q in the above expressions assume the following forms:

q in equations:

$$(244) = \frac{h}{f}\left[\frac{ah^2}{12l}(w_1 + w_1') - \frac{1}{2}(a^2p_1 + f^2w)\right] - \frac{h^2}{2}w_1$$

$$+ \frac{ah}{lf}\left[l_1\left(b + \frac{l_1}{2}\right)p + ap_1\left(l_1 + b + \frac{a}{2}\right) + \frac{b^2}{2}p_1'\right.$$

$$\left. - f\left(h + \frac{f}{2}\right)(w + w') - \frac{h^2}{2}(w_1 + w_1')\right] \; . \; . \; . \; . \; . \; . \; . \; . \; (246)$$

$$(244a) = \frac{h}{f}\left[\frac{bh^2}{12l}(w_1 + w_1') + \frac{1}{2}(b^2p_1' - f^2w')\right] - \frac{h^2}{2}w_1'$$

$$- \frac{bh}{lf}\left[l_1\left(a + \frac{l_1}{2}\right)p + \frac{a^2}{2}p_1 + b\left(a + l_1 + \frac{b}{2}\right)p_1'\right.$$

$$\left. + f\left(h + \frac{f}{2}\right)(w + w') + \frac{h^2}{2}(w_1 + w_1')\right] \; . \; . \; . \; . \; . \; . \; . \; . \; (246a)$$

$$(244b) = \frac{h^2}{2}(w_1 + w_1') + hf(w + w') \ \ldots \ldots \ldots \ldots \ldots (246b)$$

$$(245) = -\frac{5}{8}h^2 w_1 - \frac{h}{2f}(a^2 p_1 + f^2 w) + \frac{ah}{lf}\left[l_1\left(b + \frac{l_1}{2}\right)p + a\left(l_1 + b + \frac{a}{2}\right)p_1 \right.$$
$$\left. + \frac{b^2}{2}p_1' - \frac{ah}{lf}\left[f\left(h + \frac{f}{2}\right)(w + w') + \frac{h^2}{2}(w_1 + w_1')\right] \ \ldots \ldots (246c)$$

$$(245a) = -\frac{5}{8}h^2 w_1' + \frac{h}{2f}(b^2 p_1' - f^2 w') - \frac{bh}{lf}\left[l_1\left(a + \frac{l_1}{2}\right)p + \frac{a^2}{2}p_1 \right.$$
$$\left. + b\left(a + l_1 + \frac{b}{2}\right)p_1'\right] - \frac{bh}{lf}\left[f\left(h + \frac{f}{2}\right)(w + w') + \frac{h^2}{2}(w_1 + w_1')\right]. \ (246d)$$

$$(245b) = \frac{5}{8}h^2(w_1 + w_1') + hf(w + w') \ \ldots \ldots \ldots \ldots \ldots (246e)$$

For the joint expressions we have:

(a) Fixed bases,

$$(K_1 + K_2)A + \frac{K_1}{2}A' + \frac{K_2}{2}B + \left[\frac{(a+b)}{l_1}K_1 - K_2\right]R$$
$$+ \frac{bh}{l_1 f}K_1(R_1 - R_1') = -FM_{AA'} - FM_{AB'},$$

$$(K_1 + K_4)A' + \frac{K_1}{2}A + \frac{K_4}{2}B' + \left[\frac{(a+b)}{l_1}K_1 - K_4\right]R$$
$$+ \left(\frac{bh}{l_1 f}K_1 - \frac{h}{f}K_4\right)(R_1 - R_1') = -FM_{A'A} - FM_{A'B'},$$

$$(K_2 + K_3)B + \frac{K_2}{2}A - K_2 R - K_3 R_1 = -FM_{BA} - FM_{BC},$$

$$(K_4 + K_5)B' + \frac{K_4}{2}A' - K_4 R - \left(K_5 - \frac{h}{f}K_4\right)R_1' - \frac{h}{f}K_4 R_1$$
$$= -FM_{B'A'} - FM_{B'C'};$$

$$\left. \right\} . \ (247)$$

(b) Hinged bases,

$$(K_1 + K_2)A + \frac{K_1}{2}A' + \frac{K_2}{2}B + \left[\frac{(a+b)}{l_1}K_1 - K_2\right]R$$
$$+ \frac{bh}{l_1 f}K_1(R_1 - R_1') = -FM_{AA'} - FM_{AB'},$$

$$(K_1 + K_4)A' + \frac{K_1}{2}A + \frac{K_4}{2}B + \left[\frac{(a+b)}{l_1}K_1 - K_4\right]R$$
$$+ \left(\frac{bh}{l_1 f}K_1 - \frac{h}{f}K_4\right)(R_1 - R_1') = -FM_{A'A} - FM_{A'B'},$$

$$\left(K_2 + \frac{3}{4}K_3\right)B + \frac{K_2}{2}A - K_2 R - \frac{K_3}{2}R_1 = -FM_{BA} - HM_{BC},$$

$$\left(K_4 + \frac{3}{4}K_5\right)B' + \frac{K_4}{2}A' - K_4 R - \left(\frac{K_5}{2} - \frac{h}{f}K_4\right)R_1' - \frac{h}{f}K_4 R_1$$
$$= -FM_{B'A'} - HM_{B'C'}.$$

$$\left. \right\} \ (247a)$$

ILLUSTRATIVE EXAMPLE

The symmetrical bent shown in Fig. 190c is subjected to a uniform lateral load of one kip per vertical foot. Assuming the legs to be fixed at the bases, determine the end moments.

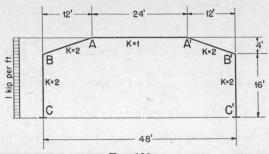

Fig. 190c.

Solution: Applying eqs. (244),

$$16R-6R_1-2R_1'=12A+8B-B'-338.67,$$
$$16R+62R_1-70R_1'=12A'-B+8B'-178.67,$$
$$4R_1+4R_1'=3B+3B'+192.00;$$

from which

$$544R=396A+12A'+365B+77B'-4826.67,$$
$$68R_1=-6(A-A')+21B+30B'+1712,$$
$$68R_1'=6(A-A')+30B+21B'+1552.$$

Substituting in eqs. (247),

$$1044A+452A'+35B+67B'=-8112,$$
$$452A+1044A'+67B+35B'=+2853.33,$$
$$-152A-120A'+1110B-634B'=+6858.67,$$
$$-120A-152A'-634B+1110B'=+25418.67;$$

from which

$$A=-13.475,\quad A'=5.642,$$
$$B=26.170,\quad B'=37.163;$$

and

$$R=4.262,\quad R_1'=44.159,$$
$$R_1=51.341,\quad R_{AA'}=-18.625,\quad R_{A'B'}=32.988.$$

The end moments become:

$$M_{AA'}=-13.475+2.821+18.625=7.971,$$
$$M_{AB}=2(-13.475+13.085-4.262)+1.333=-7.791;$$

$$M_{BA}=2(26.170-6.737-4.262)-1.333=29.009,$$
$$M_{BC}=2(26.170+0.-51.341)+21.333=-29.009;$$

$$M_{A'A}=5.642-6.737+18.625=17.530,$$
$$M_{A'B'}=2(5.642+18.581-32.988)=-17.530;$$

$$M_{B'A'} = 2(37.163 + 2.821 - 32.988) = 13.992,$$
$$M_{B'A'} = 2(37.163 + 2.821 - 32.988) = 13.992,$$
$$M_{B'C'} = 2(37.163 + 0 - 44.159) = -13.992;$$

$$M_{CB} = 2(13.085 - 51.341) - 21.333 = -97.845;$$

$$M_{C'B'} = 2(18.581 - 44.159) = -51.156.$$

PROBLEMS

71. Obtain the load constants q in the deflection expressions for a bracket loading on member BC of the bent shown in Fig. 191 (d).

72. Determine the end moments for the bent shown in Fig. 190c, assuming the legs to be hinged at the bases.

68. Symmetrical Monitor Bent with Symmetrical Vertical Loading.—When sketching the deformations of the bent shown in Fig. 192,

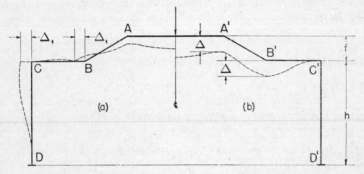

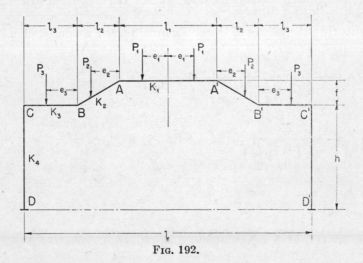

FIG. 192.

it is convenient to consider the deflection of the legs CD and $C'D'$, and that of members CB and $C'B'$, independently. The relative displacements of the joints due to these two independent deflections are shown in (a) and (b). Because of the symmetry of loading, the deflection of the member AA' will be zero; that is, the joints A and A' will move downward the same distance. The deflection of the sloping roof members AB and $A'B'$ is dependent only upon the deflection Δ_1 of the legs, since the deflection Δ of members CB and $C'B'$ produces no relative displacement of the ends. Denoting the deflection term of the member CB by R, and that of the leg CD by R_1, the corresponding term for the member AB becomes, as in the gabled bents,

$$R_{AB}=-\frac{h}{f}R_1 \ . \ . \ . \ . \ . \ . \ . \ . \ . \ . \quad (a)$$

The expression of R is obtained from the shear equation of the member BC:

$$M_{CB}+M_{BC}+(P_1+P_2+P_3)l_3-P_3e_3=0;$$

or, substituting the values of the end moments,

$$\frac{3}{2}K_3(B+C)-2K_3R+(FM_{CB}+FM_{BC})+(P_1+P_2+P_3)l_3-P_3e_3=0,$$

$$R=\frac{3}{4}(B+C)+\frac{1}{2K_3}[(FM_{CB}+FM_{BC})+(P_1+P_2+P_3)l_3-P_3e_3] \ . \ . \quad (248)$$

Similarly, for the expression of R_1, obtained from the shear equations of members CD and AB, we have:

$$\frac{1}{h}(M_{CD}+M_{DC})=\frac{1}{f}[M_{AB}+M_{BA}+(P_1+P_2)l_2-P_2e_2].$$

Substituting the values of the end moments, and assuming fixed bases,

$$R_1=-\frac{3}{4}\cdot\frac{\frac{f}{h}(A+B)}{\left(1+\frac{1}{4}\frac{f^2}{h^2}\frac{K_4}{K_2}\right)}+\frac{3}{4}\cdot\frac{C}{\left(1+\frac{h^2}{f^2}\frac{K_2}{K_4}\right)}$$

$$-\frac{\frac{f}{h}}{2K_4\left(\frac{K_2}{K_4}+\frac{f^2}{h^2}\right)}[(FM_{AB}+FM_{BA})+(P_1+P_2)l_2-P_2e_2] \ . \quad (249)$$

and, in the case of hinged bases,

$$R_1 = -\frac{3}{4} \cdot \frac{\frac{f}{h}(A+B)}{\left(1+\frac{1}{4}\frac{f^2}{h^2}\frac{K_4}{K_2}\right)} + \frac{3}{8} \cdot \frac{C}{\left(\frac{1}{4}\frac{h^2}{f^2}\frac{K_2}{K_4}\right)}$$

$$-\frac{\frac{f}{h}}{2K_4\left(\frac{K_2}{K^4}+\frac{1}{4}\frac{f^2}{h^2}\right)}[(FM_{AB}+FM_{BA})+(P_1+P_2)l_2-P_2e_2] \ . \ (249a)$$

If the loading is uniform, of intensity w_1, w_2 and w_3 per linear foot in the respective spans, the load factors in the brackets of eqs. (248) and (249) reduce to the following:

$$(248) = \left(\frac{1}{2}w_1l_1+w_2l_2\right)l_3+\frac{1}{2}w_3l_3^2, \ \ldots \ldots \ldots \ (b)$$

$$(249) = \frac{1}{2}(w_1l_1l_2+w_2l_2^2) \ \ldots \ldots \ldots \ldots \ (c)$$

The joint expressions, before elimination of the deflection terms, are in the following forms:

(a) Fixed bases,

$$\left.\begin{aligned}\left(\frac{K_1}{2}+K_2\right)A+\frac{K_2}{2}B+\frac{h}{f}K_2R_1+FM_{AA'}+FM_{AB}=0,\\(K_2+K_3)B+\frac{K_2}{2}A+\frac{K_3}{2}C+\frac{h}{f}K_2R_1-K_3R+FM_{BA}+FM_{BC}=0,\\(K_3+K_4)C+\frac{K_3}{2}B-K_3R-K_4R_1+FM_{CB}=0;\end{aligned}\right\} \ . \ . \ (250)$$

(b) Hinged bases,

$$\left.\begin{aligned}\left(\frac{K_1}{2}+K_2\right)A+\frac{K_2}{2}B+\frac{h}{f}K_2R_1+FM_{AA'}+FM_{AB}=0,\\(K_2+K_3)B+\frac{K_2}{2}A+\frac{K_3}{2}C+{}^h K_2R_1-K_3R+FM_{BA}+FM_{BC}=0,\\\left(K_3+\frac{3}{4}K_4\right)C+\frac{K_3}{2}B-K_3R-\frac{K_4}{2}R_1+FM_{CB}=0.\end{aligned}\right\} \ . \ (250a)$$

ILLUSTRATIVE EXAMPLE

The symmetrical bent shown in Fig. 192c is carrying a uniform roof load of one kip per horizontal foot. Assuming the legs to be fixed at the bases, determine the end moments.

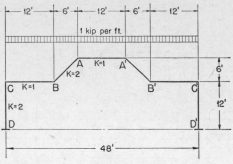

Fig. 192c.

Solution: Applying eqs. (248), (249), (a), (b) and (c),

$$R = \frac{3}{4}(B+C) + 108,$$
$$R_1 = -0.3(A+B) + 0.15C - 5.4;$$

and substituting in eq. (150),

$$1.3A - 0.2B + 0.6C = 30.6,$$
$$-0.2A + 1.05B + 0.35C = 120.6,$$
$$0.6A + 0.35B + 1.95C = 109.2;$$

from which

$$A = 27.94, \; B = 111.01, \; C = 27.47;$$

and

$$R = 211.86, \; R_1 = -42.96, \; R_{AB} = 85.92.$$

With these values, the end moments become:

$$M_{AA'} = 13.97 - 12 = 1.97,$$
$$M_{AB} = 2(27.94 + 55.50 - 85.92) + 3 = -1.96;$$

$$M_{BA} = 2(111.01 + 13.97 - 85.92) - 3 = 75.12,$$
$$M_{BC} = 111.01 + 13.73 - 211.86 + 12 = -75.12;$$

$$M_{CB} = 27.48 + 55.50 - 211.86 - 12 = -140.88,$$
$$M_{CD} = 2(27.48 + 42.96) = 140.88;$$

$$M_{DC} = 2(13.74 + 42.96) = 113.40.$$

PROBLEMS

73. Obtain the deflection expressions R and R_1 for the symmetrical bent with vertical monitor shown in Fig. 193.

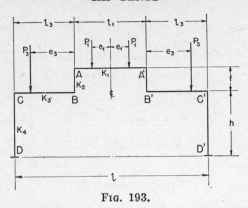

FIG. 193.

74. Determine the end moments for the bent shown in Fig. 192c, assuming the legs to be hinged at the bases.

69. Three-legged Symmetrical Hip Bent with Symmetrical Vertical Loading.—The joint displacements of the symmetrically loaded bent in Fig. 194 are shown in (a) and (b). Assuming that the top members

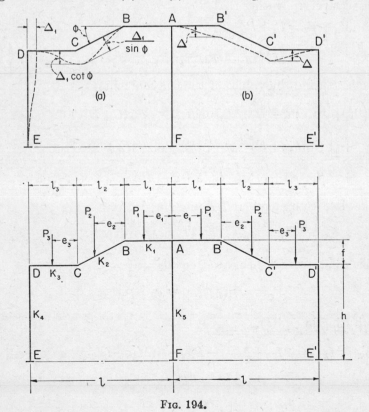

FIG. 194.

AB and AB', and the legs DE and $D'E'$ deflect a distance Δ and Δ_1, respectively, the corresponding deflections of the other members are then as indicated in the respective half of the figure. With the usual notations, for the deflections terms R we can write:

$$R_{AB}=R,$$

$$R_{DE}=R_1,$$

$$R_{BC}=-\frac{h}{f}R_1,$$

$$R_{DC}=-\frac{l_1}{l_3}R+\frac{hl_2}{fl_3}R_1.$$

The derivation for the expressions of R and R_1, obtained from vertical and horizontal shear equations of the members, follows:

$$\left.\begin{array}{l} -V_Al_1+P_1(l_1-e_1)+(M_{AB}+M_{BA})=0, \\ V_Dl_3-P_3e_3+(M_{CD}+M_{DC})=0; \end{array}\right\} \quad \cdots \cdots \; (a)$$

in which V_A and V_D indicate the vertical shears or reactions at A and D, respectively. Noting that

$$V_A+V_D=P_1+P_2+P_3$$

$$=\frac{1}{l_1}(M_{AB}+M_{BA})-\frac{1}{l_3}(M_{CD}+M_{DC})+\frac{P_1}{l_1}(l_1-e_1)+\frac{P_3}{l_3}e_3;$$

and substituting the values of the end moments,

$$\left(K_1+\frac{l_1^2}{l_3^2}K_3\right)R-\frac{hl_1l_2}{fl_3^2}K_3R_1=\frac{3}{4}K_1B-\frac{3l_1}{4l_3}K_3(C+D)$$

$$+\frac{1}{2}\bigg[(FM_{AB}+FM_{BA})-\frac{l_1}{l_3}(FM_{CD}+FM_{DC})$$

$$+P_1(l_1-e_1)+\frac{l_1}{l_3}P_3e_3-l_1(P_1+P_2+P_3)\bigg] \; \cdots \cdots \cdots \; (251)$$

Likewise, from members DE and BC,

$$\frac{1}{h}(M_{DE}+M_{ED})=\frac{1}{f}[(M_{CB}+M_{BC})+V_Cl_2-P_2e_2] \; \cdots \cdots \; (b)$$

in which V_C, vertical shear at C, equals

$$V_C=-\frac{1}{l_3}[(M_{DC}+M_{CD})+P_3(l_3-e_3)]$$

Substituting in eq. (b),

$$\frac{f}{h}(M_{DE}+M_{ED})=(M_{CB}+M_{BC})-P_2e_2-\frac{l_2}{l_3}[(M_{DC}+M_{CD})+P_3(l_3-e_3)] \; . \; (c)$$

Substituting also the values of the end moments, the deflection expressions for the two conditions of support become:

(a) Fixed bases,

$$\frac{l_1 l_2}{l_3^2} K_3 R - \left(\frac{h}{f} K_2 + \frac{f}{h} K_4 + \frac{h l_2^2}{f l_3^2} K_3\right) R_1 = \frac{3}{4} K_2 B + \frac{3}{4}\left(K_2 - \frac{l_2}{l_3} K_3\right) C$$

$$- \frac{3}{4}\left(\frac{f}{h} K_4 + \frac{l_2}{l_3} K_3\right) D + \frac{1}{2}\left[(FM_{BC} + FM_{CB}) - \frac{l_2}{l_3}(FM_{CD} + FM_{DC})\right.$$

$$\left. - P_2 e_2 - \frac{l_2}{l_3} P_3(l_3 - e_3)\right]. \quad\dots\dots\dots\dots\dots\quad (252)$$

(b) Hinged bases,

$$\frac{l_1 l_2}{l_3^2} K_3 R - \left(\frac{h}{f} K_2 + \frac{f}{4h} K_4 + \frac{h l_2^2}{f l_3^2} K_3\right) R_1 = \frac{3}{4} K_2 B + \frac{3}{4}\left(K_2 - \frac{l_2}{l_3} K_3\right) C$$

$$- \frac{3}{4}\left(\frac{f}{2h} K_4 + \frac{l_2}{l_3} K_3\right) D + \frac{1}{2}\left[(FM_{BC} + FM_{CB}) - \frac{l_2}{l_3}(FM_{CD} + FM_{DC})\right.$$

$$\left. - P_2 e_2 - \frac{l_2}{l_3} P_3(l_3 - e_3)\right]. \quad\dots\dots\dots\dots\dots\quad (252a)$$

For the joint expressions we have:

(a) Fixed bases,

$$\left.\begin{aligned}
&(K_1 + K_2)B + \frac{K_2}{2}C - K_1 R + \frac{h}{f} K_2 R_1 + FM_{BA} + FM_{BC} = 0, \\[1em]
&(K_2 + K_3)C + \frac{K_2}{2}B + \frac{K_3}{2}D + \frac{l_1}{l_3} K_3 R + \frac{h}{f}\left(K_2 - \frac{l_2}{l_3} K_3\right) R_1 \\
&\qquad\qquad + FM_{CB} + FM_{CD} = 0, \\[1em]
&(K_3 + K_4)D + \frac{K_3}{2}C + \frac{l_1}{l_3} K_3 R - \left(K_4 + \frac{h l_2}{f l_3} K_3\right) R_1 + FM_{DC} = 0;
\end{aligned}\right\} \quad (253)$$

(b) Hinged bases,

$$\left.\begin{aligned}
&(K_1 + K_2)B + \frac{K_2}{2}C - K_1 R + \frac{h}{f} K_2 R_1 + FM_{BA} + FM_{BC} = 0, \\[1em]
&(K_2 + K_3)C + \frac{K_2}{2}B + \frac{K_3}{2}D + \frac{l_1}{l_3} K_3 R + \frac{h}{f}\left(K_2 - \frac{l_2}{l_3} K_3\right) R_1 \\
&\qquad\qquad + FM_{CB} + FM_{CD} = 0, \\[1em]
&\left(K_3 + \frac{3}{4} K_4\right)D + \frac{K_3}{2}C + \frac{l_1}{l_3} K_3 R - \left(\frac{K_4}{2} + \frac{h l_2}{f l_3} K_3\right) R_1 + FM_{DC} = 0.
\end{aligned}\right\} \quad (253a)$$

70. Four-legged Symmetrical Hip Bent with Symmetrical Vertical Loading.

—This case, shown in Fig. 195, is very much similar to the

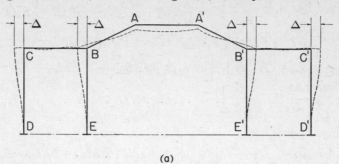

(a)

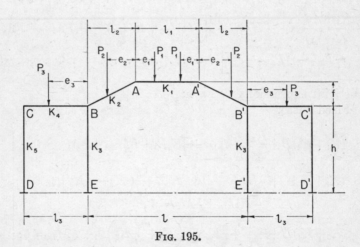

FIG. 195.

one discussed in Art. 66. As sketched in (a), the tops of the legs displace the same distance Δ. Then, indicating the deflection term of the legs BE and CD by R, the corresponding term for the inclined roof member AB will again be given by the familiar expression

$$R_{AB}=-\frac{h}{f}R.$$

The deflection expressions are similar to those given by eqs. (240), Rewritten for the slight changes in notation, we have:

(a) Fixed bases,

$$-\left(\frac{h^2}{f^2}K_2+K_3+K_5\right)R=\frac{3h}{4f}K_2A+\frac{3}{4}\left(\frac{h}{f}K_2-K_3\right)B-\frac{3}{4}K_5C$$
$$+\frac{h}{2f}[(FM_{AB}+FM_{BA})+(P_1+P_2)l_2-P_2e_2]; \quad . \quad . \quad . \quad (240b)$$

(b) Hinged bases,

$$-\left(\frac{h^2}{f^2}K_2+\frac{K_3+K_5}{4}\right)R=\frac{3h}{4f}K_2A+\frac{3}{4}\left(\frac{h}{f}K_2-\frac{K_3}{2}\right)B-\frac{3}{8}K_5C$$

$$+\frac{h}{2f}[(FM_{AB}+FM_{BA})+(P_1+P_2)l_2-P_2e_2] \quad . \quad . \quad . \quad . \quad (240c)$$

The joint expressions are in the following forms:

(a) Fixed bases,

$$\left(\frac{K_1}{2}+K_2\right)A+\frac{K_2}{2}B+\frac{h}{f}K_2R+FM_{AA'}+FM_{AB}=0,$$

$$(K_2+K_3+K_4)B+\frac{K_2}{2}A+\frac{K_4}{2}C+\left(\frac{h}{f}K_2-K_3\right)R+FM_{BA}+FM_{BC}=0, \quad \} (254)$$

$$(K_4+K_5)C+\frac{K_4}{2}B-K_5R+FM_{CB}=0;$$

(b) Hinged bases,

$$\left(\frac{K_1}{2}+K_2\right)A+\frac{K_2}{2}B+\frac{h}{f}K_2R+FM_{AA'}+FM_{AB}=0,$$

$$\left(K_2+\frac{3}{4}K_3+K_4\right)B+\frac{K_2}{2}A+\frac{K_4}{2}C+\left(\frac{h}{f}K_2-\frac{K_3}{2}\right)R+FM_{BA}+FM_{BC}=0,$$

$$\left(K_4+\frac{3}{4}K_5\right)C+\frac{K_4}{2}B-\frac{K_5}{2}R+FM_{CB}=0.$$

$$(254a)$$

ILLUSTRATIVE EXAMPLE

The symmetrical bent shown in Fig. 195b is carrying a uniform vertical load of 1 kip per linear foot. Assuming the legs to be fixed at the bases, determine the end moments.

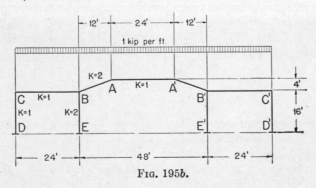

FIG. 195b.

Solution: Applying eqs. (240b) and (254),

$$-35R = 6A + 4.5B - 0.75C + 432;$$
$$79A - 2B + 12C = 9432,$$
$$-2A + 296B + 44C = 2664,$$
$$12A + 44B + 138.5C = 2496;$$

from which

$$A = 118.888, \quad B = 9.085, \quad C = 4.835;$$

and

$$R = -33.788, \quad R_{AB} = 135.152.$$

Then

$$M_{AA'} = 59.444 - 48 = 11.44,$$
$$M_{AB} = 2(118.888 + 4.542 - 135.152) + 12 = -11.44;$$

$$M_{BA} = 2(9.085 + 59.444 - 135.152) - 12 = -145.25,$$
$$M_{BC} = 9.085 + 2.417 + 48 = 59.50,$$
$$M_{BE} = 2(9.085 + 33.788) = 85.75;$$

$$M_{CB} = 4.835 + 4.542 - 48 = -38.62,$$
$$M_{CD} = 4.835 + 33.788 = 38.62;$$

$$M_{DC} = 2.417 + 33.788 = 36.20;$$
$$M_{ED} = 2(4.542 + 33.788) = 76.66.$$

PROBLEMS

75. Obtain the deflection expressions for the bent shown in Fig. 196, corresponding to fixed and hinged bases.

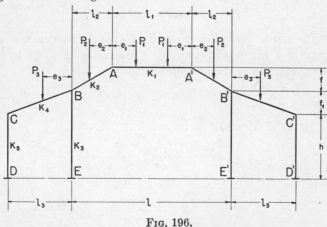

Fig. 196.

76. Determine the end moments for the bent shown in Fig. 195b, assuming the legs to be hinged at the bases.

71. Symmetrical Monitor Bent with Unsymmetrical Loading.—Under the system of loading shown in Fig. 197, the bent will have

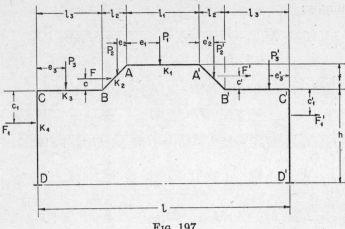

Fig. 197.

five unknown deflections; namely, the deflection of AB or $A'B'$ in the trapezoidal panel $BAA'B'$ and the deflections of the remaining four members. The corresponding deflection terms can be indicated as follows:

$$
\left.
\begin{aligned}
R_{AB} &= R, \\
R_{A'B'} &= R + \frac{h}{f}(R_2 - R_2'), \\
R_{AA'} &= \frac{l_2}{l_1}\frac{h}{f}(R_2' - R_2) - \frac{2l_2}{l_1}R - \frac{l_3}{l_1}(R_1 + R_1'), \\
R_{BC} &= R_1, \\
R_{B'C'} &= R_1', \\
R_{CD} &= R_2, \\
R_{C'D'} &= R_2'.
\end{aligned}
\right\} \quad \ldots \ldots \; (a)
$$

In deriving the deflection expressions, use will be made of the following relations:

(1) The horizontal shear at C, in member CD, equals that at B, in member AB;
(2) The horizontal shear at C', in member $C'D'$, equals that at B', in member $A'B'$;
(3) The vertical shear at C, obtained from CB, equals the vertical reaction at D;
(4) The vertical shear at C', obtained from $C'B'$, equals the vertical reaction at D';
(5) The sum of the horizontal reactions at the bases D and D' equals the sum of the external lateral loads.

Accordingly:

$$\frac{1}{h}[(M_{CD}+M_{DC})+F_1(h-c_1)]=\frac{1}{f}[(M_{AB}+M_{BA})-P_2e_2$$
$$-F(f-c)+V_Bl_2],$$

$$\frac{1}{h}[(M_{C'D'}+M_{D'C'})+F_1'(h-c_1')]=\frac{1}{f}[(M_{A'B'}+M_{B'A'})$$
$$+P_2'e_2'-F'(f-c')-V_{B'}l_2],$$

$$\frac{1}{l_3}[(M_{CB}+M_{BC})-P_3(l_3-e_3)]=\frac{1}{l}(M_{DC}+M_{D'C'}+EM_{D'}),$$

$$\frac{1}{l_3}[(M_{C'B'}+M_{B'C'})+P_3'(l_3-e_3')]=\frac{1}{l}(M_{DC}+M_{D'C'}+EM_D),$$

$$\frac{1}{h}[(M_{CD}+M_{DC})+(M_{C'D'}+M_{D'C'})-F_1c_1-F_1'c_1']$$
$$=-(F+F'+F_1'+F_1');$$

$$\left. \right\} \cdot \quad (b)$$

in which V_B and $V_{B'}$ indicate the vertical shears at B and B', EM_D and $EM_{D'}$ the moments due to the external forces—taken about D and D', respectively, and equal:

$$V_B=-\frac{1}{l_3}[(M_{BC}+M_{CB})+P_se_s],$$
$$V_{B'}=\frac{1}{l_3}[(M_{B'C'}+M_{C'B'})-P_3'e_3'];$$

$$\left. \right\} \cdots \cdots \cdots (c)$$

$$EM_D=F(h+c)+F'(h+c')+F_1(h-c_1)$$
$$+F_1'(h-c_1')+P_3e_3+P_2(l_3+l_2-e_2)+P_1(l_3+l_2+e_1)$$
$$+P_2'(l_3+l_2+l_1+e_2')+P_3'(l-e_3'),$$

$$EM_{D'}=F(h+c)+F'(h+c')+F_1(h-c_1)+F_1'(h-c_1')$$
$$-P_3'e_3'-P_2'(l_3+l_2-e_2')-P_1(l_3+l_2+l_1-e_1)$$
$$-P_2(l_3+l_2+l_1+e_2)-P_3(l-e_3).$$

Substituting the values of V_B, $V_{B'}$ and the end moments in eqs. (b), and assuming fixed bases, the deflection expressions become:

$$2\left(K_2R-\frac{l_2}{l_3}K_3R_1-\frac{f}{h}K_4R_2\right)=\frac{3}{2}K_2A+\frac{3}{2}\left(K_2-\frac{l_2}{l_3}K_3\right)B$$

$$-\frac{3}{2}\left(\frac{l_2}{l_3}K_3+\frac{f}{h}K_4\right)C-(FM_{CD}+FM_{DC})+(FM_{AB}+FM_{BA})$$

$$-\frac{l_2}{l_3}(FM_{BC}+FM_{CB})-F(f-c)-\frac{f}{h}F_1(h-c_1)-P_2e_2-\frac{l_2}{l_3}P_3e_3; \quad (255a)$$

$$2\left[K_2R-\left(\frac{f}{h}K_4+\frac{h}{f}K_2\right)R_2'-\frac{l_2}{l_3}K_3R_1'+\frac{h}{f}K_2R_2\right]=\frac{3}{2}K_2A'$$

$$+\frac{3}{2}\left(K_2-\frac{l_2}{l_3}K_3\right)B'-\frac{3}{2}\left(\frac{l_2}{l_3}K_3+{}_hK_4\right)C'-(FM_{C'D'}+FM_{D'C'})$$

$$+(FM_{A'B'}+FM_{B'A'})-\frac{l_2}{l_3}(FM_{B'C'}+FM_{C'B'})-F'(f-c')$$

$$-\frac{f}{h}F_1'(h-c_1')+P_2'e_2'+\frac{l_2}{l_3}P_3'e_3';\quad\dots\dots\dots\quad(255b)$$

$$K_4(R_2+R_2')-2\frac{l}{l_3}K_3R_1=-\frac{3l}{2l_3}K_3B+\frac{1}{2}\left(K_4-3\frac{l}{l_3}K_3\right)C$$

$$+\frac{K_4}{2}C'+FM_{DC}+FM_{D'C'}-\frac{l}{l_3}(FM_{BC}+FM_{CB})$$

$$+EM_{D'}+\frac{l}{l_3}P_3(l_3-e_3).\dots\dots\dots\dots\dots\quad(255c)$$

$$K_4(R_2+R_2')-2\frac{l}{l_3}K_3R_1'=-\frac{3l}{2l_3}K_3B'+\frac{1}{2}\left(K_4-3\frac{l}{l_3}K_3\right)C'$$

$$+\frac{K_4}{2}C+FM_{DC}+FM_{D'C'}-\frac{l}{l_3}(FM_{B'C'}+FM_{C'B'})$$

$$+EM_D-\frac{l}{l_3}P_3'(l_2-e_3')\;;\dots\dots\dots\dots\dots\quad(255d)$$

$$2K_4(R_2+R_2')=\frac{3}{2}K_4(C+C')+(FM_{CD}+FM_{DC})+(FM_{C'D'}$$

$$+FM_{D'C'})-F_1c_1-F_1'c_1'+h(F+F'+F_1+F_1').\dots\dots\quad(255e)$$

In the case of hinged bases, we have:

$$2\left(K_2R-\frac{l_2}{l_3}K_3R_1-\frac{f}{4h}K_4R_2\right)=\frac{3}{2}K_2A+\frac{3}{2}\left(K_2-\frac{l_2}{l_3}K_3\right)B$$

$$-\frac{3}{2}\left(\frac{l_2}{l_3}K_3+\frac{f}{2h}K_4\right)C-HM_{CD}+(FM_{AB}+FM_{BA})$$

$$-\frac{l_2}{l_3}(FM_{BC}+FM_{CB})-F(f-c)-\frac{f}{h}F_1(h-c_1)-P_2e_2-\frac{l_2}{l_3}P_3e_3;\quad(255f)$$

$$2\left[K_2R-\left(\frac{f}{4h}K_4+\frac{h}{f}K_2\right)R_2'-\frac{l_2}{l_3}K_3R_1'+\frac{h}{f}K_2R_2\right]=\frac{3}{2}K_2A'$$

$$+\frac{3}{2}\left(K_2-\frac{l_2}{l_3}K_3\right)B'-\frac{3}{2}\left(\frac{l_2}{l_3}K_3+\frac{f}{2h}K_4\right)C'-HM_{C'D'}$$

$$+(FM_{A'B'}+FM_{B'A'})-\frac{l_2}{l_3}(FM_{B'C'}+FM_{C'B'})$$

$$-F'(f-c')-\frac{f}{h}F_1'(h-c_1')+P_2'e_2'+\frac{l_2}{l_3}P_3'e_3';\quad\dots\dots\quad(255g)$$

$$2K_3R_1 = \frac{3}{2}K_3(B+C) + (FM_{BC} + FM_{CB}) - P_3(l_3 - e_3) - \frac{l_3}{l}EM_{D'}; \quad . \quad (255h)$$

$$2K_3R_1' = \frac{3}{2}K_3(B' + C') + (FM_{B'C'} + FM_{C'B'}) + P_3'(l_3 - e_3')$$
$$- \frac{l_3}{l}EM_D; \; . \; . \; . \; . \; . \; . \; . \; . \; . \; . \; . \; . \; (255i)$$

$$\frac{K_4}{2}(R_2 + R_2') = \frac{3}{4}K_4(C + C') + HM_{CD} + HM_{C'D'} - F_1C_1 - F_1'c_1'$$
$$+ h(F' + F'' + F_1 + F_1') \; . \; . \; . \; . \; . \; . \; . \; (255k)$$

The joint expressions at A, A', B and B', for fixed and hinged bases, are in the following forms:

$$\left.\begin{aligned}
&(K_1 + K_2)A + \frac{K_1}{2}A' + \frac{K_2}{2}B + \left(\frac{2l^2}{l_1}K_1 - K_2\right)R \\
&+ K_1\left[\frac{l_3}{l_1}(R_1 + R_1') - \frac{hl_2}{fl_1}(R_2' - R_2)\right] + FM_{AB} + FM_{AA'} = 0, \\
&(K_1 + K_2)A' + \frac{K_1}{2}A + \frac{K_2}{2}B' + \left(\frac{2l_2}{l_1}K_1 - K_2\right)R + \frac{l_3}{l_1}K_1(R_1 + R_1') \\
&+ \left(\frac{h}{f}K_2 - \frac{hl_2}{fl_1}K_1\right)(R_2' - R_2) + FM_{A'B'} + FM_{A'A} = 0, \\
&(K_2 + K_3)B + \frac{K_2}{2}A + \frac{K_3}{2}C - K_2R - K_3R_1 + FM_{BA} + FM_{BC} = 0, \\
&(K_2 + K_3)B' + \frac{K_2}{2}A' + \frac{K_3}{2}C' - K_3R_1' - K_2\left[R + \frac{h}{f}(R_2 - R_2')\right] \\
&+ FM_{B'A'} + FM_{B'C'} = 0.
\end{aligned}\right\} \quad . \quad (256)$$

For the joint expressions at C and C', corresponding to the two conditions of support, we have:

(a) Fixed bases,

$$\left.\begin{aligned}
&(K_3 + K_4)C + \frac{K_3}{2}B - K_3R_1 - K_4R_2 + FM_{CB} + FM_{CD} = 0, \\
&(K_3 + K_4)C' + \frac{K_3}{2}B' - K_3R_1' - K_4R_2' + FM_{C'B'} \\
&\qquad\qquad + FM_{C'D'} = 0;
\end{aligned}\right\} \quad . \; .(256f)$$

(b) Hinged bases,

$$\left.\begin{aligned}
&\left(K_3 + \frac{3}{4}K_4\right)C + \frac{K_3}{2}B - K_3R_1 - \frac{K_4}{2}R_2 + FM_{CB} + HM_{CD} = 0, \\
&\left(K_2 + \frac{3}{4}K_4\right)C' + \frac{K_3}{2}B' - K_3R_1' - \frac{K_4}{2}R_2' + FM_{C'B'} \\
&\qquad\qquad + HM_{C'D'} = 0.
\end{aligned}\right\} \quad (256h)$$

72. Three-legged Symmetrical Hip Bent with Unsymmetrical Loading.—For the system of loading shown in Fig. 198, the deflection

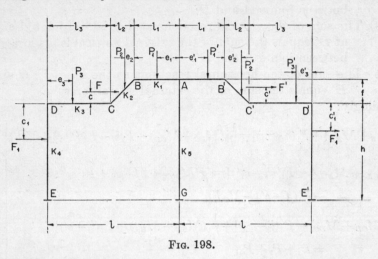

FIG. 198.

terms of the bent—corresponding to five unknown deflections—may be notated as follows:

$$
\left.\begin{aligned}
R_{AB} &= R,\\[2pt]
R_{AB'} &= R',\\[2pt]
R_{DE} &= R_1,\\[2pt]
R_{AG} &= R_2,\\[2pt]
R_{D'E'} &= R_1',\\[2pt]
R_{BC} &= \frac{(f+h)}{f}R_2 - \frac{h}{f}R_1,\\[4pt]
R_{B'C'} &= \frac{(f+h)}{f}R_2 - \frac{h}{f}R_1',\\[4pt]
R_{CD} &= \frac{l_2}{l_3}\cdot\frac{h}{f}R_1 - \frac{l_1}{l_3}\cdot\frac{(f+h)}{f}R_2,\\[4pt]
R_{C'D'} &= \frac{l_2}{l_3}\cdot\frac{h}{f}R_1' - \frac{l_1}{l_3}R' - \frac{l_2}{l_3}\cdot\frac{(f+h)}{f}R_2.
\end{aligned}\right\} \quad \ldots \ldots \ldots (d)
$$

The five deflection expressions are derived from the following considerations:

(1) The horizontal shear at D, in member DE, equals that at C, in member BC;

(2) The horizontal shear at D', in member $D'E'$, equals that at C', in member $B'C'$;

(3) The sum of the vertical reactions at the left of joint A and at D equals the sum of the external vertical loads located between joints A and D;

(4) The sum of the vertical reactions at the right of joint A and at D' equals the sum of the external vertical loads located between joints A and D';

(5) The sum of the horizontal reactions at the bases E, G and E' equals the sum of the external lateral forces.

Accordingly:

$$\frac{1}{h}[(M_{DE}+M_{ED})+F_1(h-c_1)]=\frac{1}{f}[(M_{BC}+M_{CB})-P_2e_2-F(f-c)+V_cl_2],$$

$$\frac{1}{h}[(M_{D'E'}+M_{E'D'})+F_1'(h-c_1')]=\frac{1}{f}[(M_{B'C'}+M_{C'B'})+P_2'e_2'$$
$$-F'(f-c')-V_{c'}l_2],$$

$$-\frac{1}{l_3}[(M_{CD}+M_{DC})-P_3(l_3-e_3)]+\frac{1}{l_1}[(M_{AB}+M_{BA})+P_1(l_1-e_1)]$$
$$=P_1+P_2+P_3,$$

$$\frac{1}{l_3}[(M_{C'D'}+M_{D'C'})+P_3'(l_3-e_3')]-\frac{1}{l_1}[(M_{AB'}+M_{B'A})-P_1'(l_1-e_1')]$$
$$=P_1'+P_2'+P_3',$$

$$\frac{1}{h}[(M_{DE}+M_{ED})-F_1c_1+(M_{D'E'}+M_{E'D'})-F_1'c_1']$$
$$+\frac{1}{f+h}(M_{AG}+M_{GA})=F+F'+F_1+F_1'.$$

$\left.\rule{0pt}{11em}\right\}(e)$

Substituting the values of the end moments, and noting that

$$V_c=-\frac{1}{l_3}[(M_{CD}+M_{DC})+P_3e_3],$$

$$V_{c'}=\frac{1}{l_3}[(M_{C'D'}+M_{D'C'})-P_3'e_3'],$$

in the case of fixed bases we have:

$$2\frac{l_1l_2}{l_3^2}K_3R-2\frac{h}{f}\Big(\frac{f^2}{h^2}K_4+K_2+\frac{l_2^2}{l_3^2}K_3\Big)R_1+2\frac{(f+h)}{f}\Big(K_2+\frac{l_2^2}{l_3^2}K_3\Big)R_2$$

$$=\frac{3}{2}K_2B+\frac{3}{2}\Big(K_2-\frac{l_2}{l_3}K_3\Big)C-\frac{3}{2}\Big(\frac{l_2}{l_3}K_3+\frac{f}{h}K_4\Big)D+(FM_{BC}+FM_{CB})$$

$$-\frac{f}{h}(FM_{DE}+FM_{ED})-\frac{l_2}{l_3}(FM_{CD}+FM_{DC})-\frac{f}{h}F_1(h-c_1)$$

$$-F(f-c)-P_2e_2-\frac{l_2}{l_3}P_3e_3, \quad \ldots \ldots \ldots \ldots \quad (257a)$$

$$2\frac{l_1 l_2}{l_3^2}K_3 R' - 2\frac{h}{f}\left(\frac{f^2}{h_2}K_4 + K_2 + \frac{l_2^2}{l_3^2}K_3\right)R_1' + 2\frac{(f+h)}{f}\left(K_2 + \frac{l_2^2}{l_3^2}K_3\right)R_2'$$

$$= \frac{3}{2}K_2 B' + \frac{3}{2}\left(K_2 - \frac{l_2}{l_3}K_3\right)C' - \frac{3}{2}\left(\frac{l_2}{l_3}K_3 + \frac{f}{h}K_4\right)D'$$

$$+ (FM_{B'C'} + FM_{C'B'}) - \frac{f}{h}(FM_{D'E'} + FM_{E'D'})$$

$$- \frac{l_2}{l_3}(FM_{C'D'} + FM_{D'C'}) - \frac{f}{h}F_1'(h - c_1') - F'(f - c')$$

$$+ P_2' e_2' + \frac{l_2}{l_3}P_3' e_3', \quad \ldots \ldots \ldots \ldots \quad (257b)$$

$$2\left(\frac{l_3}{l_1}K_1 + \frac{l_1}{l_3}K_3\right)R - 2\frac{hl_2}{fl_3}K_3 R_1 + 2\frac{(f+h)l_2}{fl_3}K_3 R_2 = \frac{3l_3}{2l_1}K_1(A+B)$$

$$- \frac{3}{2}K_3(C+D) + \frac{l_3}{l_1}(FM_{AB} + FM_{BA}) - (FM_{CD} + FM_{DC})$$

$$+ P_1\frac{l_3}{l_1}(l_1 - e_1) + P_3(l_3 - e_3) - l_3(P_1 + P_2 + P_3), \quad \ldots \ldots \quad (257c)$$

$$2\left(\frac{l_3}{l_1}K_1 + \frac{l_1}{l_3}K_3\right)R' - 2\frac{hl_2}{fl_3}K_3 R_1' + 2\frac{(f+h)l_2}{fl_3}K_3 R_2 = \frac{3l_3}{2l_1}K_1(A + B')$$

$$- \frac{3}{2}K_3(C' + D') + \frac{l_3}{l_1}(FM_{AB'} + FM_{B'A}) - (FM_{C'D'} + FM_{D'C'})$$

$$= P_1'\frac{l_3}{l_1}(l_1 - e_1') - P_3'(l_3 - e_3') + l_3(P_1' + P_2' + P_3'), \quad \ldots \quad (257d)$$

$$2K_4(R_1 + R_1') + \frac{2h}{(f+h)}K_5 R_2 = \frac{3h}{2(f+h)}K_5 A + \frac{3}{2}K_4(D + D') - F_1 c_1$$

$$- F_1' c_1' + (FM_{DE} + FM_{ED}) + (FM_{D'E'} + FM_{E'D'})$$

$$- h(F + F' + F_1 + F_1') \quad \ldots \ldots \ldots \ldots \quad (257e)$$

If the bases are hinged, eqs. (257a), (257b) and (257e) will change as follows:

$$2\frac{l_1 l_2}{l_3^2}K_3 R - 2\frac{h}{f}\left(\frac{f^2}{4h^2}K_4 + K_2 + \frac{l_2^2}{l_3^2}K_3\right)R_1 + 2\frac{(f+h)}{f}\left(K_2 + \frac{l_2^2}{l_3^2}K_3\right)R_2$$

$$= \frac{3}{2}K_2 B + \frac{3}{2}\left(K_2 - \frac{l_2}{l_3}K_3\right)C - \frac{3}{2}\left(\frac{l_2}{l_3}K_3 + \frac{f}{2h}K_4\right)D + (FM_{BC} + FM_{CB})$$

$$- \frac{f}{h}HM_{DE} - \frac{l_2}{l_3}(FM_{CD} + FM_{DC}) - \frac{f}{h}F_1(h - c_1)$$

$$- F(f - c) - P_2 e_2 - \frac{l_2}{l_3}P_3 e_3, \quad \ldots \ldots \ldots \vdots \ldots \ldots \quad (257f)$$

$$2\frac{l_1 l_2}{l_3^2}K_3 R' - 2\frac{h}{f}\left(\frac{f^2}{4h^2}K_4 + K_2 + \frac{l_2^2}{l_3^2}K_3\right)R_1' + 2\frac{(f+h)}{f}\left(K_2 + \frac{l_2^2}{l_3^2}K_3\right)R_2'$$

$$=\frac{3}{2}K_2 B' + \frac{3}{2}\left(K_2 - \frac{l_2}{l_3}K_3\right)C' - \frac{3}{2}\left(\frac{l_2}{l_3}K_3 + \frac{f}{2h}K_4\right)D'$$

$$+(FM_{B'C'} + FM_{C'B'}) - \frac{f}{h}HM_{D'E'} - \frac{l_2}{l_3}(FM_{C'D'} + FM_{D'C'})$$

$$-\frac{f}{h}F_1'(h-c_1') - F'(f-c') + P_2'e_2' + \frac{l_2}{l_3}P_3'e_3'\ ,\ \dots\dots \quad (257g)$$

$$\frac{K_4}{2}(R_1 + R_1') + \frac{h}{2(f+h)}K_5 R_2 = \frac{3h}{4(f+h)}K_5 A + \frac{3}{4}K_4(D+D') - F_1 c_1$$

$$-F_1'c_1' + HM_{DE} + HM_{D'E'} - h(F + F' + F_1 + F_1').\ \dots \quad (257h)$$

The joint expressions at B, B', C and C', for both fixed and hinged bases, are in the following forms:

$$(K_1 + K_2)B + \frac{K_1}{2}A + \frac{K_2}{2}C - K_1 R + K_2\left(\frac{h}{f}R_1 - \frac{(f+h)}{f}R_2\right)$$

$$+FM_{BA} + FM_{BC} = 0\ ,\ \dots\dots\dots\dots\dots \quad (258a)$$

$$(K_1 + K_2)B' + \frac{K_1}{2}A' + \frac{K_2}{2}C' - K_1 R' + K_2\left(\frac{h}{f}R_1' - \frac{(f+h)}{f}R_2\right)$$

$$+FM_{B'A} + FM_{B'C'} = 0\ ,\ \dots\dots\dots\dots \quad (258b)$$

$$(K_2 + K_3)C + \frac{K_2}{2}B + \frac{K_3}{2}C + \frac{l_1}{l_3}K_3 R - \frac{h}{f}\left(\frac{l_2}{l_3}K_3 - K_2\right)R_1$$

$$+\frac{(f+h)}{f}\left(\frac{l_2}{l_3}K_3 - K_2\right) + FM_{CB} + FM_{CD} = 0,\ \dots\dots \quad (258c)$$

$$(K_2 + K_3)C' + \frac{K_2}{2}B' + \frac{K_3}{2}C' + \frac{l_1}{l_3}K_3 R' - \frac{h}{f}\left(\frac{l_2}{l_3}K_3 - K_2\right)R_1'$$

$$+\frac{(f+h)}{f}\left(\frac{l_2}{l_3}K_3 - K_2\right)R_2 + FM_{C'B'} + FM_{C'D'} = 0\ \dots \quad (258d)$$

At A, D and D', we have:

(a) Fixed bases,

$$(2K_1 + K_5)A + \frac{K_1}{2}(B+B') - K_1(R+R') - K_5 R_2 + FM_{AB}$$
$$+ FM_{AB}' = 0,$$

$$(K_3 + K_4)D + \frac{K_3}{2}C + \frac{l_1}{l_3}K_3 R - \left(K_4 + \frac{hl_2}{fl_3}K_3\right)R_1 + \frac{(f+h)l_2}{fl_3}K_3 R_2$$
$$+ FM_{DC} + FM_{DE} = 0,$$

$$(K_3 + K_4)D' + \frac{K_3}{2}C' + \frac{l_1}{l_3}K_3 R' - \left(K_4 + \frac{hl_2}{fl_3}K_3\right)R_1' + \frac{(f+h)l_2}{fl_3}K_3 R_2$$
$$+ FM_{D'C'} + FM_{D'E'} = 0;$$

$$\left.\vphantom{\begin{array}{c}a\\a\\a\\a\\a\\a\\a\end{array}}\right\}\ (258f)$$

(b) Hinged bases,

$$\left(2K_1+\frac{3K_5}{4}\right)A+\frac{K_1}{2}(B+B')-K_1(R+R')-\frac{K_5}{2}R_2$$
$$+FM_{AB}+FM_{AB'}=0,$$

$$\left(K_3+\frac{3}{4}K_4\right)D+\frac{K_3}{2}C+\frac{l_1}{l_3}K_3R-\left(\frac{K_4}{2}+\frac{hl_2}{fl_3}K_3\right)R_1$$
$$+\frac{(f+h)l_2}{fl_3}K_3R_2+FM_{DC}+HM_{DE}=0,$$

$$\left(K_3+\frac{3}{4}K_4\right)D'+\frac{K_3}{2}C'+\frac{l_1}{l_3}K_3R'-\left(\frac{K_4}{2}+\frac{hl_2}{fl_3}K_3\right)R_1'$$
$$+\frac{(f+h)l_2}{fl_3}K_3R_2+FM_{D'C'}+HM_{D'E'}=0.$$

$$\left.\right\} \quad \cdots \quad (258h)$$

73. Four-legged Symmetrical Hip Bent with Unsymmetrical Loading.—The deformations of the bent in Fig. 199 are similar to those

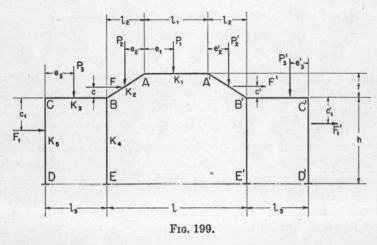

FIG. 199.

shown in Fig. 191. The deflection terms of the bent, corresponding to three unknown deflections, may be listed as follows:

$$R_{AB}=R,$$
$$R_{BE}=R_{CD}=R_1,$$
$$R_{B'E'}=R_{C'D'}=R_1',$$
$$R_{A'B'}=R+\frac{h}{f}(R_1-R_1'),$$
$$R_{AA'}=-\frac{2l_2}{l_1}R+\frac{hl_2}{fl_1}(R_1'-R_1).$$

$$\left.\right\} \quad \cdots \cdots \quad (f)$$

The three deflection expressions are derived from the following considerations:

(1) The horizontal shear at B, obtained from AB, equals the sum of shears at B and C—obtained from BE and CD;

(2) The horizontal shear at B', obtained from $A'B'$, equals the sum of shears at B' and C'—obtained from $B'E'$ and $C'D'$;

(3) The sum of the horizontal reactions at the bases D, E, E' and D' equals the sum of the external lateral loads.

Thus

$$\frac{1}{f}[(M_{AB}+M_{BA})-F(f-c)-P_2e_2+V_Bl_2]=\frac{1}{h}[(M_{BE}+M_{EB})$$
$$+(M_{CD}+M_{DC})+F_1(h-c_1)B,$$

$$\frac{1}{f}[(M_{A'B'}+M_{B'A'})-F'(f-c)+P_2'e_2'-V_{B'}l_2]=\frac{1}{h}[(M_{B'E'}$$
$$+M_{E'B'})+(M_{C'D'}+M_{D'C'})+F_1'(h-c_1')], \quad\quad \Bigg\} \cdot \cdot (g)$$

$$\frac{1}{h}[(M_{CD}+M_{DC})+(M_{BE}+M_{EB})+(M_{B'E'}+M_{E'B'})$$
$$+(M_{C'D'}+M_{D'C'})-F_1c_1-F_1'c_1']$$
$$=-(F+F'+F_1+F_1').$$

Substituting the values of the end moments, and noting that the vertical shears at B and B' equal

$$V_B=-\frac{1}{l}[M_{BA}+M_{B'A'}+Fc+F'c'-P_1(l_1+l_2-e_1)$$
$$-P'_2(l_2-e_2')-P_2(l_1+l_2+e_2)], \quad\quad \Bigg\} \cdot \cdot \cdot (h)$$

$$V_{B'}=\frac{1}{l}[M_{BA}+M_{B'A'}+Fc+F'c'+P_2(l_2-e_2)$$
$$+P_1(l_2+e_1)+P_2'(l_2+l_1+e_2')],$$

for fixed bases we have:

$$2\left(1-\frac{l_2}{l}\right)K_2R-\left[2\frac{f}{h}(K_4+K_5)+\frac{hl_2}{fl}K_2\right]R_1-\frac{hl_2}{fl}K_2R_1'=\left(3-\frac{l_2}{l}\right)\frac{K_2}{2}A$$

$$-\frac{l_2}{2l}K_2A'+\frac{3}{2}K_2\left(1-\frac{fK_4}{hK_2}-\frac{2l_2}{3l}\right)B-\frac{l_2}{l}K_2B'-\frac{3f}{2h}K_5C-\frac{f}{h}F_1(h-c_1)$$

$$-F(f-c)-P_2e_2+(FM_{AB}+FM_{BA})-\frac{f}{h}(FM_{CD}+FM_{DC})$$

$$-\frac{l_2}{l}[FM_{BA}+FM_{B'A'}+Fc+F'c'-P_1(l_1+l_2-e_1)$$

$$-P_2'(l_2-e_2)-P_2(l_1+l_2+e_2)], \quad \ldots \ldots \ldots \ldots \quad (259a)$$

$$2\left(1-\frac{l_2}{l}\right)K_2R+\frac{h}{f}\left(2-\frac{l_2}{l}\right)K_2R_1-\left[2\frac{f}{h}(K_4+K_5)+\frac{h}{f}\left(2-\frac{l_2}{l}\right)K_2\right]R_1'$$

$$=\left(3-\frac{l_2}{l}\right)\frac{K_2}{2}A'-\frac{l_2}{2l}K_2A+\frac{3}{2}\left(1-\frac{fK_4}{hK_2}-\frac{2l_2}{3l}\right)K_2B'-\frac{l_2}{l}K_2B$$

$$-\frac{3f}{2h}K_5C'-\frac{f}{h}F_1'(h-c_1')-F''(f-c')+P_2'e_2'+(FM_{A'B'}$$

$$+FM_{B'A'})-\frac{f}{h}(FM_{C'D'}+FM_{D'C'})-\frac{l_2}{l}[FM_{BA}+FM_{B'A'}+Fc$$

$$+F'c'+P_2(l_2-e_2)+P_1(l_2+e_1)+P_2'(l_2+l_1+e_2')],\quad\ldots\quad(259b)$$

$$2(K_4+K_5)\,(R_1+R_1')=\frac{3}{2}K_4(B+B')+\frac{3}{2}K_5(C+C')$$

$$+(FM_{CD}+FM_{DC})+(FM_{C'D'}+FM_{D'C'})-F_1c_1-F_1'c_1'$$

$$+h(F+F'+F_1+F_1')\ \ldots\ldots\ldots\ldots\ldots\ldots\quad(259c)$$

For hinged bases the expressions become:

$$2K_2\left(1-\frac{l_2}{l}\right)R-\left[\frac{f}{2h}(K_4+K_5)+\frac{hl_2}{fl}K_2\right]R_1-\frac{hl_2}{fl}K_2R_1'=\left(3-\frac{l_2}{l}\right)\frac{K_2}{2}A$$

$$-\frac{l_2}{2l}K_2A'+\frac{3}{4}\left(2-\frac{fK_4}{hK_2}-\frac{4l_2}{3l}\right)K_2B-\frac{l_2}{l}K_2B'-\frac{3f}{4h}K_5C-\frac{f}{h}F_1(h-c_1)$$

$$-F(f-c)-P_2e_2+(FM_{AB}+FM_{BA})-\frac{f}{h}HM_{CD}-\frac{l_2}{l}[FM_{BA}$$

$$+FM_{B'A'}+Fc+F'c'-P_1(l_1+l_2-e_2)-P_2'(l_2-e_2)$$

$$-P_2(l_1+l_2+e_2)],\ \ldots\ldots\ldots\ldots\ldots\ldots\quad(259d)$$

$$2\left(1-\frac{l_2}{l}\right)K_2R+\frac{h}{f}K_2\left(2-\frac{l_2}{l_1}\right)R_1-\left[\frac{f}{2h}(K_4+K_5)+\frac{h}{f}\left(2-\frac{l_2}{l}\right)K_2\right]R_1'$$

$$=\left(3-\frac{l_2}{l}\right)\frac{K_2}{2}A'-\frac{l_2}{2l}K_2A+\frac{3}{4}\left(2-\frac{fK_4}{hK_2}-\frac{4l_2}{3l}\right)K_2B'-\frac{l_2}{l}K_2B$$

$$-\frac{3f}{4h}K_5C'-\frac{f}{h}F_1'(h-c_1')-F'(f-c')+P_2'e_2'$$

$$+(FM_{A'B'}+FM_{B'A'})-\frac{f}{h}HM_{C'D'}-\frac{l_2}{l}[FM_{BA}+FM_{B'A'}+Fc$$

$$+F'c'+P_2(l_2-e_2)+P_1(l_2+e_1)+P_2'(l_2+l_1+e_2')],\quad\ldots\quad(259e)$$

$$\frac{1}{2}(K_4+K_5)\,(R_1+R_1')=\frac{3}{4}K_4(B+B')+\frac{3}{4}K_5(C+C')+HM_{DC}+HM_{C'D'}$$

$$-F_1c_1-F_1'c_1'+h(F+F'+F_1+F_1')\ \ldots\ldots\ldots\ldots\quad(259f)$$

The joint expressions are in the following forms:

(a) Joints A and A', fixed and hinged bases,

$$\left.\begin{aligned}(K_1+K_2)A+\frac{K_1}{2}A'+\frac{K_2}{2}B+\left(2\frac{l_2}{l_1}K_1-K_2\right)R+\frac{hl_2}{fl_1}K_1(R_1-R_1')\\+FM_{AA'}+FM_{AB}=0,\\[4pt](K_1+K_2)A'+\frac{K_1}{2}A+\frac{K_2}{2}B'+\left(2\frac{l_2}{l_1}K_1-K_2\right)R\\+\frac{h}{f}\left(\frac{l_2}{l_1}K_1-K_2\right)(R_1-R_1')+FM_{A'A}+FM_{A'B'}=0;\end{aligned}\right\}\quad(260)$$

(b) Joints B, B', C and C', fixed bases,

$$
\left.
\begin{aligned}
&(K_2+K_3+K_4)B+\frac{K_2}{2}A+\frac{K_3}{2}C,\, K_2R-K_4R_1 \\
&\quad +FM_{BA}+FM_{BC}=0, \\
&(K_2+K_3+K_4)B'+\frac{K_2}{2}A'+\frac{K_3}{2}C'-K_2R-\frac{h}{f}K_2R_1 \\
&\quad +\left(\frac{h}{f}K_2-K_4\right)R_1{}'+FM_{B'A'}+FM_{B'C'}=0, \\
&(K_3+K_5)C+\frac{K_3}{2}B-K_5R_1+FM_{CB}+FM_{CD}=0, \\
&(K_3+K_5)C'+\frac{K_3}{2}B'-K_5R_1{}'+FM_{C'B'}+FM_{C'D'}=0;
\end{aligned}
\right\} \qquad \cdot \quad (260f)
$$

(c) Joints B, B', C, C', hinged bases,

$$
\left.
\begin{aligned}
&\left(K_2+K_3+\frac{3}{4}K_4\right)B+\frac{K_2}{2}A+\frac{K_3}{2}C-K_2R-\frac{K_4}{2}R_1 \\
&\quad +FM_{BA}+FM_{BC}=0, \\
&\left(K_2+K_3+\frac{3}{4}K_4\right)B'+\frac{K_2}{2}A'+\frac{K_3}{2}C'-K_2R-K_2\frac{h}{f}R_1 \\
&\quad +\left(\frac{h}{f}K_2-\frac{K_4}{2}\right)R_1{}'+FM_{B'A'}+FM_{B'C'}=0, \\
&\left(K_3+\frac{3}{4}K_5\right)C+\frac{K_3}{2}B-\frac{K_5}{2}R_1+HM_{CD}+FM_{CB}=0, \\
&\left(K_3+\frac{3}{4}K_5\right)C'+\frac{K_3}{2}B'-\frac{K_5}{2}R_1{}'+HM_{C'D'}+FM_{C'B'}=0.
\end{aligned}
\right\} \qquad (260h)
$$

CHAPTER VII

BENTS OF IRREGULAR OUTLINE

74. Method of Approach.—The great advantage of slope deflection, as a method of solution of stresses in framed structures, is due to its simplicity of application. It is a general method which can be applied to simple as well as complicated framings with equal ease. The procedure, repeatedly stated and amply illustrated by the solution of various problems in part II, consists of the following steps:

1. Determine the number of unknown deflections in the bent;
2. Using the shear equations of members, obtain an expression for each unknown deflection;
3. Write the joint expression for each joint of the bent;
4. From the expressions of steps 2 and 3 solve for the values of the deflections and deflection angles—by first eliminating the deflections (i. e., deflection terms R).

The number of unknown deflections in a bent is readily determined by the simple formula

$$u=n-2 \qquad \ldots \ldots \ldots \ldots \quad (a)$$

in which n indicates the number of members in a bay or panel under consideration, and u is the number of unknown deflections. Accordingly, the three-member rectangular bent shown in (a), Fig. 200, will

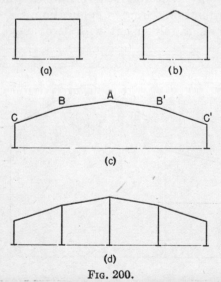

Fig. 200.

319

have only one unknown deflection; the gable bent in (b), 2 unknown deflections; and the 6-member arched bent in (c), 4 unknown deflections. In the case of the five-legged bent in (d), since the adjacent bays have a common member, there will be a single unknown deflection—the common deflection of the upper five joints of the bent.

If the framing is symmetrical and the loading symmetrically applied, the formula becomes

$$u=\frac{n-2}{2} \text{ or } u=\frac{n-1}{2}-1 \quad \ldots \ldots \ldots \quad (b)$$

according whether the panel is composed of an even or odd number of members.

The deflection expressions are characteristic of a bent, their forms varying in accordance with the framing arrangement of the members. To obtain these expressions, the shears or reactions of members at certain joints of the bent are equated to the external loading. For rectangular panels, the derivation involving only horizontal reactions, the resulting equations are of rather simple form; while in nonrectangular panels, due to the necessitated use of both horizontal and vertical reactions, the expressions may become somewhat lengthy. However, except for the computation routine, the required work involves no difficulties.

Since the cross-sectional outline of a building bent may vary in a great number of ways, no attempt will be made to cover the wide range of variation. The following examples will, however, further illustrate the general procedure of application.

Fig. 201 shows a gable bent with two unsymmetrical lean-tos.

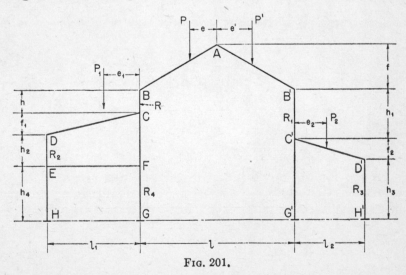

Fig. 201.

According to eq. (a), the bent will have five unknown deflections: two from the upper panel $CBAB'C'$, and one from each of the remaining three panels. In obtaining the corresponding five deflection expressions, the considerations are that:

(a) Members AB and BC must have the same horizontal shear at B;

(b) Members AB' and $B'C'$ must have the same horizontal shear at B';

(c) The sum of horizontal reactions of legs CF and DE equals the shear in BC;

(d) The sum of horizontal reactions of legs $C'G'$ and $D'H'$ equals the shear in $B'C'$; and

(e) The sum of horizontal reactions of legs EH and FG equals that of DE and CF.

Accordingly:

$$\left.\begin{aligned}
&\frac{1}{h}(M_{BC}+M_{CB})=\frac{1}{f}\left(M_{AB}+M_{BA}-Pe+V_B\frac{l}{2}\right),\\[6pt]
&\frac{1}{h_1}(M_{B'C'}+M_{C'B'})=\frac{1}{f}\left(M_{AB'}+M_{B'A}+P'e'-V_{B'}\frac{l}{2}\right),\\[6pt]
&\frac{1}{(f_1+h_2)}(M_{CF}+M_{FC})+\frac{1}{h_2}(M_{DE}+M_{ED})=\frac{1}{h}(M_{BC}+M_{CB}),\\[6pt]
&\frac{1}{(f_2+h_3)}(M_{C'G'}+M_{G'C'})+\frac{1}{h_3}(M_{D'H'}+M_{H'D'})\\[4pt]
&\qquad=\frac{1}{h_1}(M_{B'C'}+M_{C'B'}),\\[6pt]
&\frac{1}{(f_1+h_2)}(M_{CF}+M_{FC})+\frac{1}{h_2}(M_{DE}+M_{ED})\\[4pt]
&\qquad=\frac{1}{h_4}[(M_{DH}+M_{HB})+(M_{FG}+M_{GF})],
\end{aligned}\right\} \quad\cdot\cdot\ (c)$$

in which V_B and $V_{B'}$ are the vertical reactions at B and B', and equal:

$$-V_B=\frac{1}{l}\left[M_{BA}+M_{B'A}-P\left(\frac{l}{2}+e\right)-P'\left(\frac{l}{2}-e'\right)\right],$$

$$V_{B'}=\frac{1}{l}\left[M_{BA}+M_{B'A}+P\left(\frac{l}{2}+e\right)+P'\left(\frac{l}{2}+e'\right)\right].$$

Except for the proper notation of deflection terms R, the joint expressions—obtained by summing up end moments of members meeting at each joint—need no further elaboration. These terms for the various members of the bent may be indicated as follows:

$$R_{BC}=R,\; R_{B'C'}=R_1,\; R_{DE}=R_2,\; R_{D'H'}=R_3,\; R_{FG}=R_4;$$

$$R_{BA}=-R_{AB'}=\frac{1}{2f}(h_1R_1+h_3R_3-hR-h_2R_2-h_4R_4);$$

$$R_{CF}=\frac{h_2}{(f_1+h_2)}R_2;\; R_{C'G'}=\frac{h_3}{(f_2+h_3)}R_3;\; R_{EH}=R_4.$$

As a second example, consider the unsymmetrical gable bent in Fig. 202. In this case, there are only two unknown deflections; namely,

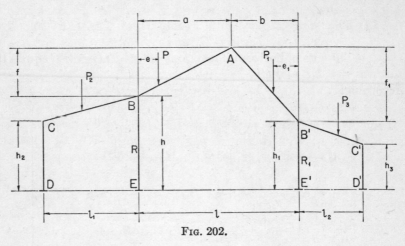

FIG. 202.

the common deflection of joints B and C and that of joints B' and C'. The corresponding two deflection expressions may be developed by equating the horizontal shears just above joints B and B' to the sum of horizontal reactions of the two legs in the respective half of the bent. From the shear equation of member AB we have:

$$M_{AB}+M_{BA}-P(a-e)+V_Ba-H_Bf=0\; .\; .\; .\; .\; .\; (d)$$

in which V_B and H_B, respectively, indicate the vertical and horizontal reactions at B. Noting also that in the portion BAB' of the bent

$$M_{BA}+M_{B'A}-P(l-e)-P_1e_1+V_Bl+H_B(f_1-f)=0,\; .\; .\; .\; (e)$$

solving for V_B, and substituting in eq. (d),

$$M_{AB}+\left(1-\frac{a}{l}\right)M_{BA}-\frac{a}{l}M_{B'A}-P\left[(a-e)-\frac{a}{l}(l-e)\right]$$
$$+\frac{a}{l}P_1e_1-H_B\left[f+\frac{a}{l}(f_1-f)\right]=0;\; .\; .\; .\; .\; .\; .\; (f)$$

and, from members BE and CD,

$$H_B = \frac{1}{h}(M_{BE}+M_{EB}) + \frac{1}{h_2}(M_{CD}+M_{EC}) \quad \cdots \cdots \quad (g)$$

or

$$\frac{1}{f+\frac{a}{l}(f_1-f)}\left[M_{AB}+\left(1-\frac{a}{l}\right)M_{AB}-\frac{a}{l}M_{B'A}+Pe\left(1-\frac{a}{l}\right)+\frac{a}{l}P_1e_1\right]$$

$$=\frac{1}{h}(M_{BE}+M_{EB})+\frac{1}{h_2}(M_{CD}+M_{DC}) \quad \cdots \cdots \quad (262)$$

Similarly, from members in the right half of the bent we obtain:

$$\frac{1}{f_1-\frac{b}{l}(f_1-f)}\left[M_{AB'}+\left(1-\frac{b}{l}\right)M_{B'A}-\frac{b}{l}M_{BA}-\left(1-\frac{b}{l}\right)P_1e_1-\frac{b}{l}Pe\right]$$

$$=\frac{1}{h_1}M_{B'E'}+M_{E'B'})+\frac{1}{h_3}(M_{C'D'}+M_{D'C'}) \quad \cdots \quad (262a)$$

If the deflection terms of members BE and $B'E'$ be indicated by R and R_1, respectively, for the corresponding terms of the remaining members of the bent we can write:

$$\left.\begin{array}{l} R_{CD}=\dfrac{h}{h_2}R,\ R_{C'D'}=\dfrac{h_1}{h_3}R_1, \\[2mm] R_{AB}=\dfrac{b}{af_1+bf}(h_1R_1-hR), \\[2mm] R_{AB'}=\dfrac{a}{af_1+bf}(hR-h_1R_1). \end{array}\right\} \quad \cdots \cdots \quad (263)$$

PART IV. SUPPLEMENTARY CONSIDERATIONS

75. Some Factors in Design Not Considered in Parts II and III.— The analysis of various frames in Part II was confined to stresses resulting from flexure only. Obviously, in most cases, this procedure constitutes the practical confine of design. In certain limited cases, however, it might be necessary—by supplementary analysis—to consider also the effect of the so-called factors of refinement and. special features of framing. The former includes the deformations due to axial and shearing stresses, commonly referred to as "secondary stresses", while under the latter heading we may list such considerations as displacement of foundations, slip or flexibility in connections and the effect of the width of supporting members at the joints. A brief treatment of these factors will now be given.

CHAPTER I

DISPLACEMENT OF FOUNDATIONS

76. Three Components of Displacement.—The displacement at a footing may be considered as the resultant of a maximum of three component motions, namely:

(a) Horizontal spread,
(b) Vertical settlement, and
(c) Rotation.

Similar to the analysis of frames involving side sway, here again, the application of fundamental slope-deflection formulas and the derivation of joint and deflection expressions will be greatly simplified if the probable deformations of the bent are first sketched on its cross-sectional outline. With this in view, it will be found more convenient to treat each of the three components of displacement separately.

HORIZONTAL SPREAD

77. Two-legged Bent.—The simplest study of the effect of horizontal spread at the foundations is presented by the two-legged rectangular bent shown in Fig. 203. The deflected outline of the bent, due to the displacement Δ of the base C, is indicated by dotted lines. It is

324

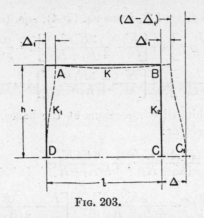

FIG. 203.

seen that when the base C moves a distance Δ to C_1, the upper joints A and B rotate through the respective deflection angles θ_A and θ_B and displace horizontally a distance Δ_1. Accordingly, Δ_1 is the unknown deflection of the leg AD, and that of BC is given by $(\Delta - \Delta_1)$. Denoting the deflection term of the former by R_1,

$$R_{AD} = \frac{6E\Delta_1}{h} = R_1,$$

then the corresponding term of BC becomes

$$R_{BC} = -\frac{6E}{h}(\Delta - \Delta_1) = R_1 - \frac{6E\Delta}{h} \quad \dots \dots \dots \quad (a)$$

As usual, the deflection expression of R_1 is obtained from the shear equations of the two legs. Thus, assuming first fixed connections at D and C, we have:

$$\frac{1}{h}[(M_{AD}+M_{DA})+(M_{BC}+M_{CB})] = \frac{3}{2}(K_1A+K_2B)$$

$$-2(K_1+K_2)R_1 + 12K_2E\frac{\Delta}{h} = 0 \quad \dots \dots \dots \quad (b)$$

from which

$$R_1 = \frac{3}{4}\frac{(K_1A+K_2B)}{(K_1+K_2)} + \frac{6E\Delta K_2}{h(K_1+K_2)}. \quad \dots \dots \quad (264)$$

The joint expressions at A and B are in the following forms:

$$\left.\begin{array}{l} M_{AB}+M_{AD} = (K+K_1)A + \dfrac{K}{2}B - K_1R_1 = 0, \\[2mm] M_{BA}+M_{BC} = (K+K_2)B + \dfrac{K}{2}A - K_2R_1 + \dfrac{6E\Delta}{h}K_2 = 0. \end{array}\right\} \quad \dots \quad (c)$$

Substituting the value of R_1 from eq. (264), eqs. (c) become:

$$\left[K+K_1-\frac{3K_1{}^2}{4(K_1+K_2)}\right]A+\left[\frac{K}{2}-\frac{3K_1K_2}{4(K_1+K_2)}\right]B=\frac{6E\Delta K_1K_2}{h(K_1+K_2)},$$
$$\left[K+K_2-\frac{3K_2{}^2}{4(K_1+K_2)}\right]B+\left[\frac{K}{2}-\frac{3K_1K_2}{4(K_1+K_2)}\right]A=-\frac{6E\Delta K_1K_2}{h(K_1+K_2)}. \quad \left.\right\} \quad (265)$$

In the case of hinged connections at the bases, the deflection and joint expression become:

$$R_1=\frac{3}{2}\frac{(K_1A+K_2B)}{(K_1+K_2)}+\frac{6E\Delta K_2}{h(K_1+K_2)} \quad \cdots \cdots \cdots \quad (264a)$$

$$\left[K+\frac{3}{4}K_1-\frac{3K_1{}^2}{4(K_1+K_2)}\right]A+\left[\frac{K}{2}-\frac{3K_1K_2}{4(K_1+K_2)}\right]B$$
$$=\frac{3E\Delta K_1K_2}{h(K_1+K_2)},$$
$$\left[K+\frac{3}{4}K_2-\frac{3K_2{}^2}{4(K_1+K_2)}\right]B+\left[\frac{K}{2}-\frac{3K_1K_2}{4(K_1+K_2)}\right]A$$
$$=-\frac{3E\Delta K_1K_2}{h(K_1+K_2)}. \quad \left.\right\} \quad (265a)$$

If the bent is symmetrical, that is $K_1=K_2$, we will have:

(a) Fixed bases,

$$A=-B=\frac{6E\Delta K_1}{h(K+2K_1)},$$
$$R_1=\frac{3E\Delta}{h};$$
$$M_{AB}=\frac{3E\Delta KK_1}{h(K+2K_1)},$$
$$M_{DA}=-\frac{3E\Delta K_1(K+K_1)}{h(K+2K_1)}; \quad \left.\right\} \quad \cdots \cdots \quad (266)$$

(b) Hinged bases,

$$A=-B=\frac{6E\Delta K_1}{h(2K+3K_1)},$$
$$R_1=\frac{3E\Delta}{h};$$
$$M_{AB}=\frac{3E\Delta KK_1}{h(2K+3K_1)}. \quad \left.\right\} \quad \cdots \cdots \quad (266a)$$

78. Three-legged Bent.—As a second example, consider the three-legged unsymmetrical bent shown in Fig. 204. The deformations of

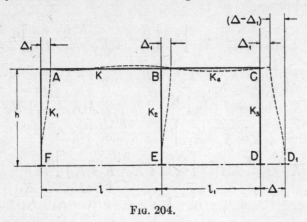

FIG. 204.

the bent, resulting from the horizontal displacement of the base D a distance Δ, and indicated by dotted lines on the diagram, are similar to those of the two-legged bent discussed above. The legs AF and BE will have the same deflection. Indicating it by Δ_1, the deflection of the leg CD will then equal $(\Delta-\Delta_1)$. Once this relation is established, the deflection and joint expressions of the bent are derived in the usual manner. Thus:

$$\left.\begin{aligned} R_{AF}=R_{BE}=\frac{6E\Delta_1}{h}=R_1, \\ R_{CD}=-\frac{6E}{h}(\Delta-\Delta_1)=R_1-\frac{6E\Delta}{h}; \end{aligned}\right\} \quad \ldots \ldots (a)$$

$$\frac{1}{h}[(M_{AF}+M_{FA})+(M_{BE}+M_{EB})+(M_{CD}+M_{DC})]=0 \ldots (b)$$

Substituting the values of the end moments in eq. (b) and solving for R_1,

(a) Fixed bases,

$$R_1=\frac{3}{4}\frac{(K_1A+K_2B+K_3C)}{(K_1+K_2+K_3)}+\frac{6E\Delta K_3}{h(K_1+K_2+K_3)} \quad \ldots \ldots (267)$$

(b) Hinged bases,

$$R_1=\frac{3}{2}\frac{(K_1A+K_2B+K_3C)}{(K_1+K_2+K_3)}+\frac{6E\Delta K_3}{h(K_1+K_2+K_3)} \quad \ldots \ldots (267a)$$

With these values, the joint expressions become:

(a) Fixed bases,

$$\left[K+K_1-\frac{3K_1{}^2}{4(K_1+K_2+K_3)}\right]A+\left[\frac{K}{2}-\frac{3K_1K_2}{4(K_1+K_2+K_3)}\right]B$$
$$-\frac{3K_1K_3}{4(K_1+K_2+K_3)}C=\frac{6E\Delta K_1K_3}{h(K_1+K_2+K_3)},$$
$$\left[\frac{K}{2}-\frac{3K_1K_2}{4(K_1+K_2+K_3)}\right]A+\left[K+K_2+K_4-\frac{3K_2{}^2}{4(K_1+K_2+K_3)}\right]B$$
$$+\left[\frac{K_4}{2}-\frac{3K_2K_3}{4(K_1+K_2+K_3)}\right]C=\frac{6E\Delta K_2K_3}{h(K_1+K_2+K_3)},$$
$$-\frac{3K_1K_3}{4(K_1+K_2+K_3)}A+\left[\frac{K_4}{2}-\frac{3K_2K_3}{4(K_1+K_2+K_3)}\right]B$$
$$+\left[K_3+K_4-\frac{3K_3{}^2}{4(K_1+K_2+K_3)}\right]C=-\frac{6E\Delta K_3(K_1+K_2)}{h(K_1+K_2+K_3)};$$

(268)

(b) Hinged bases,

$$\left[K+\frac{3}{4}K_1-\frac{3K_1{}^2}{4(K_1+K_2+K_3)}\right]A+\left[\frac{K}{2}-\frac{3K_1K_2}{4(K_1+K_2+K_3)}\right]B$$
$$-\frac{3K_1K_3}{4(K_1+K_2+K_3)}C=\frac{3E\Delta K_1K_3}{h(K_1+K_2+K_3)},$$
$$\left[\frac{K}{2}-\frac{3K_1K_2}{4(K_1+K_2+K_3)}\right]A+\left[K+\frac{3}{4}K_2+K_4\right.$$
$$\left.-\frac{3K_2{}^2}{4(K_1+K_2+K_3)}\right]B$$
$$+\left[\frac{K_4}{2}-\frac{3K_2K_3}{4(K_1+K_2+K_3)}\right]C=\frac{3E\Delta K_2K_3}{h(K_1+K_2+K_3)},$$
$$-\frac{3K_1K_3}{4(K_1+K_2+K_3)}A+\left[\frac{K_4}{2}-\frac{3K_2K_3}{4(K_1+K_2+K_3)}\right]B$$
$$+\left[K_4+\frac{3}{4}K_3-\frac{3K_3{}^2}{4(K_1+K_2+K_3)}\right]C$$
$$=-\frac{3E\Delta K_3(K_1+K_2)}{h(K_1+K_2+K_3)}.$$

(268a)

If the displacement occurs at the base E,

$$R_{AF}=R_{CD}=\frac{6E\Delta_1}{h}=R_1,$$
$$R_{BE}=-\frac{6E}{h}(\Delta-\Delta_1)=R_1-\frac{6E\Delta}{h};$$

(c)

and the right sides of eqs. (268) and (268a) assume the following forms:

(a) Fixed bases,

$$Q_A = \frac{6E\Delta K_1 K_2}{h(K_1+K_2+K_3)},$$

$$Q_B = -\frac{6E\Delta K_2 (K_1+K_3)}{h(K_1+K_2+K_3)},$$

$$Q_C = \frac{6E\Delta K_2 K_3}{h(K_1+K_2+K_3)};$$

(b) Hinged bases,

$$Q_A = \frac{3E\Delta K_1 K_2}{h(K_1+K_2+K_3)},$$

$$Q_B = -\frac{3E\Delta K_2 (K_1+K_3)}{h(K_1+K_2+K_3)},$$

$$Q_C = \frac{3E\Delta K_2 K_3}{h(K_1+K_2+K_3)}.$$

$$\cdots \quad (d)$$

79. Gable Bent.—To examine the effect of horizontal spread in a gable bent, consider the unsymmetrical framing shown in Fig. 205.

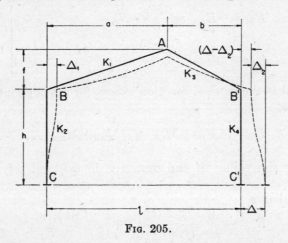

FIG. 205.

From the dotted outline of the deformation diagram it is noted that, due to displacement Δ of the base C', the legs BC and $B'C'$ deflect a distance Δ_1 and Δ_2, respectively. The relative displacement of joint B' with respect to joint B then equals $(\Delta-\Delta_1-\Delta_2)$. Denoting the deflection terms of members BC and $B'C'$ respectively by R_1 and R_2, for the corresponding terms of AB and AB', in accordance with the discussion in Art. 51, we can write:

$$\left.\begin{array}{l} R_{AB} = \dfrac{6bE}{fl}(\Delta-\Delta_1-\Delta_2) = \dfrac{6bE\Delta}{fl} - \dfrac{bh}{fl}(R_1+R_2), \\[3mm] R_{AB'} = \dfrac{6aE}{fl}(\Delta_1+\Delta_2-\Delta) = \dfrac{ah}{fl}(R_1+R_2) - \dfrac{6aE\Delta}{fl}. \end{array}\right\} \quad \cdots \quad (269)$$

The deflection terms thus established, the joint and deflection expressions are derived as in Art. 51.

If the bent is symmetrical, as that shown in Fig. 206, the two legs

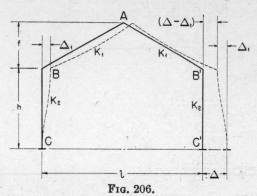

will have the same deflection, that is Δ_1 equals Δ_2. Then

$$\left.\begin{aligned}
R_{BC} &= -R_{B'C'} = \frac{6E\Delta_1}{h} = R_1, \\
R_{AB} &= -R_{AB'} = \frac{3E}{f}(\Delta - 2\Delta_1) = \frac{3E\Delta}{f} - \frac{h}{f}R_1;
\end{aligned}\right\} \quad \cdots \quad (a)$$

and noting that the vertical reaction is zero, for the horizontal reaction we can write:

$$H_B = \frac{1}{h}(M_{BC} + M_{CB}) = \frac{1}{f}(M_{AB} + M_{BA}) \quad \cdots \cdots (b)$$

Substituting the values of end moments in (g), and solving for R_1, we have:

(a) Fixed bases,

$$R_1 = -\frac{3f(hK_1 - fK_2)}{4(h^2K_1 + f^2K_2)}B + \frac{3E\Delta hK_1}{(h^2K_1 + f^2K_2)}; \quad \cdots (270)$$

(b) Hinged bases,

$$R_1 = -\frac{3f(2hK_1 - fK_2)}{2(4h^2K_1 + f^2K_2)}B + \frac{12E\Delta hK_1}{(4h^2K_1 + f^2K_2)} \quad \cdots (270a)$$

The joint expressions become:

(a) Fixed bases,

$$\left[K_1 + K_2 - \frac{3(hK_1 - fK_2)^2}{4(h^2K_1 + f^2K_2)}\right]B = \frac{3E\Delta K_1 K_2(f+h)}{(h^2K_1 + f^2K_2)}; \quad \cdots (271)$$

(b) Hinged bases,

$$\left[K_1 + \frac{3}{4}K_2 - \frac{3(2hK_1 - fK_2)^2}{4(h^2K_1 + f^2K_2)}\right]B = \frac{3E\Delta K_1 K_2(f+2h)}{(4h^2K_1 + f^2K_2)} \quad \cdots (271a)$$

VERTICAL SETTLEMENT

80. Two-legged Bent.—To study the effect of the vertical component of settlement in a simple frame, the two-legged bent in Fig. 203 is redrawn in Fig. 203a, with a new deformation outline corre-

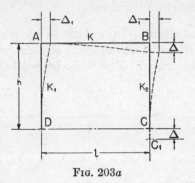

FIG. 203a

sponding to fixed bases and a vertical displacement Δ of the base C. It is seen that, when C moves to C_1, the top member AB deflects a like distance Δ and the joints A and B rotate and sway a distance Δ_1. Then

$$\left.\begin{array}{l}R_{AD}=R_{BC}=\dfrac{6E\Delta_1}{h}=R_1, \\[2mm] R_{AB}=\dfrac{6E\Delta}{l}; \\[2mm] \dfrac{3}{2}(K_1A+K_2B)-2(K_1+K_2)R_1=0;\end{array}\right\} \quad \ldots \ldots (a)$$

$$R_1=\frac{3(K_1A+K_2B)}{4(K_1+K_2)}; \quad \ldots \ldots \ldots \ldots \ldots (b)$$

and the joint expressions become:

$$\left.\begin{array}{l}\left[K+K_1-\dfrac{3K_1{}^2}{4(K_1+K_2)}\right]A+\left[\dfrac{K}{2}-\dfrac{3K_1K_{22}}{4(K_1+K_2)}\right]B=\dfrac{6E\Delta K}{l}, \\[4mm] \left[\dfrac{K}{2}-\dfrac{3K_1K_2}{4(K_1+K_2)}\right]A+\left[K+K_2-\dfrac{3K^2}{4(K_1+K_2)}\right]B=\dfrac{6E\Delta K}{l}.\end{array}\right\} (272)$$

If the bent is symmetrical, that is, $K_1=K_2$, we have:

$$\left.\begin{array}{l}A=\quad B\ =\dfrac{24E\Delta K}{l(6K+K_1)}, \\[3mm] R_1=\quad \dfrac{3}{4}A=\dfrac{18E\Delta K}{l(6K+K_1)}, \\[3mm] M_{AD}=-M_{DA}=\dfrac{6E\Delta KK_1}{l(6K+K_1)}.\end{array}\right\} \quad \ldots \ldots (273)$$

In the case of hinged bases, when C moves vertically to C_1, the bent freely rotates about the base D. Hence, except for stresses of negligible order, due to the spread of the bases a distance equaling the difference between the final and original base lengths ($\overline{DC_1}-\overline{DC}=\dfrac{\Delta^2}{2l}$ approx.), the members will remain unstrained.

81. Three-Legged Bent.—In a bent with more than two legs, however, vertical settlement will produce stresses regardless of the type of connections of the bases. The three-legged bent in Fig. 204a will

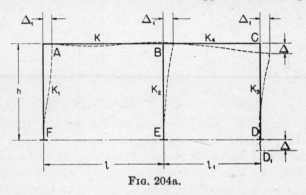

Fig. 204a.

serve for illustration. Due to the displacement of the base D a distance Δ to D_1, the top member BC deflects downward a like distance, while the joints A, B and C rotate and sway a distance Δ_1. Then

$$\left.\begin{aligned} R_{AF}=R_{BE}=R_{CD}=\frac{6E\Delta_1}{h}=R_1,\\ R_{AB}=0,\ R_{BC}=\frac{6E\Delta}{l_1}; \end{aligned}\right\} \quad \ldots \ldots \quad (a)$$

and the deflection expressions become:

(a) Fixed bases,

$$R_1=\frac{3}{4}\cdot\frac{(K_1A+K_2B+K_3C)}{(K_1+K_2+K_3)};\quad \ldots \ldots \quad (274)$$

(b) Hinged bases,

$$R_1=\frac{3}{2}\cdot\frac{(K_1A+K_2B+K_3C)}{(K_1+K_2+K_3)}\ \ldots \ldots \quad (274a)$$

In deriving the joint expressions, it is evident that the left sides of eqs. (268) and (268a) remain unchanged, while for the right sides or the displacement factors for both fixed and hinged bases we can write:

$$Q_A=0,\ Q_B=Q_C=\frac{6E\Delta K_4}{l}\ \ldots \ldots \ldots \quad (275)$$

82. Gable Bent.—The behavior of a gable bent in vertical settlement is similar to that of a two-legged rectangular bent. If the bases are hinged, vertical displacement of one base will simply cause a free rotation of the frame about the other base. If the bases are fixed, however, the bent will deform in accordance with the dotted outline shown in Fig. 206a. Since the bent is symmetrical, when the base

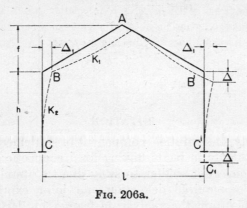

FIG. 206a.

C' moves down a distance Δ to C_1, the joints B and B' sway laterally a distance Δ_1, the sway of the latter joint being accompanied by a vertical displacement Δ which, in turn, causes similar deflections in the members AB and AB'. Thus

$$\left.\begin{aligned}R_{BC}=R_{B'C'}=\frac{6E\Delta_1}{h}=R_1,\\ R_{AB}=R_{AB'}=\frac{6E\Delta}{l};\end{aligned}\right\} \quad \cdots \cdots \cdots \cdots \; (a)$$

and since B equals B', and the horizontal shears or reactions are zero,

$$\left.\begin{aligned}M_{BC}+M_{CB}=\frac{3}{2}K_2B-2K_2R_1=0;\\ R_1=\frac{3}{4}B.\end{aligned}\right\} \quad \cdots \cdots \cdots \; (b)$$

With this value of R_1, the joint expressions at A and B become:

$$\left.\begin{aligned}2K_1A+K_1B=\frac{12E\Delta K_1}{l},\\ \frac{K^1}{2}A+\left(K^1+\frac{K^2}{4}\right)B=\frac{6E\Delta K_1}{l};\end{aligned}\right\} \quad \cdots \cdots \cdots \; (c)$$

from which

$$A = \frac{6E\Delta(2K_1+K_2)}{l(3K_1+K_2)},$$

$$B = \frac{12R\Delta K_1}{l(3K_1+K_2)},$$

$$R_1 = \frac{9E\Delta K_1}{l(3K_1+K_2)};$$

and

$$M_{B\dot{C}} = -M_{CB} = \frac{3E\Delta K_1 K_2}{l(3K_1+K_2)},$$

$$M_{AB} = 0.$$

$$\left.\begin{array}{c} \\ \\ \\ \\ \\ \\ \end{array}\right\} \quad \ldots \ldots \ldots , \quad (276)$$

ROTATION

83. Obviously, the rotation component of settlement produces additional stresses only in bents having fixed connections at the bases. The effect is somewhat similar to sway due to lateral loading; and, accordingly, the required deflection and joint expressions are directly obtainable from the analysis of frames in Part II. The application will again be confined to the three typical bents used in the preceding discussions.

84. Two-legged Bent.—Fig. 203b represents the deformations of a

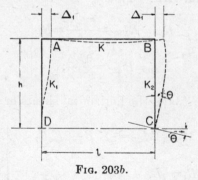

Fig. 203b.

two-legged bent resulting from rotation at one of the bases. Due to the relation of the base C through an angle Θ, the upper joints A and B rotate and sway a distance Δ_1. Then we have:

$$R_{AD} = R_{BC} = \frac{6E\Delta_1}{h} = R_1;$$

$$M_{BC} = K_2(B+2E\Theta-R_1),$$

$$M_{CB} = K_2\left(\frac{B}{2}+4E\Theta-R_1\right);$$

$$\left.\begin{array}{c} \\ \\ \\ \end{array}\right\} \quad \ldots \ldots \ldots \quad (a)$$

$$M_{AD}+M_{DA}+M_{BC}+M_{CB}=0,$$

$$R_1=\frac{3(K_1A+K_2B)}{4K_1+K_2}+\frac{3E\Theta K_2}{K_1+K_2} \quad \ldots \ldots \ldots \quad (277)$$

$$\left.\begin{aligned}
\left[K+K_1-\frac{3K_1^2}{4(K_1+K_2)}\right]A+\left[\frac{K}{2}-\frac{3K_1K_2}{4(K_1+K_2)}\right]B&=\frac{3E\Theta K_1K_2}{(K_1+K_2)},\\
\left[\frac{K}{2}-\frac{3K_1K_2}{4(K_1+K_2)}\right]A+\left[K+K_2-\frac{3K_2^2}{4(K_1+K_2)}\right]B&\\
=\frac{E\Theta K_2(K_2-2K_1)}{(K_1+K_2)}.&
\end{aligned}\right\} \ (278)$$

85. Three-legged Bent.—In the case of the three-legged bent shown in Fig. 204b, due to the rotation of the base D through an angle Θ,

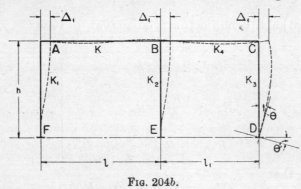

FIG. 204b.

we have:

$$\left.\begin{aligned}
R_{AF}=R_{BE}=R_{CD}&=\frac{6E\Delta_1}{h}=R_1;\\
M_{CD}&=K_3(C+2E\Theta-R_1),\\
M_{DC}&=K_3\left(\frac{C}{2}+4E\Theta-R_1\right);
\end{aligned}\right\} \quad \ldots \ldots \ldots \ldots \quad (a)$$

$$M_{AF}+M_{FA}+M_{BE}+M_{EB}+M_{CD}+M_{DC}=0,$$

$$R_1=\frac{3(K_1A+K_2B+K_3C)}{4(K_1+K_2+K_3)}+\frac{3E\Theta K_3}{(K_1+K_2+K_3)}; \quad \ldots \ldots \quad (279)$$

and the right sides or rotation factors of the joint eqs. 268) become:

$$\left.\begin{aligned}
Q_A&=\frac{3E\Theta K_1K_3}{(K_1+K_2+K_3)},\\
Q_B&=\frac{3E\Theta K_2K_3}{(K_1+K_2+K_3)},\\
Q_C&=\frac{E\Theta K_3(K_2-2K_1-2K_3)}{(K_1+K_2+K_3)}.
\end{aligned}\right\} \quad \ldots \ldots \ldots \ldots \quad (280)$$

86. Gable Bent.—Fig. 206b represesents the deformations of a

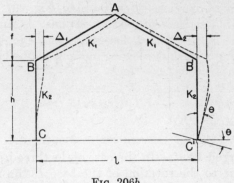

FIG. 206b.

symmetrical gable bent due to a rotation Θ at the base C'. Here again indicating

$$
\left.
\begin{aligned}
R_{BC} &= \frac{6E\Delta_1}{h} = R_1, \\[2mm]
R_{B'C'} &= \frac{6E\Delta_2}{h} = R_2, \\[2mm]
R_{AB} &= -R_{AB'} = \frac{h}{2f}(R_2 - R_1);
\end{aligned}
\right\} \quad \dots \dots \dots (a)
$$

and noting that

$$
M_{B'C'} = K_2(B' + 2E\Theta - R_2),
$$

$$
M_{C'B'} = K_2\left(\frac{B'}{2} + 4E\Theta - R_2\right);
$$

for the deflection expressions of R_1 and R_2, as in Art. 47, we can write:

$$
\left.
\begin{aligned}
\left(\frac{hK_1}{f^2} + \frac{2K_2}{h}\right)R_1 - \frac{hK_1}{f^2}R_2 &= -\frac{K_1}{f}A + \left(\frac{3K_2}{2h} - \frac{K_1}{f}\right)B + \frac{K_1}{2f}B', \\[2mm]
\left(\frac{hK_1}{f^2} + \frac{2K_2}{h}\right)R_2 - \frac{hK_1}{f^2}R_1 &= -\frac{K_1}{f}A + \left(\frac{3K_2}{2h} - \frac{K_1}{f}\right)B' + \frac{K_1}{2f}B + 6E\frac{\Theta}{h}K_2.
\end{aligned}
\right\} (281)
$$

The joint expressions, before elimination of R_1 and R_2, are in the following forms:

$$
\left.
\begin{aligned}
2K_1 A + \frac{K_1}{2}B + \frac{K_1}{2}B' &= 0, \\[2mm]
\frac{K_1}{2}A + (K_1 + K_2)B - \left(K_2 - \frac{h}{2f}K_1\right)R_1 - \frac{h}{2f}K_1 R_2 &= 0, \\[2mm]
\frac{K_1}{2}A + (K_1 + K_2)B' - \left(K_2 - \frac{h}{2f}K_1\right)R_2 - \frac{h}{2f}K_1 R_1 &= -2E\Theta K_2.
\end{aligned}
\right\} (282)
$$

A steel gable bent of symmetrical framing, Fig. 207, is to be investigated for probable settlement of foundations. Assuming originally fixed connections at the bases, determine the end moments of the members resulting from the following motions at the base C':

(a) Horizontal spread of 1 inch;

(b) Vertical displacement of 1 inch;

(c) Clockwise rotation of 0.01 radian.

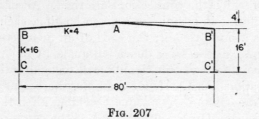

FIG. 207

Solution: (a) From eqs. (271), (270) and (f),

$$B = 0.0125E\Delta, \quad R_{BC} = 0.0125E\Delta, \quad R_{AB} = 0.0125E\Delta.$$

Then

$$M_{AB} = -0.025E\Delta = -62.5 \text{ ft.-kips,}$$

$$M_{BC} = 0,$$

$$M_{CB} = -0.1E\Delta = -250 \text{ ft.-kips.}$$

(b) From eqs. (276)

$$M_{AB} = 0,$$

$$M_{BC} = -M_{CB} = \frac{E\Delta}{140} = 17.86 \text{ ft.-kips.}$$

(c) Applying eqs. (281) and (282),

$$A = -0.5712E\theta, \quad R_{BC} = 2.0568E\theta,$$

$$B = 1.9428E\theta, \quad R_{B'C'} = 2.6568E\theta,$$

$$B' = 0.3428E\theta; \quad R_{AB} = 1.2000E\theta.$$

Then

$$M_{AB} = -3.200E\theta = -80.0 \text{ ft.-kips,}$$

$$M_{BC} = -1.824E\theta = -45.6 \text{ ft.-kips,}$$

$$M_{B'C'} = -5.024E\theta = -125.6 \text{ ft.-kips,}$$

$$M_{CB} = -17.368E\theta = -434.2 \text{ ft.-kips,}$$

$$M_{C'B'} = 24.232E\theta = 605.8 \text{ ft.-kips.}$$

CHAPTER II

SEMIRIGID FRAMING

87. Slip in Connections of Framing.—By definition, a rigid frame is a framing in which the connections are rigid. Accordingly, when a rigid frame deforms in sustaining a given loading, each joint deflects and rotates as a unit; that is, the ends of all members meeting at a joint rotate through the same deflection angle. Obviously, in a steel framing this condition of full rigidity will depend entirely upon the type of connections used. If, for example, the beams or girders are connected to the columns by adequate welding, then the condition of rigidity is satisfied. On the other hand, if the connections are composed of seat and relatively thin top angles, riveted or welded at the toes, then there will be only partial rigidity, resulting in some slip in the connection due to the yielding or "opening" of the top angles at the heels. A framing in which connections possess such flexibility is often called a semirigid framing. Due to the introduction of this "slip" factor, the analysis of a semirigid frame is considerably more involved than that of a rigid frame. However, in deriving the fundamental moment expressions by slope deflection, there is but little deviation from the procedure previously outlined in Arts. 25 and 26.

88. Fundamental Moment Expressions for Members in a Semirigid Framing. (1) *Constant moment of inertia.*—Slip in a joint is usually expressed as a function of the moment transmitted through the connection; and, in order to simplify the analysis, it is assumed that the relation is linear; that is, the slip angle varies in direct ratio with the moment developed by the connection. While, in reality, the relation is not strictly linear, laboratory tests* of seat-and-top-angle-type connections indicate that this assumption is justified within the ordinary working range of stress. Accordingly, if θ_A, Fig. 208 (*a*), indicates the deflection angle of a joint A to which a member AB is connected, and θ'_A is the end deflection angle of the member when a moment M'_{AB} is transmitted through the connection, then the relative rotation of the member with respect to the joint is given by the expression

$$\theta_A - \theta'_A = \lambda_A M'_{AB}; \quad \ldots \ldots \ldots \quad (a)$$

---

*See, for example, Wilson and Moore, "Tests to Determine the Rigidity of Riveted Joints of Steel Structures," Univ. of Ill. Eng. Exp. Sta., Bul. No. 104, 1917.

338

in which λ_A is the connection constant, determined experimentally for each type of connection, and, since

$$\lambda_A = \frac{\theta_A - \theta'_A}{M'_{AB}}, \quad \cdots \cdots \cdots \quad (b)$$

it may be defined as the "slip" of the connection due to the transfer of a unit moment.

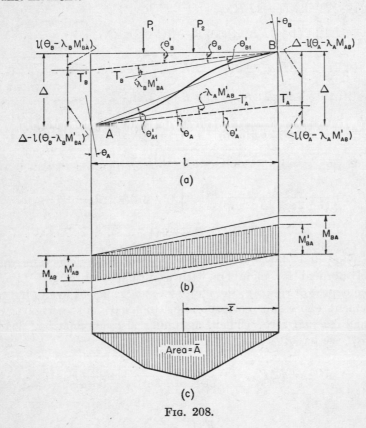

FIG. 208.

As in Art. 25, for the change in deflection angle between the two ends of the member, and the displacement of end B with respect to the tangent at A, we have:

$$(\theta_A - \lambda_A M'_{AB}) - (\theta_B - \lambda_B M'_{BA}) = \frac{l}{2EI}M'_{AB} - \frac{l}{2EI}M'_{BA} + \frac{\overline{A}}{EI}; \quad (283)$$

$$[\Delta - l(\theta_A - \lambda_A M'_{AB})] = -\frac{l^2}{3EI}M'_{AB} + \frac{l^2}{6EI}M'_{BA} - \frac{x\overline{A}}{EI}. \quad \cdots \quad (284)$$

Solving for the end moments M'_{AB} and M'_{BA},

$$[2(1+2EK\lambda_B)(1+3EK\lambda_A)-(1+2EK\lambda_A)]M'_{AB}$$
$$=2EK\left[2(1+3EK\lambda_B)\theta_A+\theta_B-3(1+2EK\lambda_B)\frac{\Delta}{l}\right]$$
$$-6(1+2EK\lambda_B)\frac{\bar{x}\bar{A}}{l^2}+\frac{2\bar{A}}{l}, \dots \dots \dots \dots \dots \quad (285)$$

$$[2(1+2EK\lambda_B)(1+3EK\lambda_A)-(1+2EK\lambda_A)]M'_{BA}$$
$$=2EK\left[2(1+3EK\lambda_A)\theta_B+\theta_A-3(1+2EK\lambda_A)\frac{\Delta}{l}\right]$$
$$+\left[2(1+3EK\lambda_A)-3(1+2EK\lambda_A)\frac{\bar{x}}{l}\right]\frac{2\bar{A}}{l}; \dots \dots \dots \quad (285a)$$

or, substituting α for $2EK\lambda_A$, and β for $2EK\lambda_B$,

$$M'_{AB}=\frac{1}{(1+2\alpha+2\beta+3\alpha\beta)}\left\{2EK\left[(2+3\beta)\theta_A+\theta_B-3(1+\beta)\frac{\Delta}{l}\right]\right.$$
$$\left.-\frac{2\bar{A}}{l^2}[3(1+\beta)\bar{x}-l]\right\}, \dots \dots \dots \dots \quad (286)$$

$$M'_{BA}=\frac{1}{(1+2\alpha+2\beta+3\alpha\beta)}\left\{2EK\left[(2+3\alpha)\theta_B+\theta_A-3(1+\alpha)\right.\right.$$
$$\left.\left.+\frac{2\bar{A}}{l^2}[l(2+3\alpha)-3(1+\alpha)\bar{x}]\right\} \dots \dots \dots \quad (286a)$$

Eqs. (286) and (286a) are the fundamental slope-deflection expressions of moment for members with semirigid connections. For an assumed degree of rigidity, the factors α and β may be evaluated from the moment expression corresponding to fixed ends; namely, when θ_A, θ_B and Δ equal zero. Then, assuming also symmetrical loading and $\alpha=\beta$, we have:

$$M'_{AP}=FM'_{AB}=-\frac{(1+3\alpha)}{(1+4\alpha+3\alpha^2)}\cdot\frac{\bar{A}}{l}=\frac{1}{1+\alpha}FM_{AB},$$

or,

$$\frac{FM'_{AB}}{FM_{AB}}=\frac{1}{1+\alpha}; \dots \dots \dots \dots \quad (287)$$

in which FM'_{AB} is the "fixed-end" moment of a member with semirigid connections.

Since $\dfrac{FM'_{AB}}{FM_{AB}}$ is the ratio of moment developed through a connection

of partial rigidity to that of complete rigidity, we may call it "ratio of rigidity." Indicating it by Q_R, the values of α corresponding to different values of Q_R are given in Table 11.

TABLE 11

Q_R	%	α
1	100	0
$\frac{3}{4}$	75	$\frac{1}{3}$
$\frac{1}{2}$	50	1
$\frac{1}{4}$	25	3
0	0	∞

(2) *Variable moment of inertia.*—In the case of variable cross section, the moment expressions may be obtained from eqs. (58) and (59), Art. 26, by replacing θ_A and θ_B by $(\theta_A - \lambda_A M'_{AB})$ and $(\theta_B - \lambda_B M'_{BA})$, respectively. Thus

$$\left.\begin{aligned}
M'_{AB} &= \frac{EK}{p(1-u-v)}\left[(1-v)(\theta_A-\lambda_A M'_{AB})+v(\theta_B-\lambda_B M'_{BA})-\frac{\Delta}{l}\right] \\
&\quad -\frac{(\bar{x}_1-vl)}{pl^2(1-u-v)}\overline{A}_1, \\
M'_{BA} &= \frac{EK}{q(1-u-v)}\left[(1-u)(\theta_B-\lambda_B M'_{BA})+u(\theta_A-\lambda_A M'_{AB})-\frac{\Delta}{l}\right] \\
&\quad +\frac{(l-ul-\bar{x}_1)}{ql^2(1-u-v)}\overline{A}_1;
\end{aligned}\right\} \quad (288)$$

or,

$$\left.\begin{aligned}
&\left[+\frac{(1-v)\alpha}{p(1-u-v)}\right]M'_{AB}+\frac{v\beta}{p(1-u-v)}M'_{BA} \\
&\quad =\frac{EK}{p(1-u-v)}\left[(1-v)\theta_A+v\theta_B-\frac{\Delta}{l}\right]-\frac{(\bar{x}_1-vl)}{pl^2(1-u-v)}\overline{A}_1, \\
&\left[+\frac{(1-u)\beta}{q(1-u-v)}\right]M'_{BA}+\frac{u\alpha}{v(1-u-v)}M'_{AB} \\
&\quad =\frac{EK}{q(1-u-v)}\left[(1-u)\theta_B+u\theta_A-\frac{\Delta}{l}\right]+\frac{(l-ul-\bar{x}_1)}{ql^2(1-u-v)}\overline{A}_1
\end{aligned}\right\} \quad (289)$$

Solving for M'_{AB} and M'_{BA},

$$M'_{AB}=\frac{2EK\left\{[2(1-v)q+\beta]\theta_A+2vq\theta_B-(2q+\beta)\dfrac{\Delta}{l}\right\}-\dfrac{2\overline{A}}{l^2}[(2q+\beta)\bar{x}_1-2qvl]}{4(1-u-v)pq+2(1-v)q\alpha+2(1-u)p\beta+\alpha\beta}$$
$$\quad\quad\quad\quad\quad\quad\quad\quad\quad\quad\quad\quad\quad\quad\quad \cdots\quad (290)$$

$$M'_{BA}=\frac{2EK\left\{[2(1-u)p+\alpha]\theta_B+2up\theta_A-(2p+\alpha)\dfrac{\Delta}{l}\right\}}{4(1-u-v)pq+2(1-v)q\alpha+2(1-u)p\beta+\alpha\beta}$$

$$\quad +\frac{\dfrac{2\overline{A}}{l^2}[2pl(1-u)+\alpha l-(2p+\alpha)\bar{x}_1]}{4(1-u-v)pq+2(1-v)q\alpha+2(1-u)p\beta+\alpha} \quad \cdots \quad (290a)$$

1. The symmetrical gable bent shown in Fig. 111 has fixed bases. The crown joint A is rigid, but the connections B and B' of roof members AB and AB' to the columns possess only 50 percent rigidity. Determine the end moments and compare with the corresponding values in Example 1 of Art. 46.

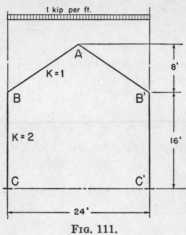

FIG. 111.

Solution: Applying eqs. (286) and noting that α at B equals 1, and β and the deflection angle at A equal zero,

$$M'_{BA}=\frac{4}{3}EK\theta_B-\frac{1}{3}KR_{AB}+\frac{1}{3}FM_{BA}=\frac{B}{3}+\frac{2}{3}R-4,$$

$$M'_{AB}=\frac{2}{3}EK\theta_B-\frac{2}{3}KR_{AB}+\frac{4}{3}FM_{AB}=\frac{B}{6}+\frac{4}{3}R+16;$$

in which $R=R_{BC}=-\frac{8}{16}R_{AB}$. For the horizontal reaction H we have:

$$H=\frac{1}{16}(3B-4R)=\frac{1}{8}\left(\frac{B}{2}+2R+84\right)\;;\;.\;.\;.\;.\;.\;.\;(c)$$

and the joint expression at B is in the form

$$2B+\frac{B}{3}-2R+\frac{2}{3}R-4=\frac{7}{3}B-\frac{4}{3}R-4=0\;.\;.\;.\;.\;.\;(d)$$

From eqs. (c) and (d),

$$B=-12,\,R=-24\text{ and }R_{AB}=+48.$$

Then

$M_{AB}=-2-32+16=-18;$	For $\alpha=0$, $M_{AB}=-10;$
$M_{BA}=-4-16-4=-24,$	$M_{BA}=-32,$
$M_{BC}=-24+48=24;$	$M_{BC}=32;$
$M_{CB}=-12+48=36.$	$M_{CB}=28.$

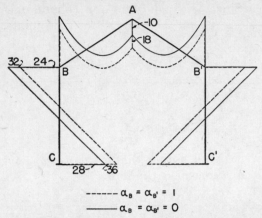

$$------ \alpha_B = \alpha_{B'} = 1$$
$$\underline{\hspace{2cm}} \alpha_B = \alpha_{B'} = 0$$

FIG. 111a.—Comparative moment diagrams.

2. Beam-to-column connections of the three-story symmetrical bent shown in Fig. 68a have only partial rigidity. Assuming the bases fixed, obtain the following:

(a) Deflection and joint expressions, using the same rigidity factor, α, at all connections;

(b) End moments resulting from numerical values given in Fig. 68, Art. 37, and corresponding to $\alpha = 1$.

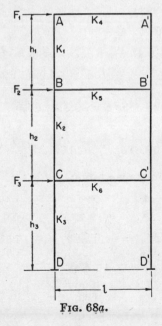

FIG. 68a.

Solution: (a) Since α equals zero for column members, the deflection expressions remain the same as for rigid joints. Thus

$$\left.\begin{aligned} R_1 &= R_{AB} = \frac{3}{4}(A+B) + \frac{F_1 h_1}{4K_1}, \\[2mm] R_2 &= R_{BC} = \frac{3}{4}(B+C) + \frac{h_2}{4K_2}(F_1+F_2), \\[2mm] R_3 &= R_{CD} = \frac{3}{4}C + \frac{h_3}{4K_3}(F_1+F_2+F_3). \end{aligned}\right\} \quad \cdots \cdots (e)$$

Applying eq. (286), and noting that $\alpha=\beta$, $\theta_A=\theta_B$, $\Delta=0$, the typical beam-moment equation takes the form

$$M'_{AA'} = \frac{6EK(1+\alpha)\theta_A}{1+4\alpha+3\alpha^2} = \frac{6EK\theta_A}{1+3\alpha} = \frac{3KA}{2(1+\alpha)} \quad \cdots \cdots (f)$$

Then the joint expressions become:

$$\left.\begin{aligned} \left[\frac{K_1}{4}+\frac{3K_4}{2(1+\alpha)}\right]A - \frac{K_1}{4}B &= \frac{h_1F_1}{4}, \\[2mm] \left[\frac{K_1}{4}+\frac{K_2}{4}+\frac{3K_5}{2(1+\alpha)}\right]B - \frac{K_1}{4}A - \frac{K_2}{4}C &= \frac{h_1F_1}{4}+\frac{h_2}{4}(F_1+F_2), \\[2mm] \left[\frac{K_2}{4}+\frac{K_3}{4}+\frac{3K_6}{2(1+\alpha)}\right]C - \frac{K_2}{4}B &= \frac{h_2}{4}(F_1+F_2)+\frac{h_3}{4}(F_1+F_2+F_3). \end{aligned}\right\} \quad \cdots (g)$$

(b) Applying eqs. (293),

$$0.775A - 0.40B = 10,$$
$$-0.40A + 1.95B - 0.80C = 22,$$
$$-0.80B + 3.90C = 24;$$

from which

$$A = 23.388, \; B = 20.314, \; C = 10.320;$$

and from eqs. (291),

$$R_1 = 39.026, \; R_2 = 26.726, \; R_3 = 9.616.$$

Then for the end moments we have:

	$\alpha=1$	$\alpha=0$
$M_{AA'}=$	8.770;	9.954;
$M_{BA}=$	−11.229,	−10.043,
$M_{BC}=$	− 4.006,	− 9.558,
$M_{BB'}=$	15.235;	19.593;
$M_{CB}=$	−19.997,	−14.442,
$M_{CD}=$	4.506,	− 6.438,
$M_{CC'}=$	15.480;	20.868;
$M_{DC}=$	−28.518.	−17.568,

EFFECT OF WIDTH OF SUPPORTS

89. Relation Between Moments at Center of Joint and Face of **Support.**—For convenience, the elastic curve of a framed member is generally assumed to extend continuously to the hypothetical joint centers of the supporting members. In reality, due to the abrupt change in cross section, the elastic curve ends at the face of the support; and, for a finite width of support, it will be more nearly correct to assume that there is no change in deflection angle and deflection within the support. This latter assumption will obviously result in a corresponding change in the moment expression at center of a joint, which is obtained from the fundamental relation

$$\overline{M}_{AB}=M_{AB}+(V_{AB}-V'_A)b_A=M_{AB}+\frac{b_A}{l}(M_{AB}+M_{BA})-V'_Ab_A; \quad (291)$$

in which, referring to Fig. 209,

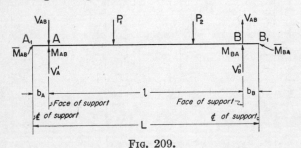

Fig. 209.

$\overline{M}_{AB}$=moment at center A_1 of support $A;$
M_{AB}=moment at face of support $A;$
$\quad b_A$=distance from face of support to center of support $A;$
$\quad l$=distance between faces of supports A and $B;$
V_{AB}=shear couple corresponding to end moments M_{AB} and $M_{BA};$ and
V'_A=simple end reaction at face of support A due to external loading.

By substituting in eq. (291) the values of M_{AB} and M_{BA} from moment equations previously derived, the corresponding expression for moment at center of a support is then readily obtained. Thus, in the case of semirigid framing, using end moment values for variable cross section, eqs. (290), we have:

$$\overline{M}_{AB}=\frac{2EK\left[\left(1+\dfrac{b_A}{l}\right)(2q-2vq+\beta)+2vp\dfrac{b_A}{l}\right]\theta_A+\left[2vq\left(1+\dfrac{b_A}{l}\right)+2(1-u)p\dfrac{b_A}{l}+\alpha\dfrac{b_A}{l}\right]\theta_B}{4(1-u-v)pq+2(1-v)q\alpha+2(1-u)p\beta+\alpha\beta}$$

$$-\frac{2EK\left[\left(1+\dfrac{b_A}{l}\right)(2q+\beta)+(2p+\alpha)\dfrac{b_A}{l}\right]\dfrac{\Delta}{l}}{4(1-u-v)pq+2(1-v)q\alpha+2(1-u)p\beta+\alpha\beta}$$

$$-\frac{\left\{\left(1+\dfrac{b_A}{l}\right)[(2q+\beta)\bar{x}_1-2qvl]-[2pl(1-u)+\alpha l-(2p+\alpha)\bar{x}_1]\dfrac{b_A}{l}\right\}\dfrac{2\bar{A}}{l^2}}{4(1-u-v)pq+2(1-v)q\alpha+2(1-u)p\beta+\alpha\beta}-V_A{}'b_A.\quad\ldots\ldots\ldots\ldots\quad(292)$$

Similarly, at B_1, center of support B,

$$\overline{M}_{BA}=\frac{2EK\left[\left(1+\dfrac{b_B}{l}\right)(2p-2up+\alpha)+2vq\dfrac{b_B}{l}\right]\theta_B+\left[2up\left(1+\dfrac{b_B}{l}\right)+2(1-v)q\dfrac{b_B}{l}+\beta\dfrac{b_B}{l}\right]\theta_A}{4(1-u-v)pq+2(1-v)q\alpha+2(1-u)p\beta+\alpha\beta}$$

$$-\frac{2EK\left[\left(1+\dfrac{b_B}{l}\right)(2p+\alpha)+(2q+\beta)\dfrac{b_B}{l}\right]\dfrac{\Delta}{l}}{4(1-u-v)pq+2(1-v)q\alpha+2(1-u)p\beta+\alpha\beta}$$

$$+\frac{\left\{\left(1+\dfrac{b_B}{l}\right)[2pl(1-u)+\alpha l-(2p+\alpha)\bar{x}_1]-[(2q+\beta)x_1-2qvl]\dfrac{b_B}{l}\right\}\dfrac{2\bar{A}}{l_2}}{4(1-u-v)pq+2(1-v)q\alpha+2(1-u)p\beta+\alpha\beta}+V_B{}'b_B\quad\ldots\ldots\ldots\ldots\quad(292a)$$

In the case of members of constant cross section, $p=q=\frac{1}{2}$, $u=v=\frac{1}{3}$, eqs. (292) become:

$$\overline{M}_{AB}=\frac{2EK\left\{\left[2+3\beta+3(1+\beta)\frac{b_A}{l}\right]\theta_A+\left[1+3(1+\alpha)\frac{b_A}{l}\right]\theta_B-3\left[1+\beta+(2+\alpha+\beta)\frac{b_A}{l}\right]\frac{\Delta}{l}\right\}}{1+2\alpha+2\beta+3\alpha\beta}$$

$$+\frac{2\overline{A}\left\{l-3(1+\beta)\overline{x}+3\frac{b_A}{l}[(1+\alpha)l-(2+\alpha+\beta)\overline{x}]\right\}}{l^2(1+2\alpha+2\beta+3\alpha\beta)}-V_A{}'b_A, \quad \dots \dots \text{(293)}$$

$$\overline{M}_{BA}=\frac{2EK\left\{\left[2+3\alpha+3(1+\alpha)\frac{b_B}{l}\right]\theta_B+\left[1+3(1+\beta)\frac{b_B}{l}\right]\theta_A-3\left[1+\alpha+(2+\alpha+\beta)\frac{b_B}{l}\right]\frac{\Delta}{l}\right\}}{1+2\alpha+2\beta+3\alpha\beta}$$

$$+\frac{2\overline{A}\left\{l(2+3\alpha)-3(1+\alpha)\overline{x}+3\frac{b_B}{l}[(1+\alpha)l-(2+\alpha+\beta)\overline{x}]\right\}}{l^2(1+2\alpha+2\beta+3\alpha\beta)}+V_B{}'b_B. \quad \dots \dots \text{(293a)}$$

And for rigid connections we have:

$$\overline{M}_{AB}=2EK\left[\left(2+3\frac{b_A}{l}\right)\theta_A+\left(1+3\frac{b_A}{l}\right)\theta_B-3\left(1+2\frac{b_A}{l}\right)\frac{\Delta}{l}\right]$$

$$+\frac{2\overline{A}}{l^2}\left[l-3\overline{x}+3\frac{b_A}{l}(1-2\overline{x})\right]-V'b_A, \quad \dots \dots \text{(294)}$$

$$\overline{M}_{BA}=2EK\left[\left(2+3\frac{b_B}{l}\right)\theta_B+\left(1+3\frac{b_B}{l}\right)\theta_A-3\left(1+2\frac{b_B}{l}\right)\frac{\Delta}{l}\right]$$

$$+\frac{2\overline{A}}{l^2}\left[2l-3\overline{x}+3\frac{b_B}{l}(1-2\overline{x})\right]+V'b_B \quad \dots \dots \text{(294a)}$$

Chapter III

AXIAL DEFORMATIONS

90. Moments Due to Deformations of Axial Stresses.—If the axial stresses of a frame due to the principal bending moments are known, the so-called secondary moments resulting from axial deformations, or change in length of the various members under axial stress, are then conveniently obtained from the geometry of the deformation diagram. The application will be illustrated by some examples of typical bents.

91. Two-legged Bent: (1) *Symmetrical vertical loading and framing.*—Axial deformations of a simple two-legged bent, under symmetrical vertical loading, are shown in Fig. 210. Indicating the

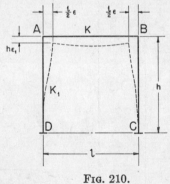

Fig. 210.

average unit shortening of the top member and the legs by ϵ and ϵ_1, respectively, it is seen that the top joints A and B move inward a distance $\frac{l}{2}\epsilon$ and downward a distance $h\epsilon_1$. Since $\frac{l}{2}\epsilon$ represents the deflection of the legs, the corresponding deflection term becomes

$$R_{AD} = -R_{BC} = 6E\frac{\Delta}{h} = 3E\epsilon\frac{l}{h} = 3\sigma\frac{l}{h}; \quad \ldots \ldots \quad (295)$$

in which σ indicates the average axial unit stress in member AB. Noting also that the deflection angles at A and B are equal and of opposit

$$\left.\begin{array}{l} \dfrac{6l\sigma K_1}{2K_1+K)}; \\[2mm] \dfrac{_1}{K)}, \\[2mm] \dfrac{(K+K_1)}{K_1+K)}. \end{array}\right\} \quad \ldots \ldots \quad (296)$$

If the

$$\left.\begin{array}{l} \dfrac{K_1}{+2K)}; \\[2mm] \dfrac{KK_1}{+2K)}. \end{array}\right\} \quad \ldots \ldots \ldots \quad (296a)$$

(2) *cal loading and unsymmetrical
ramin ormations* of the bent for the

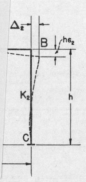

Fig. 210a.

general case, in which the strains and stiffnesses of the two legs may
differ. Again indicating the average unit strains of the members
AB, AD and BC by ϵ, ϵ_1 and ϵ_2, respectively, we have:

$$\left.\begin{array}{l} R_{AB}=6E\dfrac{h}{l}(\epsilon_1+\epsilon_2)=6\dfrac{h}{l}(\sigma_1+\sigma_2); \\[3mm] \Delta_1-\Delta_2=l\epsilon; \\[3mm] R_{BC}=6E\dfrac{\Delta_2}{h}=R_2; \\[3mm] R_{AD}=6E\dfrac{\Delta_1}{h}=R_2+6E\epsilon\dfrac{l}{h}. \end{array}\right\} \quad \ldots \ldots \quad (297)$$

The deflection relations thus determined, the joint and deflection
expressions of the bent are then obtained in the usual manner. For

fixed bases we have:

$$R_2 = \frac{3(K_1 A + K_2 B)}{4(K_1 + K_2)} - \frac{6l\sigma K_1}{h(K_1 + K_2)};$$

and

$$\left[K + K_1 - \frac{3K_1{}^2}{4(K_1 + K_2)}\right]A + \left[\frac{K}{2} - \frac{3K_1 K_2}{4(K_1 + K_2)}\right]B$$

$$= 6\frac{h}{l}K(\sigma_1 + \sigma_2) + \frac{6l\sigma K_1 K_2}{h(K_1 + K_2)},$$ . . . . (298)

$$\left[K + K_2 - \frac{3K_2{}^2}{4(K_1 + K_2)}\right]B + \left[\frac{K}{2} - \frac{3K_1 K_2}{4(K_1 + K_2)}\right]A$$

$$= 6\frac{h}{l}K(\sigma_1 + \sigma_2) - \frac{6l\sigma K_1 K_2}{h(K_1 + K_2)}.$$

In the case of hinged bases, eqs. (298) become:

$$R_2 = \frac{3(K_1 A + K_2 B)}{2(K_1 + K_2)} - \frac{6l\sigma K_1}{h(K_1 + K_2)};$$

$$\left[K + \frac{3}{4}K_1 - \frac{3K_1{}^2}{4(K_1 + K_2)}\right]A + \left[\frac{K}{2} - \frac{3K_1 K_2}{4(K_1 + K_2)}\right]B$$

$$= 6\frac{h}{l}K(\sigma_1 + \sigma_2) + \frac{3l\sigma K_1 K_2}{h(K_1 + K_2)},$$ . . (298a)

$$\left[K + \frac{3}{4}K_2 - \frac{3K_2{}^2}{4(K_1 + K_2)}\right]B + \left[\frac{K}{2} - \frac{3K_1 K_2}{4(K_1 + K_2)}\right]A$$

$$= 6\frac{h}{l}K(\sigma_1 + \sigma_2) - \frac{3l\sigma K_1 K_2}{h(K_1 + K_2)}.$$

92.—Three-legged Bent: (1) *Symmetrical vertical loading and symmetrical stiffnesses.*—Fig. 211 shows the axial deformations of a

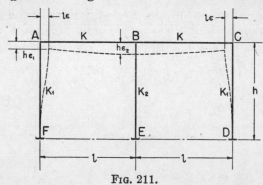

Fig. 211.

three-legged bent under symmetrical strains.   In obtaining the deflection terms R, it is noted that the deflection of member AB equals the difference in the strain shortening of the middle and end legs of the bent; and that of AF is given by the total shortening of the top strut AB. Accordingly, we can write:

$$\left.\begin{aligned} R_{AB}&=3E\frac{h}{l}(\epsilon_2-\epsilon_1)=3\frac{h}{l}(\sigma_2-\sigma_1), \\ R_{AF}&=6E\epsilon\frac{l}{h}=6\sigma\frac{l}{h};\ R_{BE}=0. \end{aligned}\right\} \ \cdots \cdots \ (299)$$

Assuming the bases fixed,

$$\left.\begin{aligned} A&=\frac{6lK_1\sigma}{h(K+K_1)}+\frac{3hK}{l(K+K_1)}(\sigma_2-\sigma_1); \\ M_{AB}&=\frac{3lKK_1}{h(K+K_1)}\left[2\sigma-\frac{h^2}{l^2}(\sigma_2-\sigma_1)\right], \\ M_{BA}&=\frac{3l\sigma KK_1}{h(K+K_1)}-\frac{3hK(K+2K_1)}{2l(K+K_1)}(\sigma_2-\sigma_1), \\ M_{FA}&\ \frac{3hKK_1}{2l(K+K_1)}(\sigma_2-\sigma_1)\ \ \frac{3l\sigma K_1}{h(K+K_1)}(2K+K_1). \end{aligned}\right\} \quad (300)$$

If the bases are assumed to be hinged,

$$\left.\begin{aligned} A&=\frac{12lK_1\sigma}{h(4K+3K_1)}+\frac{12hK}{l(4K+3K_1)}(\sigma_2-\sigma_1); \\ M_{AB}&=\frac{12lKK_1\sigma}{h(4K+3K_1)}-\frac{9hKK_1}{l(4K+3K_1)}(\sigma_2-\sigma_1), \\ M_{BA}&=\frac{6lKK_1\sigma}{h(4K+3K_1)}-\frac{3hK(2K+3K_1)}{l(4K+3K_1)}(\sigma_2-\sigma_1). \end{aligned}\right\} \ \cdots \ (300a)$$

(2) *Unsymmetrical Bent.*—In the general case of a bent with varying stiffnesses, or unsymmetrical framing, as in Fig. 212, the joint

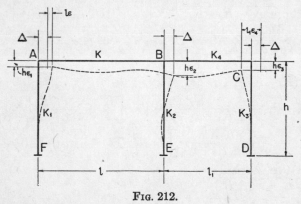

FIG. 212.

deflections may be considered as the resultant displacements due to side sway and axial shortenings. In Fig. 212, if the middle leg be assumed to deflect laterally a distance Δ, the lateral displacements of joints A and C, resulting from sway Δ and strain shortenings $l\epsilon$ and $l_1\epsilon_4$, will then become $(\Delta+l\epsilon)$ and $-(l_1\epsilon_4-\Delta)$, respectively. The vertical deflections of the same joints with respect to joint B are similarly given by $h(\epsilon_2-\epsilon_1)$ and $h(\epsilon_3-\epsilon_2)$. Indicating the unit axial strains by σ, with the same sub mark as for the corresponding K, we can write:

$$
\left.
\begin{aligned}
R_{BE} &= 6E\frac{\Delta}{h}=R_2, \\
R_{AF} &= 6E\frac{(\Delta+l\epsilon)}{h}=R_2+6\frac{l}{h}\sigma, \\
R_{CD} &= 6E\frac{(\Delta-l_1\epsilon_4)}{h}=R_2-6\frac{l_1}{h}\sigma_4, \\
R_{AB} &= 6E\frac{h}{l}(\epsilon_2-\epsilon_1)=6\frac{h}{l}(\sigma_2-\sigma_1), \\
R_{BC} &= 6E\frac{h}{l}(\epsilon_3-\epsilon_2)=6\frac{h}{l_1}(\sigma_3-\sigma_2).
\end{aligned}
\right\}
\quad \ldots \ldots (301)
$$

Having established these relations, the value of the unknown R_2 is then obtained from the shear expressions of the three legs. Thus, for fixed bases, we have:

$$
R_2=\frac{3}{4}\cdot\frac{(K_1A+K_2B+K_3C)}{(K_1+K_2+K_3)}+\frac{6(l_1K_3\sigma_4-lK_1\sigma)}{h(K_1+K_2+K_3)}; \quad (302)
$$

and for hinged bases,

$$
R_2=\frac{3}{4}\cdot\frac{(K_1A+K_2B+K_3C)}{4(K_1+K_2+K_3)}+\frac{6(l_1K_3\sigma_4-lK_1\sigma)}{h(K_1+K_2+K_3)}. \quad \ldots (302a)
$$

The joint expressions are in the following forms:
Fixed bases,

$$
\left[K+K_1-\frac{3K_1^2}{4(K_1+K_2+K_3)}\right]A+\left[\frac{K}{2}-\frac{3K_1K_2}{4(K_1+K_2+K_3)}\right]B
$$

$$
-\frac{3K_1K_3}{4(K_1+K_2+K_3)}C=6\frac{h}{l}K(\sigma_2-\sigma_1)+6\frac{l}{h}K_1\sigma
$$

$$
+\frac{6K_1(l_1K_3\sigma_4-lK_1\sigma)}{h(K_1+K_2+K_3)},
$$

$$
\left[K+K_2+K_4-\frac{3K_2^2}{4(K_1+K_2+K_3)}\right]B+\left[\frac{K}{2}-\frac{3K_1K_2}{4(K_1+K_2+K_3)}\right]A
$$

$$
+\left[\frac{K_4}{2}-\frac{3K_2K_3}{4(K_1+K_2+K_3)}\right]C=6\frac{h}{l}K(\sigma_2-\sigma_1)+6\frac{h}{l_1}K_4(\sigma_3-\sigma_2)
$$

$$
+\frac{6K_2(l_1K_3\sigma_4-lK_1\sigma)}{h(K_1+K_2+K_3)},
$$

$$
\left[K_3+K_4-\frac{3K_3^2}{4(K_1+K_2+K_3)}\right]C+\left[\frac{K_4}{2}-\frac{3K_2K_3}{4(K_1+K_2+K_3)}\right]B
$$

$$
-\frac{3K_1K_3}{4(K_1+K_2+K_3)}A=6\frac{h}{l_1}K_4(\sigma_3-\sigma_2)-6\frac{l_1}{h}K_3\sigma_4
$$

$$
+\frac{6K_3(l_1K_3\sigma_4-lK_1\sigma)}{h(K_1+K_2+K_3)};
$$

Hinged bases,

$$\left[K+\frac{3}{4}K_1-\frac{3K_1^2}{4(K_1+K_2+K_3)}\right]A+\left[\frac{K}{2}-\frac{3K_1K_2}{4(K_1+K_2+K_3)}\right]B$$

$$-\frac{3K_1K_3}{4(K_1+K_2+K_3)}C=6\frac{h}{l}K(\sigma_2-\sigma_1)+3\frac{l}{h}K_1\sigma+\frac{3K_1(l_1K_3\sigma_4-lK_1\sigma)}{h(K_1+K_2+K_3)},$$

$$\left[K+\frac{3}{4}K_2+K_4-\frac{3K_2^2}{4(K_1+K_2+K_3)}\right]B+\left[\frac{K}{2}-\frac{3K_1K_2}{4(K_1+K_2+K_3)}\right]A$$

$$+\left[\frac{K_4}{2}-\frac{3K_2K_3}{4(K_1+K_2+K_3)}\right]C=6\frac{h}{l}K(\sigma_2-\sigma_1)+6\frac{h}{l_1}K_4(\sigma_3-\sigma_2)$$

$$+\frac{3K_2(l_1K_3\sigma_4-lK_1\sigma)}{h(K_1+K_2+K_3)},$$

$$\left[K_4+\frac{3}{4}K_3-\frac{3K_3^2}{4(K_1+K_2+K_3)}\right]C+\left[\frac{K_4}{2}-\frac{3K_2K_3}{4(K_1+K_2+K_3)}\right]B$$

$$-\frac{3K_1K_3}{4(K_1+K_2+K_3)}A=6\frac{h}{l_1}K_4(\sigma_3-\sigma_2)-3\frac{l}{h}K_3\sigma_4$$

$$+\frac{3K_3(l_1K_3\sigma_4-lK_1\sigma)}{h(K_1+K_2+K_3)}.$$

93. Gable Bent: (1) *Symmetrical vertical loading and framing.*—
Fig. 213 shows the manner of joint displacement in a gable bent under

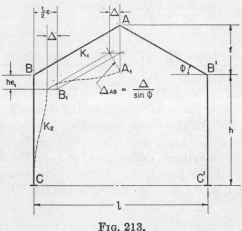

FIG. 213.

symmetrical axial strains. It is to be noted that, due to shortening
of top member AB by a horizontal distance $\frac{l}{2}\epsilon$, the first displacement
of joint B to position B_1 is accompanied by a second displacement
Δ yet to be determined. The latter displacement which is of the

same character as that due to flexure, produces a corresponding deflection in member AB. Thus we have:

$$\left.\begin{aligned} R_{BC}&=\frac{6E}{h}\left(\frac{l}{2}\epsilon-\Delta\right)=3\frac{l}{h}\sigma-R,\\ R_{AB}&=\frac{6E\Delta}{\sin\phi}\cdot\frac{\sin\phi}{f}\cdot\frac{h}{h}=\frac{h}{f}R; \end{aligned}\right\} \quad \cdots \cdots \quad (303)$$

and, from the shear expressions of members AB and BC,

$$\frac{1}{h}(M_{BC}+M_{CB})=\frac{1}{f}(M_{AB}+M_{BA}) \quad \cdots \cdots \quad (a)$$

Substituting for the values of the end moments in eq. (a), the deflection expression becomes:

Fixed bases,

$$R=\frac{3f(hK_1-fK_2)}{4(h^2K_1+f^2K_2)}B+\frac{3f^2lK_2\sigma}{h(h^2K_1+f^2K_2)}; \quad \cdots \cdots \quad (304)$$

Hinged bases,

$$R=\frac{3f(2hK_1-fK_2)}{2(4h^2K_1+f^2K_2)}B+\frac{3f^2lK_2\sigma}{h(4h^2K_1+f^2K_2)} \quad \cdots \cdots \quad (304a)$$

And for the joint expression at B, after eliminating R, we have:

Fixed bases,

$$\left[K_1+K_2-\frac{3}{4}\frac{(hK_1-fK_2)^2}{(h^2K_1+f^2K_2)}\right]B=\frac{3l}{h}K_2\sigma+\frac{3flK_2\sigma(hK_1-fK_2)}{h(h^2K_1+f^2K_2)}; \quad (305)$$

Hinged bases,

$$\left[K_1+\frac{3}{4}K_2-\frac{3}{4}\frac{(2hK_1-fK_2)^2}{4h^2K_1+f^2K_2}\right]B=\frac{3lK_2\sigma}{2h}+\frac{3flK_2\sigma(2hK_1-fK_2)}{2h(4h^2K_1+f^2K_2)} \quad (305a)$$

(2) *Symmetrical bent with unsymmetrical loading or strains.*— In the more general case of unsymmetrical loading, resulting in unequal strains for members symmetrically located with respect to the vertical axis of the bent, the joint displacements may again be considered as the resultant deflections due to bending sway and change in length of the members. These displacements are shown, on an exaggerated scale, in Fig. 214. Indicating the average axial

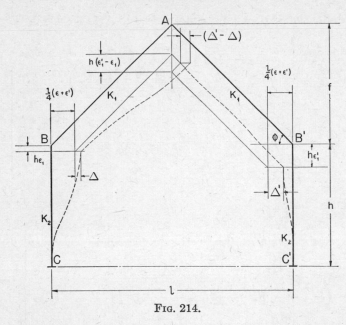

FIG. 214.

strains for members AB, AB', BC and $B'C'$ respectively by ϵ, ϵ', ϵ_1 and ϵ_1', and the corresponding unit stresses by σ, σ', σ_1 and σ_1', the deflection terms become:

$$
\left.
\begin{aligned}
\Delta_{BC} &= \Delta + \frac{l}{4}(\epsilon + \epsilon'),\ R_{BC} = 6E\frac{\Delta}{h} + \frac{3El}{2h}(\epsilon + \epsilon') \\
&= R + \frac{3l}{2h}(\sigma + \sigma'); \\
\Delta_{B'C'} &= \Delta' - \frac{l}{4}(\epsilon + \epsilon'),\ R_{B'C'} = 6E\frac{\Delta'}{h} - \frac{3El}{2h}(\epsilon + \epsilon') \\
&= R' - \frac{3l}{2h}(\sigma + \sigma'); \\
\Delta_{AB} &= \frac{h(\epsilon_1' - \epsilon_1)}{2\cos\phi} + \frac{\Delta' - \Delta}{2\sin\phi}, \\
R_{AB} &= -R_{AB'} = 6\frac{h}{l}(\sigma_1' - \sigma_1) + \frac{h}{2f}(R' - R).
\end{aligned}
\right\} \quad \dots \quad (306)
$$

The deflection expressions, obtained as in Art. 47, are in the following forms:

Fixed bases,

$$
\left.
\begin{aligned}
&\left(\frac{hK_1}{f^2}+\frac{2K_2}{h}\right)R-\frac{hK_1}{f^2}R'=-\frac{K_1}{f}A+\left(\frac{3K_2}{2h}-\frac{K_1}{f}\right)B+\frac{K_1}{2f}B' \\
&\quad -\frac{3lK_2}{h}(\sigma+\sigma')+\frac{12hK_1}{fl}(\sigma_1'-\sigma_1), \\
&\left(\frac{hK_1}{f^2}+\frac{2K_2}{h}\right)R'-\frac{hK_1}{f^2}R=-\frac{K_1}{f}A+\left(\frac{3K_2}{2h}-\frac{K_1}{f}\right)B'+\frac{K_1}{2f}B \\
&\quad +\frac{3lK_2}{h^2}(\sigma+\sigma')-\frac{12hK_1}{fl}(\sigma_1'-\sigma_1);
\end{aligned}
\right\} \cdot (307)
$$

Hinged bases,

$$
\left.
\begin{aligned}
&\left(\frac{hK_1}{f^2}+\frac{K_2}{2h}\right)R-\frac{hK_1}{f^2}R'=-\frac{3K_1}{2f}A+\left(\frac{3K_2}{4h}-\frac{3K_1}{2f}\right) \\
&\quad -\frac{3lK_2}{4h^2}(\sigma+\sigma')+\frac{12hK_1}{fl}(\sigma_1'-\sigma_1), \\
&\left(\frac{hK_1}{f^2}+\frac{K_2}{2h}\right)R'-\frac{hK_1}{f^2}R=-\frac{3K_1}{2f}A+\left(\frac{3K_2}{4h}-\frac{3K_1}{2f}\right)B' \\
&\quad +\frac{3lK_2}{4h^2}(\sigma+\sigma')-\frac{12hK_1}{fl}(\sigma_1'-\sigma_1).
\end{aligned}
\right\} \cdot \cdot (307a)
$$

The joint expressions at B and B' are given in eqs. (136), (137), (142) and (143), with the following modified load constants:

Fixed bases,

$$
Q_B=-Q_{B'}=(t-t')\left[\frac{3lK_2}{h^2}(\sigma+\sigma')-\frac{12hK_1}{fl}(\sigma_1'-\sigma_1)\right]
$$

$$
-\frac{6hK_1}{l}(\sigma_1'-\sigma_1)-\frac{3lK_2}{2h}(\sigma+\sigma');
$$

Hinged bases,

$$
Q_B=-Q_{B'}=(t-t')\left[\frac{3lK_2}{4h^2}(\sigma+\sigma')-\frac{12hK_1}{fl}(\sigma_1'-\sigma_1)\right]
$$

$$
-\frac{6hK_1}{l}(\sigma_1'-\sigma_1)-\frac{3lK_2}{4h}(\sigma+\sigma').
$$

ILLUSTRATIVE EXAMPLE

The average unit axial stress in top members AB and AB' of the symmetrical bent shown in Fig. 111b, resulting from uniform vertical loading, is 1.5 kips per square inch. The relative stiffnesses K are as indicated in the figure, and the true K of the top members equals 4. Assuming the bases to be fixed, obtain the end moments due to the axial deformations.

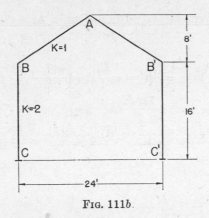

FIG. 111b.

Solution: Applying eqs. (305), (304) and (303),

$$B = 4.5, \quad R_{BC} = 2.25, \quad R_{AB} = 4.5;$$

and

$$M_{AB} = 4(2.25 - 4.5) = -9 \text{ inch kips};$$
$$M_{BA} = 4(4.5 - 4.5) = 0;$$
$$M_{CB} = 4 \times 2(2.25 - 4.5) = -18 \text{ inch kips.}$$

94. Moments Due to Temperature Deformations.—Deformations resulting from temperature changes are similar to deformations due to axial stresses. In the case of uniform shrinkage (or expansion) of members, Figs. 210, 211 and 212 may also be used to illustrate temperature deformations for the three types of bents. Assuming ϵ, ϵ_1 and ϵ_2 to indicate the unit shortening of the members, the corresponding relations in Arts. 91, 92 and 93 then become directly applicable.

In the case of temperature differential, that is, when the temperature of the two faces of the bent differs, the resultant deformation may be conveniently studied by separate consideration of its two components: first, the effect of axial shortening (or lengthening) of members due to one-half the temperature differential, analyzed as explained above; second, the effect of relative shortening (or lengthening) of the inside boundary line with respect to the outside line, resulting in joint rotations. Fig. 215 illustrates the deformations due to the latter effect in a simple two-legged bent. In (a), the temperature differential is assumed to be for top member AB; in (b), for the two legs AD and BC; and in (c), the temperature differential is assumed to occur in the leg AD. Denoting the deflection angle at the

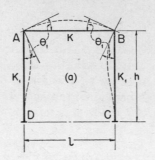

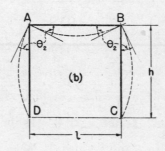

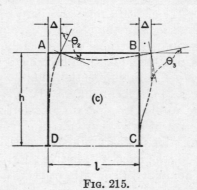

FIG. 215.

upper ends of members AD and BC of the bent in Fig. 215(b) by θ_2, then for the corresponding moment in member AB we have:

$$M_{AB} = 2EK\theta_2.$$

Similarly, if the deflection angle at each end of member AB in (a) be denoted by θ_1, the resulting moments in the two legs become:

Fixed bases,

$$M_{AD} = -4EK_1\theta_1,$$
$$M_{DA} = -2EK_1\theta_1;$$

Hinged bas

In Fig. 215(c .... at upper end of member
AD, the ben .... oint B rotates through an
angle θ_3. As .... tion of the unknowns is
obtained fro .... of the bent.

Assuming .... change in deflection angle
per unit leng ....

$$\ldots \ldots \ldots \ldots (a)$$

in which ϵ i .... iber per one degree change
in temperatu .... , d is the depth of the member and T .... n degrees) between its two
faces. Acco .... we have:

$$\ldots \ldots \ldots \ldots (b)$$

and θ_2 in (b ....

$$\frac{h\epsilon}{2d_{AD}}T, \ldots \ldots \ldots (c)$$

depending .... ixed on hinged at D.

CHAPTER IV

SHEARING DEFORMATIONS

95. Effect of Shearing Deformations.—In the derivation of fundamental slope-deflection expressions in Part I, deflections due to the shearing forces on the cross sections of a member were neglected. As in the case of axial deformations, in an ordinary framing, stresses resulting from shearing deformations are of too little importance to require analysis. However, in some special framings, such as bomb-proof bents of reinforced concrete—where members of unusual depths and relatively shorter spans are used, and bent supports for turbo-generators where deflections are of primary importance, an investigation including the effect of shearing deformations may be found justifiable. The derivation of the fundamental moment expression to include this effect is quite simple and it will be given both for members with constant cross section and variable cross section.

96. Moment Expression for Members with Constant Cross Section.— The fundamental relation between shearing stress and shearing strain is given by

$$\frac{\tau}{\gamma} = G, \quad \ldots \ldots \ldots \ldots \ldots \quad (a)$$

in which τ and γ indicate the unit shearing stress and unit shearing strain, respectively, and G is the modulus of elasticity in shear. Accordingly, for the slope of the deflection curve due to shear we can write:

$$\frac{dy}{dx} = \gamma = \frac{\tau}{G} = \frac{kS}{A_cG}; \quad \ldots \ldots \ldots \ldots \quad (b)$$

where S indicates the total shear on the section, A_c the cross-sectional area and k is a cross-sectional constant for shear (for rectangular sections $k=1.2$). Then the shear deflection corresponding to a length dx becomes

$$dy = \frac{kS}{A_cG}dx; \quad \ldots \ldots \ldots \ldots \ldots \quad (c)$$

in which the product Sdx represents the shear area of a strip dx. For a member AB, Fig. 216, subjected to end moments M_{AB} and M_{BA} and a load P, the shear S at any point along the span l equals

$$S = -\frac{1}{l}(M_{AB}+M_{BA}) \pm V_x; \quad \ldots \ldots \ldots \quad (d)$$

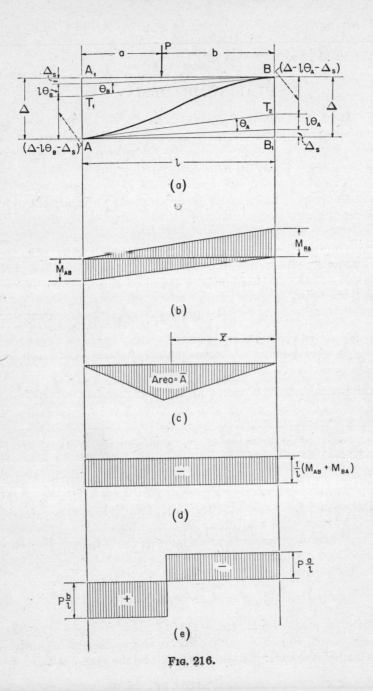

FIG. 216.

in which V_x indicates the shear due to the external loading, and the sign is positive ($+$) when the shear couple rotates in a clockwise direction. Substituting this value of S in eq. (c),

$$dy = -\frac{k}{lA_cG}(M_{AB}+M_{BA})dx \pm \frac{k}{A_cG}V_x dx \quad \dots \dots \quad (e)$$

the total deflection, Δ_s, of the member due to shear becomes

$$y = \Delta_s = -\frac{k}{A_cG}(M_{AB}+M_{BA}) + \frac{k}{A_cG}\left(\frac{Pab}{l}-\frac{Pab}{l}\right)$$

$$= -\frac{k}{A_cG}(M_{AB}+M_{BA}); \quad \dots \dots \dots \dots \quad (f)$$

that is, the sum of dx strips of shear areas shown in (d) and (e), Fig. 216. Noting also that

$$A_c = \frac{I}{r^2}, \; G = \frac{E}{2(1+\mu)}, \quad \dots \dots \dots \quad (g)$$

where I and r, respectively, indicate the moment of inertia and radius of gyration of the section and μ is Poisson's ratio, for eq. (f) we can write:

$$\Delta_s = -\frac{2(1+\mu)}{1E}kr^2(M_{AB}+M_{BA}); \quad \dots \dots \quad (308)$$

or, letting $t = 2(1+\mu)k$,

$$\Delta_s = -\frac{tr^2}{EI}(M_{AB}+M_{BA}) \dots \dots \dots \quad (308a)$$

Having obtained the value of the shear deflection the moment expressions are then derived as in Art. 25:

$$\theta_A - \theta_B = \frac{l}{2EI}M_{AB} - \frac{l}{2EI}M_{BA} + \frac{\overline{A}}{EI} \quad \dots \dots \dots \quad (h)$$

$$\Delta - l\theta_A - \Delta_s = \frac{l^2}{3EI}M_{AB} + \frac{l^2}{6EI}M_{BA} - \frac{\overline{x}\overline{A}}{EI}, \quad \dots \dots \quad (i)$$

or, substituting for Δ_s its value from eq. $(308a)$,

$$\Delta - l\theta_A = -\frac{(l^2+3tr^2)}{3EI}M_{AB} + \frac{(l^2-6tr^2)}{6EI}M_{BA} - \frac{\overline{x}\overline{A}}{EI}, \quad \dots \quad (j)$$

and solving for the end moments M_{AB} and M_{BA},

$$M_{AB} = \frac{2EK}{l^2+12tr^2}[2(l^2+3tr^2)\theta_A + (l^2-6tr^2)\theta_B - 3\Delta l]$$

$$- \frac{2\overline{A}[l(3\overline{x}-l)+6tr^2]}{l(l^2+12tr^2)}, \quad \dots \dots \dots \quad (309)$$

$$M_{BA} = \frac{2EK}{l^2+12tr^2}[2(l^2+3tr^2)\theta_B + (l^2-6tr^2)\theta_A - 3\Delta\, l]$$

$$+ \frac{2\overline{A}[l(2l-3\overline{x})+6tr^2]}{l(l^2+12tr^2)} \quad \dots \dots \dots \quad (309a)$$

It is to be noted that, if the loading is symmetrical, the last terms of eqs. (309) and (309a) will assume the familiar form of $\dfrac{\overline{A}}{l}$ or the fixed end moment, FM, for members with constant cross section.

97. Moment Expression for Members with Variable Cross Section.—

In the case of variable cross section, the slope of the deflection curve due to shear, eq. (b), may be written in the form

$$\frac{dy}{dx} = \frac{kS}{mA_cG}; \quad \cdots \cdots \cdots \cdots \quad (k)$$

in which A_c indicates the minimum cross-sectional area of the member and m is the ratio of the cross-sectional area, A_{cx}, taken at any point x, to A_c; that is,

$$m = \frac{A_{cx}}{A_c} \quad \cdots \cdots \cdots \cdots \cdots \quad (l)$$

Then

$$dy = \frac{kS}{mA_cG}dx, \quad \cdots \cdots \cdots \cdots \quad (m)$$

and

$$y = \Delta_s = \frac{k}{A_cG}\int \frac{S}{m}dx \quad \cdots \cdots \cdots \quad (310)$$

The term $\int \dfrac{S}{m}dx$ may be considered as the modified shear area of the member, corresponding to the modified moment area discussed in Art. 18. Let

$\bar{q}$ = modified area of the shear diagram for a unit shear and span of unity;

$\overline{Q}$ = modified area of the shear diagram due to the external loading.

Then, for the beam shown in Fig. 217, the shear deflection, eq. (310), becomes:

$$\Delta_s = \frac{k}{A_cG}[-\bar{q}(M_{AB}+M_{BA})+\overline{Q}]; \quad \cdots \cdots \quad (311)$$

or,

$$\Delta_s = \frac{tr^2}{EI}[-\bar{q}(M_{AB}+M_{BA})+\overline{Q}] \quad \cdots \cdots \quad (311a)$$

The shear deflection thus defined, from the modified moment and shear areas shown in Fig. 217 we have:

$$EI(_A\theta-\theta_B) = plM_{AB}-qlM_{AB}+\overline{A}_1 \quad \cdots \cdots \cdots \cdots \quad (n)$$

$$\begin{aligned}
EI(\Delta-l\theta_A) &= -pl^2(1-u)M_{AB}+qvl^2M_{BA}-\bar{x}_1\overline{A}_1 \\
&\quad +tr^2[-\bar{q}(M_{AB}+M_{BA})+\overline{Q}] \\
&= -[pl^2(1-u)+\bar{q}tr^2]M_{AB}+(qvl^2 \\
&\quad -qtr^2)M_{BA}-\bar{x}_1\overline{A}_1+tr^2\overline{Q}; \quad \cdots \cdots \cdots \quad (p)
\end{aligned}$$

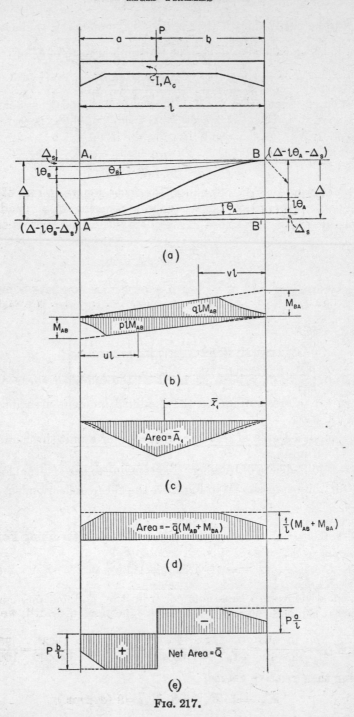

FIG. 217.

from which

$$M_{AB} = \frac{EI}{l} \cdot \frac{[ql^2(1-v)+\bar{q}tr^2]\theta_A+(qvl^2-\bar{q}tr^2)\theta_B-ql\Delta}{pql^2(1-u-v)+(p+q)\bar{q}tr^2}$$

$$-\frac{[ql(x_1-vl)+\bar{q}tr^2]\overline{A}_1+qltr^2\overline{Q}}{l[pql^2(1-u-v)+(p+q)\bar{q}tr^2]}, \quad \ldots \ldots \quad (312)$$

$$M_{BA} = \frac{EI}{l} \cdot \frac{[pl^2(1-u)+\bar{q}tr^2]\theta_B+(pul^2-\bar{q}tr^2)\theta_A-pl\Delta}{pql^2(1-u-v)+(p+q)\bar{q}tr^2}$$

$$+\frac{[pl(l-ul-\bar{x}_1)+\bar{q}tr^2]\overline{A}_1+pltr^2\overline{Q}}{l[pql^2(1-u-v)+(p+\bar{q})\bar{q}tr^2]} \quad \ldots \ldots \quad (312a)$$

Eqs. (312) and (312a) represent the most general forms of slope-deflection expressions for end moments resulting from bending as well as shearing deformations in members with variable cross section.

ILLUSTRATIVE EXAMPLE

The loading per foot of width of a reinforced concrete bombproof bent is shown in Fig. 218. The depth of the top slab is 6 feet, that

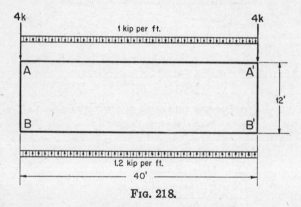

FIG. 218.

of the bottom slab 3 feet and the walls 4 feet. Assuming Poisson's ratio equal to 0.2, obtain the end moments:

(a) Considering shearing deformations;

(b) Neglecting shearing deformations.

Solution: (a) For the $\frac{I}{l}$ of the members, per foot of width, we have:

$$K_{AA'} = \frac{1\times6^3}{12\times40} = \frac{9}{20}, \ K_{AB} = \frac{1\times4^3}{12\times12} = \frac{4}{9}, \ K_{BB'} = \frac{1\times3^3}{12\times40} = \frac{9}{160};$$

or, using their relative values,

$$K_{BB'}=1, \ K_{AA'}=8, \ K_{AB}=8 \ (approx.).$$

Since $\theta_A = -\theta_{A'}$ and $\theta_B = -\theta_{B'}$, for members AA' and BB' the end moment expression, eq. (309), will assume the ordinary form

$$M_{AA'} = 2EK\theta_A + FM_{AA'} = 16E\theta_A - \frac{400}{3};$$
$$M_{BB'} = 2EK\theta_B + FM_{BB'} = 2E\theta_B + 160.$$

In the case of member AB we have:

$$r^2 = \frac{4}{3}; \quad t = 2(1+0.2)1.2 = 2.88;$$

and

$$M_{AB} = \frac{16E}{190.08}(311.04\theta_A + 120.96\theta_B) = 26.181E\theta_A + 10.181E\theta_B,$$
$$M_{BA} = \frac{16E}{190.08}(311.04\theta_B + 120.96\theta_A) = 26.181E\theta_B + 10.181E\theta_A.$$

Accordingly, the joint expressions at A and B become:

$$42.181E\theta_A + 10.181E\theta_B = 133.33,$$
$$10.181E\theta_A + 28.181E\theta_B = -160.00;$$

from which

$$E\theta A = 4.964, \quad E\theta_B = -7.471;$$

and

$$M_{AA'} = 16 \times 4.964 - 133.33 = -53.91,$$
$$M_{AB} = 26.181 \times 4.964 - 10.181 \times 7.471 = 53.90;$$

$$M_{BA} = 10.181 \times 4.964 - 26.181 \times 7.471 = -145.06,$$
$$M_{BB'} = -2 \times 7.471 + 160 = 145.06.$$

(b)

$$12A + 4B = 133.33,$$
$$4A + 8.5B = -160.00;$$

$$A = 20.620, \quad B = -28.527;$$

$$M_{AA'} = 8(10.310) - 133.33 = -50.85,$$
$$M_{AB} = 8(20.620 - 14.264) = 50.85;$$

$$M_{BA} = 8(10.310 - 28.527) = -145.74,$$
$$M_{BB'} = -14.264 + 160 = 145.74.$$

ANSWERS TO PROBLEMS

1. $\dfrac{11}{48}\dfrac{Pl^3}{EI}$.

2. (a), 0;

   (b), $\dfrac{Pl^2}{8EI}$;

   (c), $\Delta=\dfrac{5}{48}\cdot\dfrac{Pl^3}{EI}$;

   $\Delta_1=0$.

3. (a), $\dfrac{Pa^2b}{2lEI}$; (b), $\dfrac{Pab(b-a)}{3lEI}$; (c), $\dfrac{Pb(l^2-b^2)}{9lEI}\sqrt{\dfrac{l^2-b^2}{3}}$.

4. (a), $\dfrac{Pl^2}{8EI}$; (b), $\dfrac{Pl^2}{16EI}$; (c), $\dfrac{5}{192}\cdot\dfrac{Pl^3}{EI}$; (d), $\dfrac{13}{384}\cdot\dfrac{Pl^3}{EI}$.

5. (a), $\dfrac{Wl^2h}{12}$; (b), $\dfrac{Wl^2}{4h(3l+2h)}$; (c), $\dfrac{Wl}{8}\left(1-\dfrac{2l}{3l+2h}\right)$;

   (d), $\dfrac{Wl^3}{384}\left(5-\dfrac{12l}{3l+2h}\right)$.

6. (a), $\dfrac{Pl}{48EI}(3l-8l_1)$; (b), $-\dfrac{Pl}{48EI}(3l-16l_1)$;

   (c), $l_1=\dfrac{3}{16}l$; (d), $\dfrac{Pl^3}{48EI\sqrt{5}}$.

7. (a), $\dfrac{Pab^2}{l^2}$; (b), $\dfrac{2Pa^2b^2}{l^3}$; (c), $\dfrac{Pa^2b}{l^2}$.

8. (a), $\dfrac{wl^2}{8}$ and 0; (b), $\dfrac{wl^2}{12}$ and $\dfrac{wl^2}{12}$; (c), $\dfrac{5}{48}wl^2$ and $\dfrac{wl^2}{24}$.

9. (a), 0; (b), $M_{CA}=-\dfrac{4}{9}Pe$; (c), $M_{CB}=-\dfrac{5}{9}Pe$; (d), $M_{BC}=-\dfrac{1}{3}Pe$.

10. (a), $\pm\dfrac{Pl}{6}$; (b), $-\dfrac{4}{17}Pl$.

11. (a), $0.259\ Pl$; (b), $0.201\ Pl$.

12. (a), 150 inch-kips; (b), 93.75 inch-kips.

13. (a), $\dfrac{5wl^4}{384EI}$; (b), $\dfrac{wl^4}{384EI}$.

14. $\theta_A = -\theta_C = +0.0096\,\dfrac{Pl^2}{EI}.$

15. (a), $\left(8\dfrac{h}{l}K + 4.94K\right)A + 4\dfrac{h}{l}KB - 4.29KR = 0;$

     (b), $\left(16\dfrac{h}{l}K + K\right)B + 4\dfrac{h}{l}KA + 4\dfrac{h}{l}KC - KR = 0.$

16. (a), $1.5K_2A + 1.5K_3B - 2(K_2 + K_3)R + FM_{AD} + FM_{DA} = -cF:$

     (b), $\dfrac{3}{4}K_2A + \dfrac{3}{4}K_3B - \dfrac{1}{2}(K_2 + K_3)R + HM_{AD} = -cF.$

17. (a), $M_{AD} = \dfrac{14}{23}\cdot\dfrac{wl_2}{12};\ M_{BC} = -\dfrac{20}{23}\cdot\dfrac{wl^2}{12};$

     (b), $M_{AD} = \dfrac{4.75}{7}\cdot\dfrac{wl^2}{12};\ M_{BC} = -\dfrac{5.5}{7}\cdot\dfrac{wl^2}{12}.$

18. (a), $M_{AF} = -\dfrac{K_2}{K_1 + K_2}FM_{AB};\ M_{BA} = -\dfrac{K_1}{2(K_1 + K_2)}FM_{AB} + FM_{BA};$

     $FM_{BE} = 0;$

     (b), $M_{AF} = -\dfrac{3K_2}{4K_1 + 3K_2}FM_{AB};\ M_{BA} = -\dfrac{2K_1}{4K_1 + 3K_2}FM_{AB} + FM_{BA};$

     $FM_{BE} = 0.$

19. (a), $F_B = 2.4,\ F_C = 1.6,\ F_D = 2.0;$

     (b), $f_{BC} = -0.25;\ f_{CB} = -0.167,\ f_{CD} = -0.2;\ f_{DC} = -0.25;$

     (c), $B = 6.423,\ C = -18.914,\ D = 9.740.$

20. $B = 3.0,\ C = 0;\ M_{AB} = -7.5,\ M_{BA} = 21,\ M_{CB} = 30.$

21.

	A	B	E	F
f	$f_{AB} - \frac{1}{4}$ $f_{AE} - \frac{1}{16}$	$f_{BA} - \frac{1}{3}$ $f_{BF} - \frac{1}{20}$	$f_{EA} - \frac{1}{6}$ $f_{EF} - \frac{1}{5}$	$f_{FB} - \frac{1}{8}$ $f_{FE} - \frac{1}{4}$

22. Joint A:

     $M_{AB} = -26.40,$

     $M_{AD} = 26.25;$

Joint B:

     $M_{BA} = 45.16,$

     $M_{BC} = -34.37,$

     $M_{BE} = -10.94;$

Joint D:

     $M_{DA} = 21.45,$

     $M_{DE} = -38.30,$

     $M_{DG} = 16.66;$

Joint E:

$M_{EB} = - 9.60,$

$M_{ED} = 55.10,$

$M_{EF} = -37.51,$

$M_{EH} = - 8.25;$

Joint C:

$M_{CB} = 9.82,$

$M_{CF} = 0;$

Joint F:

$M_{FE} = 12.74,$

$M_{FC} = M_{FJ} = 0.$

23.

Joint	A	A1	B	B1	C	C1
Joint Coefficient	2	2	5	5	10	10
Coeffs. of Correction	A1= .05 B =−.04 B1= .12	A = .05 B = .12 B1=−.04	A =−.10 A1= .16 B1= .16 C =−.04 C1= .12	A = .30 A1=−.10 B = .16 C = .12 C1=−.04	B −−.08 B1= .24 C1= .16	B = .24 B1=−.08 C = .16
Load constant	0	−5	−22	−17	−24	−24

24. $\dfrac{R}{2}\left[\dfrac{K_5}{h_1}(1.5\alpha_A - a_1) + \dfrac{K_6}{h_2}(1.5\alpha_B - a_2) + \dfrac{K_7}{h}(1.5\alpha_C - 1\right.$

$\left. + \dfrac{K_8}{h_3}(1.5\alpha_D - a_3) + \dfrac{K_9}{h_2}(1.5\alpha_E - a_2)\right] = -F.$

25. $M_{AD} = -5.41; M_{DA} = -25.83;$

$M_{BC} = -12.08; M_{CB} = -11.16.$

26. $M_{AB} = M_{BA} = 24.$

At right base: $R_V = 6; R_H = 2.$

At left base: $R_V = 6; R_H = 4.$

27. (a), Q of $A = FM_{AB} + \dfrac{(nK_1 - K_2)[m(e+b) - b]P}{(2-m)(K_2 + K_3)},$

Q of $D = -\dfrac{K_2[m(e+b) - b]P}{(2-m)(K_2 + K_3)};$

(b), Q of $R = \dfrac{[m(e+b) - b]P}{(2-m)(K_2 + K_3)}.$

28. $M_{AB} = -M_{AD} = 14.54;$

$M_{DC} = -M_{DA} = 10.91.$

29. (a), $\dfrac{(F_1 + F_2)h_3 - m_3 M_3}{(2-m_3)(K_8 + K_9)}$; ($b$), $\dfrac{(n_3 K_7 - K_8)}{(2-m_3)(K_8 + K_9)}[(F_1 + F_2)h_3 - m_3 M_3];$

(c), $\dfrac{(n_3 K_7 - K_9)}{(2-m_3)(K_8 + K_9)}[(F_1 + F_2)h_3 - m_3 M_3].$

30.

Table for bent shown in figure 86

	Panel----	Top		Bottom	
	Joint-----	A	B	B	C
1----------	f_i-------	2. 1	4. 8	6. 14	∞
	f_c-------	0. 0625	−0. 0716	0	
2----------	$-Q'$-----	9. 6	19. 2	41. 14	
	α'-------	4. 266	4. 266	6. 70	0
	R'------	25. 6		18. 96	
	M'------	−19. 20	−19. 20	−49. 04	−62. 44
3----------	$-Q''$----	0	49. 04	19. 20	-
	α''-------	−0. 725	10. 15	3. 12	0
	R''------	6. 54		2. 45	
	M''------	−2. 00	3. 25	2. 68	−3. 56
4----------	$-Q'''$----	0	−2. 68	−3. 25	
	α'''------	0. 04	−0. 556	−0. 528	0
	R'''------	−0. 356		−0. 414	
	M'''-----	0. 11	−0. 20	−0. 46	0. 60
$M=M'+M''+M'''$-----		−21. 09	−16. 15	−46. 82	−65. 40
Location of M----------		M_{AB}	M_{BA}	M_{BC}	M_{CB}

31.

Joint----	A	B	C	D	E	F
$-Q$----	180	420	96	−240	−324	−132
Joint----	A'	B'	C'	D'	E'	F'
$-Q$-----	90	186	72	−120	−162	−66

32. $A=A'=254.54$; $B=B'=281.82$; $C=C'=0$;

     $R_1=777.27$; $R_2=336.37$.

  $M_{AB}=-381.82$; $M_{BA}=-368.18$;

  $M_{BC}=-54.55$; $M_{CB}=-195.46$.

$$339B + 29B' + 18C - 50C' = 4320,$$
$$269B' + 51B - 30C + 46C' = -480,$$
$$106C - 15B - 33B' - 16C' = -4800,$$
$$74C' - 33B + 17B' - 16C = -480.$$

34. *Table for truss shown in figure 104*

	Panel	(1)		(2)		(3)
	Joint	A	B	B	C	C
Initial Values	−Q	0	800	222. 22	226. 67	0
	α	−61. 54	307. 70	103. 22	159. 14	0
	R	553. 85		343. 37		0
	M′	−923. 08	−553. 84	−289. 0	−238. 71	0
First Increments	−Q	0	289. 0	553. 84	0	238. 71
	α	−22. 23	111. 15	232. 0	58. 0	95. 48
	R	55. 58		222. 33		0
	M″	−44. 48	88. 92	69. 6	−87. 0	95. 48
Second Increments	−Q	0	−69. 6	−88. 92	−95. 48	87. 0
	α	5. 35	−26. 76	−41. 04	−58. 0	34. 8
	R	−13. 38		−73. 8		0
	M‴	10. 7	−21. 42	6. 77	−8. 48	34. 8
M′+M″+M‴		−956. 86	−486. 34	−212. 63	−334. 19	130. 28
Location of M		M_{AB}	M_{BA}	M_{BC}	M_{CB}	M_{CD}

35. (a), $R = -\dfrac{3f(hK_1 - fK_2)}{4(h^2K_1 + f^2K_2)} B + \dfrac{f^2(FM_{BC} + FM_{CB} + Pe)}{2(h^2K_1 + f^2K_2)}$;

$$\left[K_1 + K_2 - \frac{3(hK_1 - fK_2)^2}{4(h^2K_1 + f^2K_2)} \right] B = -FM_{BC}$$

$$- \frac{f(hK_1 - fK_2)}{2(h^2K_1 + f^2K_2)} (FM_{BC} + FM_{CB} + Pe).$$

(b), $R = -\dfrac{3f(2hK_1 - fK_2)}{2(4h^2K_1 + f^2K_2)} B + \dfrac{2f^2}{4h^2K_1 + f^2K_2} (HM_{BC} + Pe)$;

$$\left[K_1 + \frac{3}{4}K_2 - \frac{3(2hK_1 - fK_2)^2}{4(4h^2K_1 + f^2K_2)} \right] B = -HM_{BC}$$

$$- \frac{f(2hK_1 - fK_2)}{4h^2K_1 + f^2K_2} (HM_{BC} + Pe).$$

36. (a), $M_{AB}=-0.25$,

$\qquad M_{BA}=-20.50$,

$\qquad M_{CB}=0$.

$\quad (b)$, $\quad V=8$;

$\qquad H=\dfrac{73}{32}$.

37. $M_{AB}=-3.56$, $\quad M_{BC}=21.03$, $\quad M_{CB}=12.04$,

$\qquad M_{B'C'}=-10.74$, $\quad M_{C'B'}=-22.33$.

38. (a), $q=\dfrac{1}{h}(FM_{BC}+FM_{CB}+Pe)$, $\quad q'=0$;

$\qquad -Q_B=-FM_{BC}+tq$, $\quad -Q_{B'}=t'q$.

$\quad (b)$, $q=\dfrac{1}{h}\Big[HM_{BC}+\dfrac{Pe}{2f}(2f+h)\Big]$, $\quad '=\dfrac{Pe}{2f}$;

$\qquad -Q_B=-HM_{BC}+tq+t'q'$, $\quad -Q_{B'}=t'q+tq'$.

39. (a), $q=\dfrac{1}{h}(FM_{BC}+FM_{CB})+\dfrac{P}{h}(b-e)$,

$\qquad q'=0$;

$\qquad -Q_B=-FM_{BC}+tq$, $\quad -Q_{B'}=t'q$.

$\quad (b)$, $q=\dfrac{1}{h}HM_{BC}+\Big[\dfrac{b}{hl_1}(l_1+e-b)-\dfrac{l}{2fl_1}(e-b)-\dfrac{e}{h}\Big]P$,

$\qquad q'=\dfrac{(b-e)}{l_1}\Big(\dfrac{l}{2f}-\dfrac{b}{h}\Big)P$;

$\qquad -Q_B=-HM_{BC}+tq+t'q'$, $\quad -Q_{B'}=t'q+tq'$.

40. $M_{AB}=17.33$;

$\qquad M_{BA}=36.85$;

$\qquad M_{B'A}=15.52$;

$\qquad M_{CB}=-117.13$;

$\qquad M_{C'B'}=-58.47$.

41. (a), $R=\dfrac{3f(fK_2-hK_1)}{4(h^2K_1+f^2K_2)}B+\dfrac{3f^2K_2C}{4(h^2K_1+f^2K_2)}$;

$\qquad \Big[K_1+K_2-\dfrac{3(hK_1-fK_2)^2}{4(h^2K_1+f^2K_2)}\Big]B+\Big[\dfrac{K_2}{2}+\dfrac{3fK_2(hK_1-fK_2)}{4(h^2K_1+f^2K_2)}\Big]C=0$,

$\qquad \Big[K_2+\dfrac{K_3}{2}+K_4-\dfrac{3f^2K_2^2}{4(h^2K_1+f^2K_2)}\Big]C+\Big[\dfrac{K_2}{2}+\dfrac{3fK_2(hK_1-fK_2)}{4(h^2K_1+f^2K_2)}\Big]B$

$\qquad =-FM_{CD}$.

$\quad (b)$, $R=\dfrac{3f(fK_2-hK_1)}{4(h^2K_1+f^2K_2)}B+\dfrac{3f^2K_2C}{4(h^2K_1+f^2K_2)}$;

$\qquad \Big[K_1+K_2-\dfrac{3(hK_1-fK_2)^2}{4(h^2K_1+f^2K_2)}\Big]B+\Big[\dfrac{K_2}{2}+\dfrac{3fK_2(hK_1-fK_2)}{4(h^2K_1+f^2K_2)}\Big]C=0$,

$\qquad \Big[K_2+\dfrac{K_3}{2}+\dfrac{3}{4}K_4-\dfrac{3f^2K_2^2}{4(h^2K_1+f^2K_2)}\Big]C+\Big[\dfrac{K_2}{2}+\dfrac{3fK_2(hK_1-fK_2)}{4(h^2K_1+f^2K_2)}\Big]B$

$\qquad =-HM_{CD}$.

42. $M_{AB}=-9.00$;
$\quad M_{BC}=32.75$;
$\quad M_{CB}=21.50$;
$\quad M_{CC'}=-10.75$,
$\quad M_{CD}=-10.75$;
$\quad M_{DC}=-5.375$.

43. (a), $Q_A=Q_B=Q_{B'}=0$;

$$-Q_C=-\frac{3}{4}FM_{CD}+\frac{1}{4}(M+FM_{DC});$$

$$-Q_{C'}=\frac{1}{4}(M+FM_{CD}+FM_{DC}).$$

(b), $Q_A=Q_B=Q_{B'}=0$;

$$-Q_C=\frac{1}{2}(M-HM_{CD});$$

$$-Q_{C'}=\frac{1}{2}(M+HM_{CD}).$$

44. $M_{AB}=4.41$;
$\quad M_{BC}=-16.42$; $\qquad M_{B'C'}=-11.01$;
$\quad M_{CB}=-25.35$, $\qquad M_{C'B'}=-11.21$,
$\quad M_{CD}=-20.71$, $\qquad M_{C'D'}=-34.51$,
$\quad M_{CC'}=-46.06$; $\qquad M_{C'C}=45.72$;
$\quad M_{DC}=-85.94$. $\qquad M_{D'C'}=-74.84$.

45. (a) 1. $\quad q=\dfrac{a}{fl}FM_{BA}-\dfrac{1}{f}(FM_{AB}+FM_{BA})+\dfrac{F}{f}\left(f-c+\dfrac{ac}{l}\right)$;

$\qquad q'=\dfrac{b}{fl}FM_{BA}+\dfrac{bcF}{fl}$.

$\qquad$ 2. $\quad q=-\dfrac{1}{f}(FM_{AB}+FM_{BA})+\dfrac{F}{f}\left[f-c+\dfrac{a}{l}(h+c)\right]$;

$\qquad q'=\dfrac{b}{fl}(h+c)F$.

(b) 1. $\quad q=\dfrac{fw}{12}\left(6+\dfrac{5a}{l}\right)$; $q'=\dfrac{5}{12}\cdot\dfrac{bf}{l}w$.

$\qquad$ 2. $\quad q=\left[\dfrac{f}{2}\left(1+\dfrac{a}{l}\right)+\dfrac{ah}{l}\right]w$; $q'=\dfrac{b}{l}\left(\dfrac{f}{2}+h\right)w$.

(c) 1. $\quad q=\dfrac{1}{h}(FM_{BC}+FM_{CB})+\left(1-\dfrac{c}{h}\right)F$; $q'=0$.

$\qquad$ 2. $\quad q=\dfrac{1}{h}HM_{BC}+(h-c)\left(\dfrac{1}{h}+\dfrac{a}{fl}\right)F$; $q'=(h-c)\dfrac{bF}{fl}$.

(d) 1. $\quad q=\dfrac{h}{2}w$; $q'=0$.

$\qquad$ 2. $\quad q=\left(\dfrac{5}{8}+\dfrac{ah}{2fl}\right)hw$; $q'=\dfrac{bh^2}{2fl}w$.

46. $M_{AB}=17.51$;
$\quad M_{BC}=-23.47$; $\qquad M_{B'C'}=-11.97$;
$\quad M_{CB}=-102.96$; $\qquad M_{C'B'}=-53.61$.

47. (a), $q=0$; $Q_A = Q_B = Q_{B'} = 0$;

$$-Q_C = \frac{wh_1^2}{12}\left(\frac{3K_6}{K_6+K_7}-1\right),$$

$$-Q_{C'} = \frac{K_7}{4(K_6+K_7)}wh_1^2.$$

(b), $q=0$; $Q_A = Q_B = Q_{B'} = 0$;

$$-Q_C = \frac{wh_1^2}{8}\left(\frac{5K_6}{K_6+K_7}-1\right),$$

$$-Q_{C'} = \frac{5K_7wh_1^2}{8(K_6+K_7)}.$$

48. $M_{AB} = 2.08$;

$M_{BA} = -35.84$; $\qquad M_{B'A} = 28.93$;

$M_{CB} = 11.87$, $\qquad M_{C'B'} = -18.78$,

$M_{CD} = -10.52$, $\qquad M_{C'D'} = 11.78$,

$M_{CC'} = -1.35$; $\qquad M_{C'C} = 7.00$;

$M_{DC} = -6.20$; $\qquad M_{D'C'} = 4.94$.

49. Q of R, fixed and hinged bases, $-\dfrac{Pl}{2f}$;

$$-Q_{Af} = \frac{h^2l(K_1-K_3)P}{f[h^2(3K_1+K_3)+8f^2K_2]}; \quad -Q_{Ah} = \frac{h^2l(K_1-K_3)P}{f[h^2(3K_1+K_3)+2f^2K_2]}$$

$$-Q_{Bf} = \frac{hl(hK_1-2fK_2)P}{f[h^2(3K_1+K_3)+8f^2K_2]}; \quad -Q_{Bh} = \frac{hl(hK_1-fK_2)P}{f[h^2(3K_1+K_3)+2f^2K_2]}.$$

50. $M_{AB} = -20.95$;

$M_{BA} = -37.04$;

$M_{CA} = 46.53$;

$M_{CE} = 0$;

$M_{DB} = M_{EC} = 0$.

51. (1) (a) and (b), $q_{181} = -\dfrac{1}{f}\left(FM_{AB}+\dfrac{1}{2}FM_{BA}\right)+F\left(1-\dfrac{c}{2f}\right)$;

$$q_{182} = 0; \quad q_{183} = hF.$$

(2) (a), $q_{181} = \dfrac{1}{h}(FM_{BD}+FM_{DB})+F\left(1-\dfrac{c}{h}\right)$;

$$q_{182} = 0; \quad q_{183} = FM_{BD}+FM_{DB}+F(h-c).$$

(b), $q_{181} = \dfrac{1}{h}HM_{BD}+F\left(1-\dfrac{c}{h}\right)$;

$$q_{182} = 0; \quad q_{183} = HM_{BD}+F(h-c).$$

(3) (a), and (b), $q_{181} = \dfrac{17}{24}wf$; $q_{182} = 0$; $q_{183} = whf$.

(4) (a), $q_{181} = w\dfrac{h}{2}$; $q_{182} = 0$; $q_{183} = w\dfrac{h^2}{2}$.

(b), $q_{181} = \dfrac{5}{8}wh$; $q_{182} = 0$; $q_{183} = \dfrac{5}{8}wh+w\dfrac{h^2}{2}$.

52. $M_{AB} = -23.668;$ $M_{CA} = 41.513,$

$M_{BD} = 36.768;$ $M_{CA'} = -5.020,$

$M_{A'B'} = -2.716;$ $M_{CB} = -36.493;$

$M_{B'D'} = -0.274;$ $M_{DB} = 0;$

                $M_{EC} = 0;$

                $M_{D'B'} = 0.$

53. $(a), R = \dfrac{3}{4} \cdot \dfrac{K_2 A + (K_2 - nK_4)B - nK_5 C}{K_2 + n^2(K_4 + K_5)};$ . . . . (191)

Joint A, as given by eq. (192);

$$\left[K_2 + K_4 - \frac{3}{4} \cdot \frac{(K_2 - nK_4)^2}{K_2 + n^2(K_4 + K_5)}\right]B + \left[\frac{1}{2}K_2 - \frac{3}{4} \cdot \frac{K_2(K_2 - nK_4)}{K_2 + n^2(K_4 + K_5)}\right]A$$

$$+ \frac{3}{4} \cdot \frac{nK_5}{K_2 + n^2(K_4 + K_5)} C = 0; \ \ . \ . \ . \ . \ . \ . \ . \ . \ . \ . \ . \ (193b)$$

$$\left[\frac{3}{4}K_3 + K_5 - \frac{3}{4} \cdot \frac{n^2 K_5{}^2}{K_2 + n^2(K_4 + K_5)}\right]C + \frac{3}{4} \cdot \frac{nK_2 K_5}{K_2 + n^2(K_4 + K_5)} A$$

$$+ \frac{3}{4} \cdot \frac{nK_5(K_2 - nK_4)}{K_2 + n^2(K_4 + K_5)} B = -HM_{CB} . \ . \ . \ . \ . \ . \ . \ . \ . \ . \ (194b)$$

$(b), R = \dfrac{3}{2} \cdot \dfrac{2K_2 A + (2K_2 - nK_4)B - nK_5 C}{4K_2 + n^2(K_4 + K_5)};$

Joint A, as given by eq. (192a);

$$\left[K_2 + \frac{3}{4}K_4 - \frac{3}{4} \cdot \frac{(2K_2 - nK_4)^2}{4K_2 + n^2(K_4 + K_5)}\right]B + \left[\frac{1}{2}K_2 - \frac{3}{2} \cdot \frac{K_2(2K_2 - nK_4)}{4K_2 + n^2(K_4 + K_5)}\right]B$$

$$+ \frac{3}{4} \cdot \frac{nK_5(2K_2 - nK_4)}{4K_2 + n^2(K_4 + K_5)} C = 0; \ \ . \ . \ . \ . \ . \ . \ . \ . \ . \ . \ . \ (193c)$$

$$\left[\frac{3}{4}K_3 + \frac{3}{4}K_5 - \frac{3}{4} \cdot \frac{n^2 K_5{}^2}{4K_2 + n^2(K_4 + K_5)}\right]C + \frac{3}{4} \cdot \frac{nK_2 K_5}{4K_2 + n^2(K_4 + K_5)} A$$

$$+ \frac{3}{4} \cdot \frac{nK_5(2K_2 - nK_4)}{4K_2 + n^2(K_4 + K_5)} B = -HM_{CB} \ . \ . \ . \ . \ . \ . \ . \ . \ . \ (194c)$$

54. $A = 34.31, \ \ B = -2.40, \ \ C = -4.54,$

$R = 17.69, \ \ R_{BE} = R_{CD} = -8.84.$

$M_{AB} = 30.84;$ $M_{CD} = 8.61;$

$M_{BA} = -5.87,$ $M_{DC} = 13.15;$

$M_{BE} = 12.88,$

$M_{BC} = -7.01;$ $M_{EB} = 15.29.$

55. $(a), R = \dfrac{3}{4}(A + B) + \dfrac{Fh}{2K_2},$ . . . . (195)

$$R_1 = \frac{3}{4} \cdot \frac{K_4 B + K_5 C}{K_4 + K_5} + \frac{h_1(F + F_1)}{2(K_4 + K_5)}; \ . \ . \ . \ . \ . \ . \ . \ . \ (196)$$

$$\left(\frac{3}{2}K_1+\frac{1}{4}K_2\right)A-\frac{1}{4}K_2B=\frac{Fh}{2}, \quad \cdots \cdots \cdots \cdots \cdots \quad (197)$$

$$\left[\frac{1}{4}K_2+K_4-\frac{3}{4}\cdot\frac{K_4{}^2}{K_4+K_5}\right]B-\frac{1}{4}K_2A-\frac{3}{4}\cdot\frac{K_4K_5}{K_4+K_5}C$$
$$=\frac{Fh}{2}+\frac{h_1(F+F_1)K_4}{2(K_4+K_5)}, \quad \cdots \cdots \cdots \cdots \quad (198b)$$

$$\left[\frac{3}{4}K_3+K_5-\frac{3}{4}\cdot\frac{K_5{}^2}{K_4+K_5}\right]C-\frac{3}{4}\cdot\frac{K_4K_5}{K_4+K_5}B=\frac{h_1(F+F_1)K_6}{2(K_4+K_5)}. \quad (199b)$$

(b), R and joint equation at A same as in (a);

$$R_1=\frac{3}{2}\cdot\frac{K_4B+K_5C}{K_4+K_5}+\frac{2h_1(F+F_1)}{K_4+K_5}, \quad \cdots \cdots \quad (196a)$$

$$\left[\frac{1}{4}K_2+\frac{3}{4}K_4-\frac{3}{4}\cdot\frac{K_4{}^2}{K_4+K_5}\right]B-\frac{1}{4}K_2A-\frac{3}{4}\cdot\frac{K_4K_5}{K_4+K_5}C$$
$$=\frac{Fh}{2}+\frac{h_1(F+F_1)K_4}{K_4+K_5} \quad \cdots \cdots \cdots \cdots \quad (198c)$$

$$\frac{3}{4}\left(K+K_5-\frac{K_5{}^2}{K_4+K_5}\right)C-\frac{3}{4}\cdot\frac{K_4K_5}{K_4+K_5}B=\frac{h_1(F+F_1)K_5}{K_4+K_5} \quad \cdot \quad (199c)$$

56. $A=40.8$, $B=95.2$, $C=181.33$;
$R=119$, $R_1=500.93$;
$M_{AB}=-61.2$;
$M_{BA}=-6.8$,
$M_{BE}=-179.06$,
$M_{BC}=185.86$;
$M_{CD}=-228.93$;
$M_{DC}=M_{EB}=0$.

57. (a), $q_{Rf}=(FM_{AB}+FM_{BA})\left(\dfrac{1}{4K_2}+\dfrac{1}{4m}\right)+\left(\dfrac{1}{4K_2}-\dfrac{1}{4m}\right)M,$

$q_{R'f}=(FM_{AB}+FM_{BA})\left(\dfrac{1}{4K_2}-\dfrac{1}{4m}\right)+\left(\dfrac{1}{4K_2}+\dfrac{1}{4m}\right)M,$

$q_{R_1f}=(FM_{AB}+FM_{BA})\left[\left(\dfrac{1}{4K_2}+\dfrac{1}{4m}\right)\dfrac{h_1K_2}{h(K_4+K_5)}\right.$

$\left.+\dfrac{h_1}{2h(K_4+K_5)}\right]+\left[\left(\dfrac{1}{4K_2}-\dfrac{1}{4m}\right)\dfrac{h_1K_2}{h(K_4+K_5)}\right.$

$\left.+\dfrac{h^1}{2h(K_4+K_5)}\right]M.$
$\qquad\qquad\qquad\qquad\qquad\qquad\qquad\qquad (219)$

$(b),\ q_{Rh}=(FM_{AB}+FM_{BA})\left(\dfrac{1}{4K_2}+\dfrac{1}{4n}\right)+\left(\dfrac{1}{4K_2}-\dfrac{1}{4n}\right)M,$

$\quad q_{R'h}=(FM_{AB}+FM_{BA})\left(\dfrac{1}{4K_2}-\dfrac{1}{4n}\right)+\left(\dfrac{1}{4K_2}+\dfrac{1}{4n}\right)M,$

$\quad q_{R_1h}=(FM_{AB}+FM_{BA})\left[\left(\dfrac{1}{4K_2}+\dfrac{1}{4n}\right)\dfrac{4h_1K_2}{h(K_4+K_5)}\right.$

$\left.\quad +\dfrac{2h_1}{h(K_4+K_5)}\right]+\left[\left(\dfrac{1}{4K_2}-\dfrac{1}{4n}\right)\dfrac{4h_1K_2}{h(K_4+K_5)}\right.$

$\left.\quad +\dfrac{2h_1}{h(K_4+K_5)}\right]M.$ \hfill (219a)

58. $A=-0.154,\quad A'=22.998,\quad B=24.794,\quad B'=18.580,$
$C=15.837,\quad C'=7.649;$
$R=23.916,\quad R'=43.749,\quad R_1=35.954,\quad R_{B'E'}=16.121;$

$M_{AB}=-11.346;$	$M_{A'B'}=-22.922;$
$M_{BA}=-10.398,$	$M_{B'A'}=-27.340,$
$M_{BE}=-22.320,$	$M_{B'E'}=4.918,$
$M_{BC}=32.713;$	$M_{B'C'}=22.405;$
$M_{CD}=-28.234;$	$M_{C'D'}=-16.944;$
$M_{DC}=-68.070;$	$M_{D'C'}=-24.592;$
$M_{EB}=-47.114;$	$M_{E'B'}=-13.662.$

59. (a), Fixed bases: R expression as given by eq. (208),
$\qquad\qquad\qquad R_1$ expression as given by eq. (208a),
$\qquad\qquad\qquad$ Joint A exp. as given by eq. (211),
$\qquad\qquad\qquad$ Joint A' exp. as given by eq. (211a),

Joint B,

$$\left\{K_2+K_4-\dfrac{3}{4}\left[\dfrac{1}{d}+\dfrac{1}{e}\left(1-\dfrac{hK_4}{h_1K_2}\right)\right]K_2{}^2-\dfrac{3}{4}\left[\dfrac{1}{d_1}-\dfrac{1}{e_1}\left(1-\dfrac{hK_4}{h_1K_2}\right)\right]K_2K_4\right\}B$$

$$+\left[\dfrac{K_2}{2}-\dfrac{3}{4}\left(\dfrac{1}{d}+\dfrac{1}{e}\right)K_2{}^2-\dfrac{3}{4}\left(\dfrac{1}{d_1}-\dfrac{1}{e_1}\right)K_2K_4\right]A-\dfrac{3}{4}\cdot\dfrac{h}{h_2}\left(\dfrac{K_2}{d}+\dfrac{K_4}{d_1}\right)K_6A'$$

$$+\dfrac{3}{4}\dfrac{h}{h_1}\left(\dfrac{K_2}{e}-\dfrac{K_4}{e_1}\right)K_5C+QB_f=0;\ \ .\ .\ .\ .\ .\ .\ .\ .\ .\ .\ .\ .\ \text{(211d)}$$

Joint C,

$$\left[\dfrac{3}{4}K_3+\left(1-\dfrac{3hK_5}{4\,h_1e_1}\right)K_5\right]C-\dfrac{3}{4}\left(\dfrac{1}{d_1}-\dfrac{1}{e_1}\right)K_2K_5A-\dfrac{3\,h}{4h_2}\dfrac{K_5}{d_1}K_6A'$$

$$+\dfrac{3}{4}\left[\dfrac{1}{d_1}-\dfrac{1}{e_1}\left(1-\dfrac{hK_4}{h_1K_2}\right)\right]K_2K_5B+QC_f=0\ \ .\ .\ .\ .\ .\ .\ \text{(211e)}$$

(b), Hinged bases: R expression as given by eq. (213),
$\qquad\qquad\qquad R_1$ expression as given by eq. (213a),
$\qquad\qquad\qquad A$ expression as given by eq. (210),
$\qquad\qquad\qquad A'$ expression as given by eq. (216a),

Joint B,

$$\left\{K_2+\frac{3}{4}K_4-\frac{3}{2}\left[\frac{1}{a}+\frac{1}{b}\left(1-\frac{hK_4}{2h_1K_2}\right)\right]K_2{}^2-\frac{3}{4}\left[\frac{1}{a_1}-\frac{1}{b_1}\left(1-\frac{hK_4}{2h_1K_2}\right)\right]K_2K_4\right\}B$$

$$+\left[\frac{K_2}{2}-\frac{3}{2}\left(\frac{1}{a}+\frac{1}{b}\right)K_2{}^2-\frac{3}{4}\left(\frac{1}{a_1}-\frac{1}{b_1}\right)K_2K_4\right]A-\frac{3h}{4h_2}\left(\frac{K_2}{}+\frac{K_4}{2a_1}\right)K_6A'$$

$$+\frac{3}{4}\cdot\frac{h}{h_1}\left(\frac{K_2}{b}-\frac{K_4}{b_1}\right)K_5C+Q_{Bh}=0; \quad \ldots \ldots \ldots \quad (216d)$$

Joint C,

$$\left[\frac{3}{4}K_3+\left(\frac{3}{4}-\frac{3hK_5}{8b_1h_1}\right)K_5\right]C-\frac{3}{8}\left(\frac{1}{a_1}-\frac{1}{b_1}\right)K_2K_5A-\frac{3hK_5K_6}{8a_1h_2}A'$$

$$-\frac{3}{4}\left[\frac{1}{a_1}-\frac{1}{b_1}\left(1-\frac{hK_4}{2h_1K_2}\right)\right]K_2K_5B+Q_{Ch}=0 \quad \ldots \ldots \quad (216e)$$

60. $A=30.570, \qquad A'=1.429, \qquad B=22.569, \quad C=12.057;$
$R=49.676, \qquad R_1=17.895, \ R_{A'E'}=33.786;$
$M_{AB}=-31.28; \qquad M_{A'E'}=-16.71;$
$\qquad\qquad\qquad\qquad M_{CD}=-23.35;$
$M_{BA}=-47.29, \qquad M_{DC}=-47.48;$
$M_{BE}=18.69, \qquad M_{EB}=-26.44;$
$M_{BC}=28.60; \qquad M_{E'A'}=-114.14.$

61. $(a), (ac+bK_2)R=\frac{3}{4}\left[c\left(K_2-\frac{h}{f}K_1\right)+bK_2\right]B$

$$+\frac{3}{4}\left[cK_2+b\left(K_2-\frac{hK_4}{h_1}\right)\right]C-\frac{3bh}{4h_1}K_5D$$

$$-\frac{ch}{2f}\left[(FM_{AB}+FM_{BA})+\left(\frac{l}{2}-e\right)P\right], \quad \ldots \ldots \quad (221b)$$

$$(ac+bK_2)R_1=\frac{3}{4}\left[K_2\left(K_2-\frac{h}{f}K_1\right)-aK_2\right]B$$

$$+\frac{3}{4}\left[K_2{}^2-a\left(K_2-\frac{h}{h_1}K_4\right)\right]C+\frac{3ah}{4h_1}K_5D$$

$$-\frac{hK_2}{2f}\left[(FM_{AB}+FM_{BA})+\left(\frac{l}{2}-e\right)P\right] \quad \ldots \ldots \quad (221c)$$

$$(b), \left(\frac{ac}{4}+bK_2\right)R=\frac{3}{4}\left[\frac{c}{4}\left(K_2-\frac{h}{f}K_1\right)+bK_2\right]B$$

$$+\frac{3}{4}\left[\frac{c}{4}K_2+b\left(K_2-\frac{h}{2h_1}K_4\right)\right]C-\frac{3bh}{8h_1}K_5D$$

$$-\frac{ch}{8f}\left[(FM_{AB}+FM_{BA})+\left(\frac{l}{2}-e\right)P\right], \quad \ldots \ldots \quad (222b)$$

$$\left(\frac{ac}{4}+bK_2\right)R_1=\frac{3}{4}\left[K_2\left(K_2-\frac{h}{f}K_1\right)-aK_2\right]B$$

$$+\frac{3}{4}\left[K_2^2-a\left(K_2-\frac{h}{2h_1}K_4\right)\right]C+\frac{3ah}{8h_1}K_5D$$

$$-\frac{hK_2}{2f}\left[(FM_{AB}+FM_{BA})+\left(\frac{l}{2}-e\right)P\right].\ .\ .\ .\ .\ .\ (222c)$$

62. $A=0$, $B=3.2795$, $C=-10.3487$, $D=18.0540$;
$R=-8.9705$, $R_1=9.2740$, $R_{AB}=-1.2140$, $R_{CF}=6.9555$;
$M_{AB}=-\ 0.43$; $M_{BA}=-\ 2.07$;
$M_{CB}=-12.07$, $M_{DE}=\ \ 35.12$;
$M_{CF}=-34.61$, $M_{ED}=-\ 0.99$;
$M_{CD}=\ \ 46.68$; $M_{FC}=-24.26$.

63. The change is made by merely omitting f_1 from the expressions.

64. $A=1.93$, $B=-5.50$, $C=-11.93$, $D=17.09$,
          $B'=-2.22$, $C'=-1.58$, $D'=-0.96$;
          $R=-12.44$, $R_1=7.87$, $R_{CF}=5.90$,
$R_{AB}=-0.61$, $R_1=-3.47$, $R_1'=-1.40$, $R_{C'F'}=-1.05$;
$M_{AB}=-0.21$; $M_{BA}=-3.92$; $M_{B'A}=-1.86$;
$M_{CB}=-8.95$, $M_{C'B'}=3.12$, $M_{DE}=36.88$;
$M_{CF}=-35.67$, $M_{C'F'}=-1.06$,
$M_{CD}=44.62$; $M_{C'D'}=-2.06$; $M_{D'E'}=1.76$;
$M_{ED}=2.70$; $M_{E'D'}=3.68$;
$M_{FC}=-23.73$; $M_{F'C'}=0.52$.

65. No changes.   (Changes in joint expressions only.)

66. $A=-19.91$, $B=2.80$, $C=38.96$, $D=103.37$,
          $B'=75.35$, $C'=54.68$, $D'=57.68$;
          $R=32.80$, $R_1=224.68$, $R_{CF}=168.52$,
$R_{AB}=-37.94$, $R'=109.55$, $R_1'=128.98$, $R_{C'F'}=96.73$;
$M_{AB}=20.18$; $M_{BC}=30.08$; $M_{B'C'}=-27.44$;
$M_{CB}=18.24$, $M_{C'B'}=-68.76$, $M_{DE}=-121.24$;
$M_{CF}=-110.08$, $M_{C'F'}=-14.72$, $M_{D'E'}=-84.92$;
$M_{CD}=91.97$; $M_{C'D'}=83.52$; $M_{ED}=M_{FC}=M_{F'C'}=M_{E'D'}=0$.

67. (a), q in eq. (237) $=0$,
           $(237a)=(FM_{B'F'}+FM_{F'B'})-P'e'$,

           $(237b)=\dfrac{h}{f_1+h_1}(FM_{CF}+FM_{FC}+Pe)$;

   (b), q in eq. (237) $=0$,
           $(237c)=HM_{B'F'}-P'e'$,

           $(237d)=\dfrac{h}{f_1+h_1}(HM_{CF}+Pe)$.

68. $A=20.32,\ B=-74.04,\ B'=-5.76,\ C=-43.02,\ D=-22.13;$
$R=101.91,\ R_1=-33.01,\ R'=-68.50,\ R_{CF}=-26.46,$
$R_{AB}=-38.41.$
$M_{AB}=21.72;\quad M_{B'F'}=33.36;\quad M_{CB}=87.48,\quad M_{ED}=87.76;$
$M_{BC}=25.44;\quad M_{DE}=43.52;\quad M_{CF}=-33.12,\quad M_{FC}=9.90;$
$$M_{CD}=-54.09;\quad M_{F'B'}=159.18.$$

69. $q(240)=-(Pe+FM_{BC}+FM_{CB}),$

$q(240a)=-(Pe+HM_{BC}),$

$$q(241)=-\frac{\dfrac{f}{h}}{2\left(1+\dfrac{f^2}{h^2}\cdot\dfrac{K_3}{K_2}\right)}(Pe+FM_{BC}+FM_{CB}),$$

$$q(241a)=-FM_{BC}-\frac{\dfrac{f}{h}\left(1-\dfrac{f}{h}\cdot\dfrac{K_3}{K_2}\right)}{2\left(1+\dfrac{f^2}{h^2}\cdot\dfrac{K_3}{K_2}\right)}(Pe+FM_{BC}+FM_{CB}),$$

$$q(242)=-\frac{\dfrac{2f}{h}}{\left(4+\dfrac{f^2}{h^2}\cdot\dfrac{K_3}{K_2}\right)}(Pe+HM_{BC}),$$

$$q(242a)=-HM_{BC}-\frac{\dfrac{f}{h}\left(2-\dfrac{f}{h}\cdot\dfrac{K_3}{K_2}\right)}{\left(4+\dfrac{f^2}{h^2}\cdot\dfrac{K_3}{K_2}\right)}(Pe+HM_{BC}).$$

70. $A=157.34,\qquad R=-52.64,$
$B=63.75,\qquad\ \ R_{AB}=210.55,$
$M_{AA'}=30.67;\qquad M_{BC}=148.26.$

71. $(a),\ q$ in eq. $(244)\ =-\dfrac{a}{l}\cdot\dfrac{h}{f}(FM_{CB}+Pe)-(FM_{BC}+FM_{CB})-Pe,$

$$(244a)=-\frac{b}{l}\cdot\frac{h}{f}(FM_{CB}+Pe),$$

$$(244b)=Pe+FM_{BC}+FM_{CB};$$

$(b),\ q$ in eq. $(245)\ =-\dfrac{a}{l}\cdot\dfrac{h}{f}(Pe)-HM_{BC}-Pe,$

$$(245a)=-\frac{b}{l}\cdot\frac{h}{f}(Pe),$$

$$(245b)=Pe+HM_{BC}.$$

72. $A=-32.189,\quad A'=-0.478,\quad B=118.208,\quad B'=143.792;$
$R=48.618,\quad R_1=314.970,\quad R_1'=302.030,\quad R_{AA'}=-74.50,$
$R_{A'B'}=100.382;$
$M_{AA'}=42.072,\qquad M_{BA}=105.659,$
$M_{A'A}=57.928,\qquad M_{B'A'}=86.342.$

73. $R=\dfrac{3}{4}(B+C)+\dfrac{1}{2K_3}[(FM_{CB}+FM_{BC})+(P_1+P_3)l_3-P_3e_3]$. (248a)

$$R_1\text{ (fixed)}=-\frac{3}{4}\cdot\frac{\frac{f}{h}(A+B)}{\left(1+\frac{f^2}{h^2}\cdot\frac{K_4}{K_2}\right)}+\frac{3}{4}\cdot\frac{C}{\left(1+\frac{h^2}{f^2}\cdot\frac{K_2}{K_4}\right)}\ \cdots\cdots\ (249b)$$

$$R_1\text{ (hinged)}=-\frac{3}{4}\cdot\frac{\frac{f}{h}(A+B)}{\left(1+\frac{1f^2}{4h^2}\cdot\frac{K_4}{K_2}\right)}+\frac{3}{8}\cdot\frac{C}{\left(\frac{1}{4}+\frac{h^2}{f^2}\cdot\frac{K_2}{K_4}\right)}\ \cdots\cdots\ (249c)$$

74. $A=90.77,\quad B=188.41,\qquad C=37.44;$
$R=277.39,\quad R_1=-101.58,\quad R_{AB}=203.16;$
$M_{AA'}=\ 33.38;$
$M_{BC}=-58.26;$
$M_{CB}=-157.75.$

75. (a) Fixed bases,

$$-\left(\frac{h^2}{f^2}K_2+-\frac{h^2}{(h+f_1)^2}K_3+K_5\right)R=\frac{3h}{4f}K_2A+\frac{3}{4}\left(\frac{h}{f}K_2-\frac{h}{(h+f_1)}K_3\right)B$$
$$-\frac{3}{4}K_5C+\frac{h}{2f}[(FM_{AB}+FM_{BA})+(P_1+P_2)l_2-P_2e_2].\ \ \cdots\ (240d)$$

(b) Hinged bases,

$$-\left(\frac{h^2}{f^2}K_2+\frac{h_2}{4(h+f_1)^2}K_3+\frac{K_5}{4}\right)R=\frac{3h}{4f}K_2A+\frac{3}{4}\left[\frac{h}{f}K_2-\frac{h}{2(h+f_1)}K_3\right]B$$
$$-\frac{3}{8}K_5C+\frac{h}{2f}[(FM_{AB}+FM_{BA})+(P_1+P_2)l_2-P_2e_2]\ \ \cdots\ (240e)$$

76. $A=143.71,\qquad R=-43.84,$
$B=27.48,\qquad R_{AB}=175.38;$
$C=7.05;$
$M_{AA'}=23.85;\qquad M_{BA}=-164.08,$
$\qquad\qquad\qquad M_{BC}=79.01,$
$M_{CD}=27.21;\qquad M_{BE}=85.07.$

APPENDIX

TABLE 12.—*BEAM COEFFICIENTS FOR BEAMS OF VARYING MOMENT OF INERTIA.*

SYMMETRICAL STRAIGHT HAUNCHES

$$b = \frac{I}{I'}$$

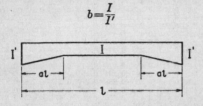

Values of a	Haunch at left support	Values of b													Haunch at right support
		1.00	0.60	0.30	0.20	0.15	0.12	0.10	0.08	0.06	0.05	0.04	0.03	0.02	
0.50	u	0.333	0.354	0.380	0.394	0.403	0.410	0.416	0.422	0.430	0.434	0.439	0.446	0.455	v
	p	0.500	0.389	0.279	0.232	0.203	0.184	0.170	0.154	0.136	0.126	0.115	0.102	0.086	q
0.40	u	0.333	0.358	0.387	0.402	0.412	0.420	0.425	0.431	0.440	0.444	0.449	0.455	0.462	v
	p	0.500	0.411	0.324	0.286	0.263	0.248	0.236	0.223	0.209	0.201	0.192	0.182	0.169	q
0.35	u	0.333	0.358	0.387	0.402	0.412	0.419	0.424	0.430	0.437	0.441	0.446	0.450	0.457	v
	p	0.500	0.422	0.346	0.312	0.292	0.279	0.269	0.258	0.245	0.238	0.230	0.221	0.210	q
0.30	u	0.333	0.357	0.385	0.400	0.408	0.415	0.419	0.425	0.431	0.434	0.438	0.443	0.448	v
	p	0.500	0.433	0.368	0.339	0.322	0.310	0.302	0.292	0.282	0.276	0.269	0.261	0.252	q
0.25	u	0.333	0.356	0.382	0.394	0.402	0.407	0.412	0.416	0.422	0.425	0.428	0.432	0.436	v
	p	0.500	0.444	0.390	0.366	0.352	0.342	0.335	0.327	0.318	0.313	0.307	0.301	0.293	q
0.20	u	0.333	0.354	0.376	0.387	0.393	0.398	0.401	0.405	0.409	0.412	0.415	0.418	0.422	v
	p	0.500	0.455	0.412	0.392	0.381	0.374	0.368	0.362	0.354	0.350	0.346	0.341	0.334	q
0.15	u	0.333	0.350	0.368	0.377	0.382	0.385	0.388	0.391	0.394	0.396	0.398	0.401	0.404	v
	p	0.500	0.466	0.434	0.420	0.411	0.405	0.401	0.396	0.391	0.388	0.384	0.380	0.376	q

383

Table 13.—*BEAM COEFFICIENTS FOR BEAMS OF VARYING MOMENT OF INERTIA.*

UNSYMMETRICAL STRAIGHT HAUNCH

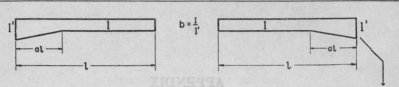

Values of a	Haunch at left support	Values of b													Haunch at right support
		1.00	0.60	0.30	0.20	0.15	0.12	0.10	0.08	0.06	0.05	0.04	0.03	0.02	
1.00	u	0.333	0.362	0.403	0.427	0.443	0.458	0.468	0.482	0.500	0.510	0.523	0.540	0.566	v
	v	0.333	0.306	0.269	0.250	0.236	0.226	0.218	0.207	0.196	0.188	0.179	0.168	0.153	u
	p	0.500	0.356	0.224	0.171	0.141	0.122	0.108	0.093	0.077	0.068	0.059	0.048	0.037	q
	q	0.500	0.422	0.335	0.292	0.266	0.247	0.232	0.215	0.196	0.184	0.171	0.156	0.136	p
0.50	u	0.333	0.373	0.425	0.455	0.475	0.490	0.501	0.515	0.531	0.540	0.551	0.564	0.580	v
	v	0.333	0.317	0.297	0.288	0.282	0.277	0.274	0.270	0.266	0.263	0.260	0.256	0.252	u
	p	0.500	0.408	0.321	0.284	0.262	0.248	0.237	0.225	0.212	0.205	0.197	0.188	0.177	q
	q	0.500	0.480	0.459	0.448	0.441	0.437	0.433	0.429	0.424	0.421	0.418	0.414	0.409	p
0.40	u	0.333	0.370	0.417	0.441	0.458	0.470	0.479	0.489	0.502	0.509	0.517	0.527	0.538	v
	v	0.333	0.321	0.308	0.301	0.297	0.294	0.292	0.289	0.286	0.284	0.282	0.280	0.277	u
	p	0.500	0.423	0.350	0.319	0.300	0.288	0.279	0.269	0.258	0.251	0.244	0.237	0.227	q
	q	0.500	0.487	0.474	0.467	0.462	0.460	0.457	0.454	0.451	0.450	0.447	0.445	0.442	p
0.35	u	0.333	0.368	0.410	0.433	0.447	0.456	0.465	0.474	0.485	0.491	0.498	0.505	0.515	v
	v	0.333	0.324	0.313	0.308	0.305	0.302	0.300	0.298	0.296	0.295	0.293	0.291	0.288	u
	p	0.500	0.432	0.366	0.338	0.321	0.310	0.302	0.293	0.283	0.277	0.271	0.264	0.255	q
	q	0.500	0.490	0.480	0.474	0.471	0.469	0.467	0.465	0.463	0.461	0.460	0.458	0.455	p
0.30	u	0.333	0.365	0.403	0.422	0.435	0.443	0.450	0.457	0.466	0.471	0.477	0.483	0.492	v
	v	0.333	0.326	0.318	0.314	0.312	0.310	0.308	0.307	0.305	0.304	0.303	0.301	0.299	u
	p	0.500	0.440	0.382	0.358	0.343	0.333	0.326	0.318	0.309	0.304	0.299	0.292	0.284	q
	q	0.500	0.493	0.485	0.481	0.479	0.477	0.476	0.474	0.473	0.472	0.470	0.469	0.467	p
0.25	u	0.333	0.362	0.394	0.410	0.420	0.427	0.433	0.439	0.446	0.450	0.455	0.460	0.466	v
	v	0.333	0.328	0.322	0.319	0.318	0.316	0.315	0.314	0.312	0.312	0.311	0.310	0.309	u
	p	0.500	0.449	0.400	0.379	0.366	0.358	0.352	0.345	0.337	0.333	0.328	0.322	0.316	q
	q	0.500	0.495	0.490	0.487	0.485	0.484	0.483	0.482	0.481	0.480	0.480	0.478	0.477	p
0.20	u	0.333	0.357	0.384	0.397	0.405	0.411	0.415	0.420	0.425	0.428	0.432	0.436	0.441	v
	v	0.333	0.330	0.326	0.324	0.323	0.322	0.321	0.321	0.319	0.319	0.318	0.318	0.317	u
	p	0.500	0.458	0.418	0.401	0.391	0.384	0.379	0.373	0.366	0.363	0.359	0.354	0.349	q
	q	0.500	0.497	0.494	0.492	0.491	0.490	0.489	0.489	0.488	0.488	0.487	0.486	0.486	p
0.15	u	0.333	0.352	0.373	0.383	0.389	0.393	0.396	0.399	0.403	0.406	0.408	0.411	0.414	v
	v	0.333	0.331	0.329	0.328	0.327	0.326	0.326	0.326	0.325	0.325	0.325	0.324	0.324	u
	p	0.500	0.468	0.438	0.424	0.416	0.411	0.407	0.403	0.398	0.395	0.392	0.388	0.384	q
	q	0.500	0.498	0.496	0.495	0.495	0.494	0.494	0.494	0.493	0.493	0.493	0.492	0.492	p

TABLE 14.—*LOAD COEFFICIENTS FOR BEAMS WITH SYMMETRICAL STRAIGHT HAUNCHES.*

UNIFORM LOAD

Total load$= W$

$$b = \frac{I}{I'} \qquad I' \qquad \overline{A_1} = CWl$$

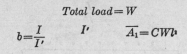

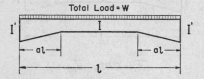

Load coefficients C

Values of a	Values of b												
	1.00	0.60	0.30	0.20	0.15	0.12	0.10	0.08	0.06	0.05	0.04	0.03	0.02
0.50	0.0833	0.0689	0.0531	0.0458	0.0409	0.0377	0.0353	0.0325	0.0292	0.0273	0.0253	0.0227	0.0195
0.40	0.0833	0.0735	0.0627	0.0575	0.0542	0.0520	0.0502	0.0481	0.0459	0.0446	0.0431	0.0414	0.0390
0.35	0.0833	0.0755	0.0670	0.0627	0.0602	0.0585	0.0570	0.0555	0.0536	0.0525	0.0512	0.0498	0.0480
0.30	0.0833	0.0773	0.0709	0.0677	0.0657	0.0643	0.0633	0.0620	0.0607	0.0599	0.0590	0.0578	0.0564
0.25	0.0833	0.0790	0.0744	0.0722	0.0708	0.0696	0.0690	0.0680	0.0670	0.0665	0.0657	0.0650	0.0639
0.20	0.0833	0.0804	0.0775	0.0758	0.0750	0.0744	0.0738	0.0733	0.0725	0.0721	0.0718	0.0712	0.0704
0.15	0.0833	0.0816	0.0799	0.0791	0.0785	0.0781	0.0778	0.0775	0.0771	0.0769	0.0765	0.0762	0.0760

Table 15.—LOAD COEFFICIENTS FOR BEAMS WITH SYMMETRICAL STRAIGHT HAUNCHES.

CONCENTRATED LOAD

$$b = \frac{I}{I'}$$

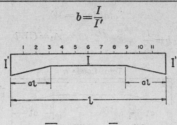

$$\overline{A_1} = CPl^2; \quad \overline{x_1} = C_1 l$$

Values of— a	b	Coefficient	\multicolumn{11}{c}{Concentrated load at point}										
			1	2	3	4	5	6	7	8	9	10	11
0.50	1.00	C	0.0382	0.0694	0.0938	0.1111	0.1215	0.1250	0.1215	0.1111	0.0938	0.0694	0.0382
		C_1	0.6389	0.6111	0.5833	0.5556	0.5278	0.5000	0.4722	0.4444	0.4167	0.3889	0.3611
	0.20	C	0.0186	0.0355	0.0501	0.0619	0.0701	0.0732	0.0701	0.0619	0.0501	0.0355	0.0186
		C_1	0.5913	0.5749	0.5583	0.5407	0.5209	0.5000	0.4791	0.4593	0.4417	0.4251	0.4087
	0.10	C	0.0138	0.0266	0.0382	0.0481	0.0551	0.0581	0.0551	0.0481	0.0382	0.0266	0.0138
		C_1	0.5746	0.5622	0.5491	0.5338	0.5179	0.5000	0.4821	0.4662	0.4509	0.4378	0.4254
	0.05	C	0.0103	0.0201	0.0292	0.0372	0.0433	0.0460	0.0433	0.0372	0.0292	0.0201	0.0103
		C_1	0.5588	0.5489	0.5395	0.5280	0.5151	0.5000	0.4849	0.4720	0.4605	0.4511	0.4412
	0.03	C	0.0084	0.0165	0.0241	0.0309	0.0364	0.0389	0.0364	0.0309	0.0241	0.0165	0.0084
		C_1	0.5488	0.5415	0.5341	0.5251	0.5132	0.5000	0.4868	0.4749	0.4659	0.4585	0.4512
0.40	0.20	C	0.0230	0.0443	0.0630	0.0782	0.0886	0.0920	0.0886	0.0782	0.0630	0.0443	0.0230
		C_1	0.5851	0.5713	0.5567	0.5397	0.5208	0.5000	0.4792	0.4603	0.4433	0.4287	0.4149
	0.10	C	0.0193	0.0376	0.0542	0.0686	0.0787	0.0820	0.0787	0.0686	0.0542	0.0376	0.0193
		C_1	0.5674	0.5571	0.5464	0.5337	0.5179	0.5000	0.4821	0.4663	0.4536	0.4429	0.4326
	0.05	C	0.0165	0.0326	0.0477	0.0611	0.0711	0.0746	0.0711	0.0611	0.0477	0.0326	0.0165
		C_1	0.5511	0.5453	0.5373	0.5284	0.5157	0.5000	0.4843	0.4716	0.4627	0.4547	0.4489
	0.03	C	0.0150	0.0297	0.0438	0.0567	0.0666	0.0700	0.0666	0.0567	0.0438	0.0297	0.0150
		C_1	0.5414	0.5377	0.5322	0.5247	0.5143	0.5000	0.4857	0.4753	0.4678	0.4623	0.4586
0.35	0.20	C	0.0252	0.0485	0.0690	0.0855	0.0959	0.0996	0.0959	0.0855	0.0690	0.0485	0.0252
		C_1	0.5866	0.5736	0.5581	0.5410	0.5216	0.5000	0.4784	0.4590	0.4419	0.4264	0.4134
	0.10	C	0.0220	0.0430	0.0621	0.0782	0.0887	0.0921	0.0887	0.0782	0.0621	0.0430	0.0220
		C_1	0.5697	0.5594	0.5505	0.5365	0.5193	0.5000	0.4807	0.4635	0.4495	0.4406	0.4303
	0.05	C	0.0196	0.0386	0.0566	0.0723	0.0826	0.0862	0.0826	0.0723	0.0566	0.0386	0.0196
		C_1	0.5558	0.5490	0.5427	0.5326	0.5179	0.5000	0.4821	0.4674	0.4573	0.4510	0.4442
	0.03	C	0.0182	0.0361	0.0534	0.0687	0.0791	0.0826	0.0791	0.0687	0.0534	0.0361	0.0182
		C_1	0.5461	0.5428	0.5377	0.5291	0.5170	0.5000	0.4830	0.4709	0.4623	0.4572	0.4539
0.30	0.20	C	0.0270	0.0528	0.0752	0.0923	0.1029	0.1064	0.1029	0.0923	0.0752	0.0528	0.0270
		C_1	0.5886	0.5770	0.5620	0.5441	0.5224	0.5000	0.4776	0.4559	0.4380	0.4230	0.4114
	0.10	C	0.0247	0.0484	0.0698	0.0870	0.0975	0.1008	0.0975	0.0870	0.0698	0.0484	0.0247
		C_1	0.5746	0.5655	0.5552	0.5401	0.5207	0.5000	0.4793	0.4599	0.4448	0.4345	0.4254
	0.05	C	0.0228	0.0450	0.0657	0.0827	0.0932	0.0967	0.0932	0.0827	0.0657	0.0450	0.0228
		C_1	0.5630	0.5574	0.5493	0.5377	0.5200	0.5000	0.4800	0.4623	0.4507	0.4426	0.4370
	0.03	C	0.0216	0.0428	0.0630	0.0802	0.0906	0.0942	0.0906	0.0802	0.0630	0.0428	0.0216
		C_1	0.5561	0.5512	0.5449	0.5353	0.5184	0.5000	0.4816	0.4647	0.4551	0.4488	0.4439
0.25	0.20	C	0.0297	0.0572	0.0808	0.0982	0.1086	0.1120	0.1086	0.0982	0.0808	0.0572	0.0297
		C_1	0.5973	0.5832	0.5679	0.5470	0.5239	0.5000	0.4761	0.4530	0.4321	0.4168	0.4027
	0.10	C	0.0275	0.0538	0.0770	0.0944	0.1049	0.1085	0.1049	0.0944	0.0770	0.0538	0.0275
		C_1	0.5829	0.5744	0.5627	0.5438	0.5224	0.5000	0.4776	0.4562	0.4373	0.4256	0.4171
	0.05	C	0.0258	0.0510	0.0741	0.0915	0.1019	0.1054	0.1019	0.0915	0.0741	0.0510	0.0258
		C_1	0.5721	0.5670	0.5583	0.5423	0.5223	0.5000	0.4777	0.4577	0.4417	0.4330	0.4279
	0.03	C	0.0250	0.0494	0.0723	0.0897	0.1001	0.1035	0.1001	0.0897	0.0723	0.0494	0.0250
		C_1	0.5682	0.5631	0.5558	0.5406	0.5207	0.5000	0.4793	0.4594	0.4442	0.4369	0.4318

Table 16.—*LOAD COEFFICIENTS FOR BEAMS WITH UNSYMMETRICAL STRAIGHT HAUNCH.*

UNIFORM LOAD

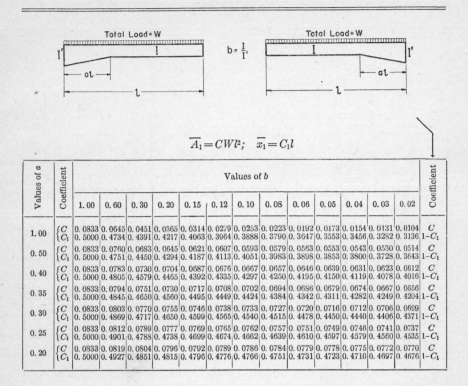

$$\overline{A_1} = CWl^2; \quad \overline{x_1} = C_1 l$$

Values of a	Coefficient	Values of b													Coefficient
		1.00	0.60	0.30	0.20	0.15	0.12	0.10	0.08	0.06	0.05	0.04	0.03	0.02	
1.00	C	0.0833	0.0645	0.0451	0.0365	0.0314	0.0279	0.0253	0.0223	0.0192	0.0173	0.0154	0.0131	0.0104	C
	C_1	0.5000	0.4734	0.4391	0.4217	0.4063	0.3964	0.3888	0.3790	0.3647	0.3553	0.3456	0.3282	0.3136	$1-C_1$
0.50	C	0.0833	0.0760	0.0683	0.0645	0.0621	0.0607	0.0593	0.0579	0.0563	0.0553	0.0543	0.0530	0.0514	C
	C_1	0.5000	0.4751	0.4450	0.4294	0.4187	0.4113	0.4051	0.3983	0.3898	0.3853	0.3800	0.3728	0.3643	$1-C_1$
0.40	C	0.0833	0.0783	0.0730	0.0704	0.0687	0.0676	0.0667	0.0657	0.0646	0.0639	0.0631	0.0623	0.0612	C
	C_1	0.5000	0.4805	0.4579	0.4465	0.4392	0.4335	0.4297	0.4250	0.4195	0.4150	0.4119	0.4078	0.4016	$1-C_1$
0.35	C	0.0833	0.0794	0.0751	0.0730	0.0717	0.0708	0.0702	0.0694	0.0686	0.0679	0.0674	0.0667	0.0656	C
	C_1	0.5000	0.4845	0.4650	0.4560	0.4495	0.4449	0.4424	0.4384	0.4342	0.4311	0.4282	0.4249	0.4204	$1-C_1$
0.30	C	0.0833	0.0803	0.0770	0.0755	0.0746	0.0738	0.0733	0.0727	0.0720	0.0716	0.0712	0.0706	0.0699	C
	C_1	0.5000	0.4869	0.4717	0.4650	0.4599	0.4565	0.4540	0.4515	0.4478	0.4450	0.4440	0.4406	0.4371	$1-C_1$
0.25	C	0.0833	0.0812	0.0789	0.0777	0.0769	0.0765	0.0762	0.0757	0.0751	0.0749	0.0746	0.0741	0.0737	C
	C_1	0.5000	0.4901	0.4785	0.4738	0.4699	0.4674	0.4662	0.4639	0.4610	0.4597	0.4579	0.4560	0.4535	$1-C_1$
0.20	C	0.0833	0.0819	0.0804	0.0796	0.0792	0.0789	0.0786	0.0784	0.0779	0.0778	0.0775	0.0772	0.0770	C
	C_1	0.5000	0.4927	0.4851	0.4815	0.4796	0.4776	0.4766	0.4751	0.4731	0.4723	0.4710	0.4697	0.4676	$1-C_1$

TABLE 17.—LOAD COEFFICIENTS FOR BEAMS WITH UNSYMMETRICAL STRAIGHT HAUNCH.
CONCENTRATED LOAD

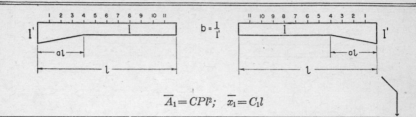

$$\overline{A}_1 = CPl^2; \quad \overline{x}_1 = C_1 l$$

Values of— a	b	Coefficient, haunch left	|	Concentrated load at point 1	2	3	4	5	6	7	8	9	10	11	Coefficient, haunch right
1.00	1.00	C C_1	{	0.0382 0.6389	0.0694 0.6111	0.0938 0.5833	0.1111 0.5556	0.1215 0.5278	0.1250 0.5000	0.1215 0.4722	0.1111 0.4444	0.0938 0.4167	0.0694 0.3889	0.0382 0.3611	C $1-C_1$
	0.20	C C_1	{	0.0135 0.5569	0.0255 0.5289	0.0358 0.5075	0.0442 0.4829	0.0503 0.4590	0.0540 0.4341	0.0549 0.4071	0.0526 0.3788	0.0466 0.3492	0.0363 0.3177	0.0211 0.2839	C $1-C_1$
	0.10	C C_1	{	0.0086 0.5145	0.0165 0.4944	0.0234 0.4735	0.0292 0.4522	0.0337 0.4286	0.0368 0.4039	0.0381 0.3781	0.0373 0.3515	0.0338 0.3213	0.0271 0.2896	0.0162 0.2558	C $1-C_1$
	0.05	C C_1	{	0.0055 0.4751	0.0106 0.4565	0.0151 0.4397	0.0191 0.4193	0.0224 0.3978	0.0248 0.3757	0.0261 0.3515	0.0261 0.3245	0.0242 0.2955	0.0199 0.2649	0.0122 0.2293	C $1-C_1$
	0.03	C C_1	{	0.0039 0.4424	0.0076 0.4246	0.0109 0.4095	0.0139 0.3925	0.0165 0.3707	0.0184 0.3523	0.0197 0.3294	0.0199 0.3032	0.0188 0.2757	0.0158 0.2441	0.0100 0.2067	C $1-C_1$
0.50	0.20	C C_1	{	0.0229 0.5317	0.0440 0.5164	0.0630 0.5006	0.0793 0.4823	0.0918 0.4630	0.0991 0.4418	0.0999 0.4177	0.0940 0.3932	0.0808 0.3678	0.0609 0.3414	0.0339 0.3157	C $1-C_1$
	0.10	C C_1	{	0.0194 0.4905	0.0379 0.4796	0.0551 0.4678	0.0702 0.4545	0.0831 0.4386	0.0916 0.4204	0.0936 0.3992	0.0888 0.3756	0.0770 0.3513	0.0583 0.3259	0.0326 0.3021	C $1-C_1$
	0.05	C C_1	{	0.0168 0.4538	0.0333 0.4488	0.0490 0.4402	0.0635 0.4301	0.0763 0.4181	0.0855 0.4035	0.0887 0.3845	0.0849 0.3624	0.0740 0.3392	0.0564 0.3143	0.0316 0.2877	C $1-C_1$
	0.03	C C_1	{	0.0155 0.4308	0.0307 0.4275	0.0456 0.4206	0.0596 0.4145	0.0722 0.4050	0.0820 0.3930	0.0857 0.3748	0.0824 0.3537	0.0722 0.3316	0.0550 0.3062	0.0310 0.2806	C $1-C_1$
0.40	0.20	C C_1	{	0.0257 0.5465	0.0497 0.5329	0.0701 0.5105	0.0892 0.5002	0.1022 0.4795	0.1084 0.4573	0.1077 0.4328	0.1001 0.4079	0.0856 0.3817	0.0639 0.3548	0.0354 0.3294	C $1-C_1$
	0.10	C C_1	{	0.0228 0.5151	0.0447 0.5045	0.0649 0.4942	0.0829 0.4819	0.0967 0.4644	0.1036 0.4436	0.1036 0.4204	0.0968 0.3961	0.0830 0.3716	0.0624 0.3449	0.0347 0.3192	C $1-C_1$
	0.05	C C_1	{	0.0207 0.4872	0.0409 0.4809	0.0602 0.4731	0.0779 0.4642	0.0921 0.4510	0.0997 0.4316	0.1005 0.4105	0.0942 0.3864	0.0811 0.3624	0.0610 0.3369	0.0340 0.3116	C $1-C_1$
	0.03	C C_1	{	0.0196 0.4724	0.0389 0.4683	0.0576 0.4616	0.0750 0.4546	0.0894 0.4438	0.0976 0.4261	0.0987 0.4050	0.0928 0.3822	0.0801 0.3570	0.0604 0.3329	0.0337 0.3076	C $1-C_1$
0.35	0.20	C C_1	{	0.0273 0.5562	0.0527 0.5434	0.0756 0.5283	0.0941 0.5098	0.1067 0.4895	0.1122 0.4653	0.1109 0.4405	0.1026 0.4149	0.0874 0.3885	0.0652 0.3615	0.0361 0.3364	C $1-C_1$
	0.10	C C_1	{	0.0247 0.5293	0.0484 0.5196	0.0703 0.5093	0.0893 0.4957	0.1025 0.4772	0.1086 0.4553	0.1079 0.4310	0.1002 0.4052	0.0856 0.3807	0.0640 0.3535	0.0355 0.3282	C $1-C^1$
	0.05	C C_1	{	0.0228 0.5066	0.0451 0.5004	0.0664 0.4933	0.0853 0.4828	0.0990 0.4665	0.1057 0.4464	0.1054 0.4230	0.0982 0.3986	0.0841 0.3735	0.0630 0.3473	0.0350 0.3220	C $1-C_1$
	0.03	C C_1	{	0.0218 0.4945	0.0433 0.4897	0.0640 0.4839	0.0831 0.4755	0.0970 0.4606	0.1040 0.4415	0.1040 0.4183	0.0972 0.3939	0.0833 0.3690	0.0625 0.3437	0.0348 0.3180	C $1-C_1$
0.30	0.20	C C^1	{	0.0290 0.5684	0.0559 0.5544	0.0799 0.5393	0.0988 0.5202	0.1105 0.4978	0.1156 0.4730	0.1137 0.4480	0.1048 0.4212	0.0891 0.3954	0.0664 0.3686	0.0367 0.3416	C $1-C_1$
	0.10	C C_1	{	0.0267 0.5435	0.0523 0.5352	0.0759 0.5247	0.0951 0.5093	0.1075 0.4886	0.1129 0.4651	0.1116 0.4401	0.1031 0.4140	0.0877 0.3880	0.0656 0.3625	0.0362 0.3359	C $1-C_1$
	0.05	C C_1	{	0.0251 0.5253	0.0495 0.5198	0.0727 0.5129	0.0922 0.4996	0.1050 0.4798	0.1108 0.4583	0.1097 0.4342	0.1017 0.4081	0.0866 0.3832	0.0647 0.3560	0.0358 0.3319	C $1-C_1$
	0.03	C C_1	{	0.0241 0.5142	0.0480 0.5115	0.0709 0.5056	0.0905 0.4943	0.1034 0.4759	0.1094 0.4539	0.1086 0.4301	0.1009 0.4053	0.0861 0.3802	0.0642 0.3537	0.0357 0.3278	C $1-C_1$
0.25	0.20	C C_1	{	0.0308 0.5809	0.0593 0.5671	0.0841 0.5509	0.1025 0.5297	0.1142 0.5056	0.1185 0.4805	0.1162 0.4542	0.1068 0.4283	0.0905 0.4004	0.0673 0.3743	0.0372 0.3476	C $1-C_1$
	0.10	C C_1	{	0.0290 0.5634	0.0565 0.5531	0.0812 0.5409	0.1001 0.5224	0.1119 0.4991	0.1167 0.4744	0.1147 0.4492	0.1056 0.4231	0.0896 0.3965	0.0667 0.3703	0.0369 0.3437	C $1-C_1$
	0.05	C C_1	{	0.0274 0.5466	0.0542 0.5415	0.0790 0.5333	0.0980 0.5155	0.1100 0.4934	0.1152 0.4697	0.1133 0.4448	0.1046 0.4186	0.0888 0.3932	0.0662 0.3665	0.0366 0.3407	C $1-C_1$
	0.03	C C_1	{	0.0266 0.5390	0.0529 0.5348	0.0775 0.5276	0.0968 0.5115	0.1089 0.4897	0.1143 0.4668	0.1126 0.4420	0.1039 0.4166	0.0883 0.3907	0.0660 0.3640	0.0364 0.3376	C $1-C_1$

TABLE 18.—*FIXED-END MOMENTS (FM).*

BEAMS OF CONSTANT CROSS SECTION.

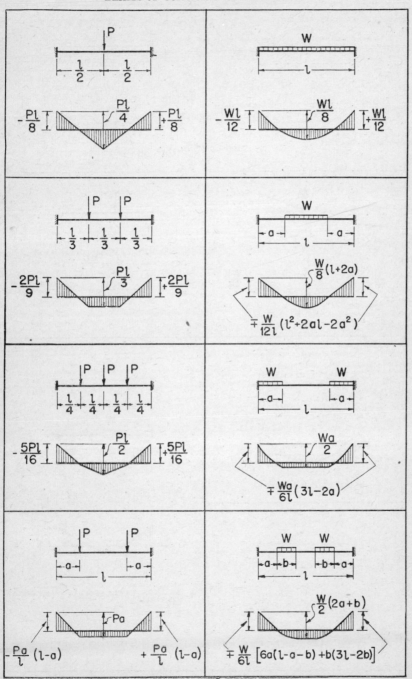

TABLE 19.—*FIXED-END MOMENTS* (FM).
BEAMS OF CONSTANT CROSS SECTION.

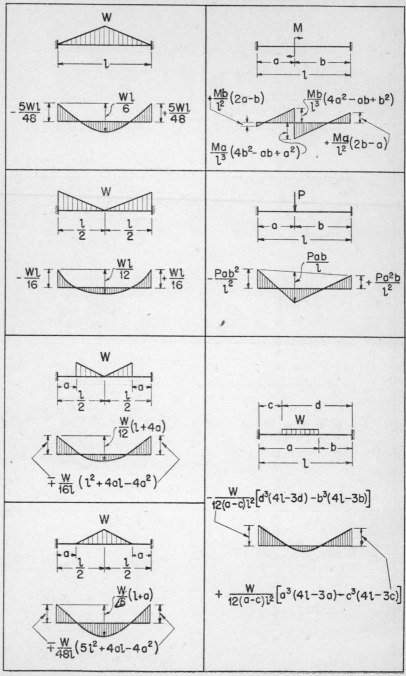

TABLE 20.—*FIXED-END MOMENTS (FM).*
BEAMS OF CONSTANT CROSS SECTION.

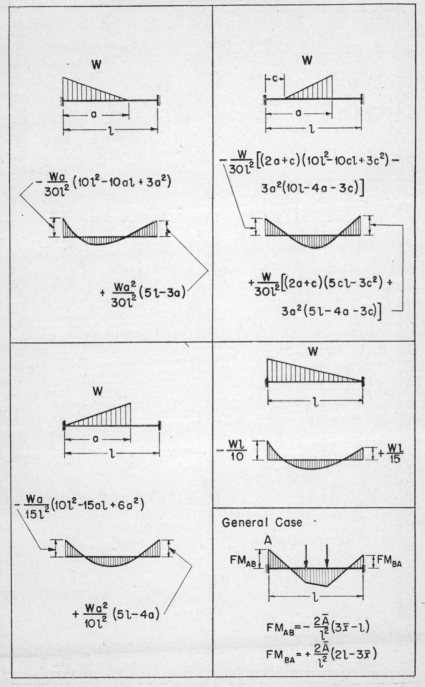

$$-\frac{Wa}{30l^2}(10l^2-10al+3a^2)$$

$$+\frac{Wa^2}{30l^2}(5l-3a)$$

$$-\frac{W}{30l^2}\Big[(2a+c)(10l^2-10cl+3c^2)-3a^2(10l-4a-3c)\Big]$$

$$+\frac{W}{30l^2}\Big[(2a+c)(5cl-3c^2)+3a^2(5l-4a-3c)\Big]$$

$$-\frac{Wa}{15l^2}(10l^2-15al+6a^2)$$

$$+\frac{Wa^2}{10l^2}(5l-4a)$$

$$-\frac{Wl}{10} \qquad +\frac{Wl}{15}$$

General Case

$$FM_{AB}=-\frac{2\bar{A}}{l^2}(3\bar{x}-l)$$

$$FM_{BA}=+\frac{2\bar{A}}{l^2}(2l-3\bar{x})$$

Table 21.—*HINGED-END MOMENTS (HM).*
BEAMS OF CONSTANT CROSS SECTION.

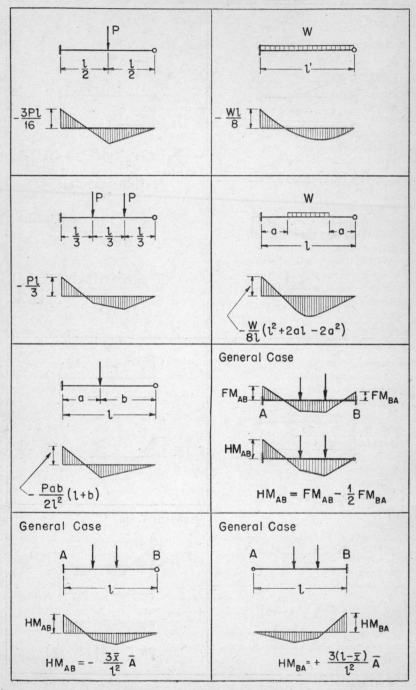

INDEX

○

AMERICAN SOCIETY OF CIVIL ENGINEERS

Founded November 5, 1852

DISCUSSIONS

ANALYSIS OF RIGID FRAMES BY SUPERPOSITION

Discussion

By F. S. Merritt, Ralph W. Stewart,
and John E. Goldberg

F. S. Merritt,[4] Jun. Am. Soc. C. E.[4a]—Although no new method of analysis is proposed (see "Synopsis"), this paper is of value in illustrating the application of the principle of superposition to different types of frames. As Professor Wilson acknowledges, the principle of superposition is usually stated in textbooks on structural analysis; but, contrary to his opinion, it is also strongly emphasized in texts discussing moment distribution, since it is the most convenient tool for analyzing rigid frames by this method. However, nowhere in this paper is the principle of superposition, the subject of the paper, clearly stated or defined; nor are the limits of its validity described.

In the outline of the method of procedure, five steps are given for the solution of any rigid frame problem. Hardy Cross and N. D. Morgan, Members, Am. Soc. C. E., describe this same procedure simply and succinctly as follows $(3a)$:[4b]

> "In analyzing a bent by moment distribution we first assume no movement of the joints and analyze for this condition, find by statics the force necessary to prevent such movements and find the moments which it would produce, and then take the difference of the two results."

The writer has developed the following procedure (16):

> "1. Apply forces to the structure to prevent sidesway while the fixed-end moments due to loads are distributed.
> "2. Compute the moments due to these forces.
> "3. Combine the moments obtained in Steps 1 and 2 to eliminate the effect of the forces."

When moment distribution by the method of moment ratios (16) is used, there is never any need to revert to the slope-deflection method, because the ques-

Note.—This paper by David M. Wilson was published in February, 1944, *Proceedings*.

[4] Field Service Engr., D. W. Haering & Co., New York, N. Y.

[4a] Received by the Secretary February 21, 1944.

[4b] Numerals in parentheses, thus: (3a), refer to corresponding items in the Bibliography (see Appendix of the paper), and at the end of discussion in this issue.

tion of convergence does not arise. The author's recommendation in conclusion 4, therefore, is not generally valid.

In applying either of these last two procedures, sketches may be desirable, but they are not necessary. From a practical viewpoint, the preparation of sketches requires time, and, where the calculations can follow a rigid procedure in which mistakes can be avoided without the use of sketches, such a procedure is recommended. In the classroom, sketches are useful in the introduction of an unfamiliar subject, but, in a drafting room, where time is money and a designer is assumed to be familiar with structural analysis, time-saving procedures should be adopted. Consequently, step 1 of the paper should be optional with the designer and should be included as a suggestion to facilitate determination of signs rather than as a step in the procedure.

In analyzing rigid frames, a designer generally wishes to obtain separately the effects of dead load, live load, wind, etc. The determination of live load moments might require the plotting of influence lines. In reality, this is the rigid frame problem, as contrasted to the classroom problem of a given structure with a fixed loading condition. Professor Wilson does not state how his procedure could be used under changing load conditions without the necessity of going through all five steps for each change in position or magnitude of loads. As a matter of fact, the writer has used the three steps outlined herein as the base of a simple procedure in which the principle of superposition is utilized to obtain the separate effects of varied loading conditions without the necessity of distributing fixed-end moments for every condition (16). The practice of computing and placing final moments on sketches, as recommended in steps 2 and 3 by the author, is cumbersome in view of the great number of sketches required and the difficulty in making summations and combinations from them.

The writer agrees with all the conclusions of the paper except conclusion 4.

RALPH W. STEWART,[5] M. AM. SOC. C. E.[5a]—In his opening sentence Professor Wilson states that the purpose of his paper "is to demonstrate the usefulness of the principle of superposition in the analysis of rigid frames by the slope-deflection and moment distribution methods." From an examination of the demonstrations the writer concludes that, for multistory frames with sloping columns and for the Vierendeel truss, the author has accomplished his purpose.

However, in his treatment of one-story and two-story frames with vertical columns, Professor Wilson introduces undesirable complexities and also so much unnecessary arithmetic that the writer does not consider this part of the paper useful. To uphold this conclusion the writer presents Fig. 11, which is the bent shown in Fig. 1, using the moment values in Eqs. 4. By equating the sums of the moments about joints B and C, respectively, to zero and then consolidating terms the author obtains Eqs. 5, containing three unknown quantities. To solve them he introduces Eqs. 7 and 8 from which $E R$ may be evaluated; and then Eqs. 5 can be solved for θ_B and θ_C.

[5] Bridge Engr., City of Los Angeles, Los Angeles. Calif.
[5a] Received by the Secretary March 20, 1944.

Fig. 12 is a graph of the traverse of the elastic curves of Fig. 11.   In Fig. 12 the geometrical values of the angles of flexure in terms of θ_B and θ_C are shown. For the beam each angle value is the same as the parenthetical term in a slope-deflection equation for this member.   The properties of these angles have been published (17).   They are located at the one-third points of the members.

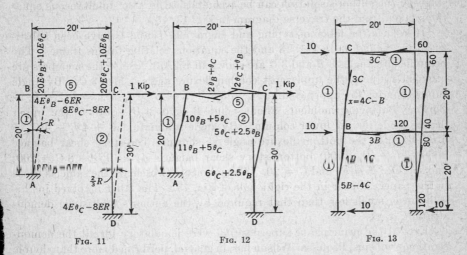

FIG. 11   FIG. 12   FIG. 13

Since the left column is only one fifth as stiff as the beam, its angle of flexure for the moment at B will be five times as great as the flexure angle in the beam, or $10\,\theta_B + 5\,\theta_C$. To obtain the flexure angle for M_A it is only necessary (from the geometry of the figure) to add θ_B to the flexure angle for the moment at B, giving $11\,\theta_B + 5\,\theta_C$. A similar procedure gives the flexure angles for the right column.   The unknown R does not appear in these angle values.   A property of an elastic curve traverse is that a flexure angle multiplied by the member stiffness equals the moment that the angle measures.   By multiplying the flexure angles by the K-values a set of relative moment values for Fig. 12 is obtained.   The geometry of the flexure of the columns gives the deflections at points B and C.   Writing the equilibrium equation, in which the sum of the column shears equals 1 kip, and the geometrical equation, which expresses the fact that the deflections at B and C are equal, and consolidating terms:

$$1.383\,\theta_B + 1.233\,\theta_C = 1 \dots\dots\dots\dots\dots\dots(33a)$$

and

$$5.5\,\theta_B = 3.667\,\theta_C \dots\dots\dots\dots\dots\dots(33b)$$

These equations, with only two unknown quantities, replace Eqs. 5 with three unknown quantities.

Solving, $\theta_B = 0.3093$ and $\theta_C = 0.464$.   The flexure angles can now be evaluated.   Multiplying these angles by the K-values of the members gives a set of moments which check Professor Wilson's moments to slide-rule accuracy.

To solve the two-story symmetrical frame illustrated by Fig. 4, the author's procedure involved the following work: Steps 1 and 2, two end-moment distribution procedures for the frame; and, step 3, the development and solution of two simultaneous formulas (Eqs. 13). The two end-moment distribution operations were unnecessary as all of the work accomplished by these three stages of the author's solution can be accomplished by two simultaneous equations taken from the traverse diagram in Fig. 13.

To reduce the labor of typing and engraving, B and C have been substituted for θ_B and θ_C in Fig. 13 and the equations relating to this frame. The beam flexure angles $3\,B$ and $3\,C$ are shown in Fig. 13. Since the members are of equal stiffness, the uppermost column flexure angle is also $3\,C$. By angle summation for the upper column: $C + 3\,C - x - B = 0$, or $x = 4\,C - B$, as shown. Balancing moments about point B gives $4\,B - 4\,C$ as the upper flexure angle for the lower column. By angle summation $B + 4\,B - 4\,C$, or $5\,B - 4\,C$, is the bottom flexure angle as shown. Top-story shear balance gives: $7\,C - B = 100$; bottom-story shear balance gives: $9\,B - 8\,C = 200$; and solving: $B = 40$ and $C = 20$. The moments (which are the same as those in the paper) appear in the right half of Fig. 13. The labor involved in this solution is much less than that required by the author's multistage demonstration.

Even if the principle of superposition were mandatory for all the demonstration problems, Professor Wilson has, in general, performed more than double the necessary preliminary work by restricting his paper to slope deflection and end-moment distribution. For example, the work in Fig. 5(a) involved one hundred and twenty-eight arithmetical operations. With the traverse method, the results can be duplicated with thirty-seven arithmetical operations and two slide-rule settings from one of which seven readings are taken; and from the other setting, four readings.

The traverse solution also has some automatic checks which end-moment distribution does not. For example, in Fig. 5(a), M_{CE} should be exactly six times M_{EC}. The author's solution yields $6 \times 208 = 1{,}268$. The correct value of M_{EC} is 211.3. This difference in moments is not important but the fact that the traverse method offers checks not offered by end-moment distribution is important. Also the author's solution is applicable to only one position of the live load whereas the traverse solution can be used for any position of the live load.

For Fig. 4(c) all the arithmetical work needed to compute the moments by the traverse method is as follows: $2 + 3 = 5$; $4\,x = 6$; $x = 1\frac{1}{2}$; $3\,x = 4.5$; $3 + 10 - 4.5 = 8.5$; and $6 \times 1 = 6$. Finally:

Traverse results	Wilson results
$4.5 = 3.176\,E\,R$	$3.17\,E\,R$
$5.0 = 3.529\,E\,R$	$3.54\,E\,R$
$\dfrac{6\,E\,R}{8.5} \times \begin{cases} \\ \\ 3.0 = 2.121\,E\,R \\ \\ \\ \end{cases}$	$2.12\,E\,R$
$2\ \ = 1.412\,E\,R$	$1.42\,E\,R$
$1\ \ = 0.706\,E\,R$	$0.72\,E\,R$

The detail of Professor Wilson's end-moment distribution is not given, but it must certainly have involved several times as much work as the foregoing. The traverse solution of Fig. 4(b) is equally simple.

To summarize: The paper is of value to engineers who design framed structures. Its usefulness is considerably impaired, however, by unnecessarily complex solutions for some of the problems due to the exclusion of the elastic curve traverse from the scope of the work.

JOHN E. GOLDBERG,[6] ASSOC. M. AM. SOC. C. E.[6a]—A commendable résumé of the application of the principle of superposition to the analysis of certain types of rigid frame structures is presented by Professor Wilson. The paper is an excellent coordination of this principle with the particular types of structures described.

The method of superposition will give a reasonable analysis in many cases where the solution by more direct methods may be comparatively tedious. This is true because in direct methods of analysis a large number of simultaneous equations must be solved, whereas in the method of superposition a limited number of modes of deformation are first analyzed and subsequently used as parameters in the solution of the complete framework. Obviously, using the latter procedure there are a smaller number of equations to solve simultaneously. The method of superposition is particularly applicable to frames of what may be termed intermediate complexity.

The writer has used similar methods for a number of years in conjunction with slope deflection and moment distribution for the analysis of several classes of structures—particularly Vierendeel trusses with cambered chords, A-frames, and simple or gabled bents—and also for the analysis of sidesway effects induced by unsymmetrical vertical loading or by transverse loading of building frames not more than a few stories in height. In such problems the method of superposition provides a simple and practicable method of analysis, particularly when used in conjunction with moment distribution or slope deflection (18)(19) and successive approximations or successive corrections. Certain of these problems have been analyzed by various writers in a number of texts and papers. The gabled bent, for example, has been "popular" in technical publications. The analysis of simple bents and bents with inclined legs likewise has been presented in several texts.

Some problems discussed by Professor Wilson may be solved at least as easily by direct methods without recourse to the method of superposition. Certain simple bents are generally in this class. A structure that may be analyzed easily by more direct methods is the Vierendeel truss with equal parallel chords or the structurally similar two-column bent with parallel equal columns. The attention of the writer was directed to this problem a number of years ago by the comparative impracticability of applying the usual popular methods to such structures when the outside members (that is, chords in the Vierendeel trusses or columns in the bents) are relatively stiff, say, five

[6] Structures Engr., Consolidated Vultee Aircraft Corp., San Diego, Calif.
[6a] Received by the Secretary March 30, 1944.

or more times as stiff as the interior members. In such cases moment or shear distribution is extremely slow in converging to the exact solution.

For a simple and practicable solution of this problem the writer derived the following exact formula from the basic slope-deflection equations:

$$\theta_n = \frac{1}{6\,K_{Gn} + K_{Cn} + K_{Co}} \left(\frac{M_n + M_o}{2} + K_{Cn}\,\theta_m + K_{Co}\,\theta_o \right) \dots (34)$$

in which K_{Gn} and K_{Cn} are the relative stiffnesses of the web members and of the chord members, respectively; and M_n is the product of the transverse external shear acting on the nth panel times the longitudinal dimension of the panel—that is, the distance between interior members. When the known K and M values are substituted, Eq. 34 reduces to an expression of the simple form,

$$\theta_n = A\,\theta_m + B\,\theta_o + C \dots (35)$$

A similar equation is set up for each panel point along either chord. The series of equations thus obtained converge very rapidly. For example, in cases where the chords are from eight to ten times as stiff as the interior members, three or four cycles of these extremely simple calculations will give an accuracy better than twenty cycles (approximately) by the usual moment distribution or shear distribution procedure. The web-member end moments are given by the formula,

$$M_{Gn} = -3\,(K_{Gn}\,\theta_n) \dots (36a)$$

and the chord-member end moments by the formula,

$$M_{Cnm} = \frac{M_n}{4} + \left(\frac{\theta_m - \theta_n}{2} \right) K_{Cn} \dots (36b)$$

Obviously, a number of problems not treated by Professor Wilson may also be analyzed by the method of superposition. The method of superposition is an extremely general and practicable method, and Professor Wilson is to be commended for his clear and concise outline.

Bibliography.—

(3) "Continuous Frames of Reinforced Concrete," by Hardy Cross and N. D. Morgan, John Wiley & Sons, Inc., New York, N. Y., 1932. (a) p. 209.

(16) "Moment Distribution by the Method of Moment Ratios," by Frederick S. Merritt (unpublished manuscript).

(17) "Relative Flexure Factors for Analyzing Continuous Structures," by Ralph W. Stewart, *Transactions*, Am. Soc. C. E., Vol. 104 (1939), p. 521.

(18) "Simplified Methods for the Analysis of Multiple Joint Rigid Frames," by George A. Maney and John E. Goldberg, *Bulletin*, Northwestern Univ., Evanston, Ill., Vol. 33, No. 7, October 17, 1932.

(19) "Vertical Load Analysis of Rigid Building Frames Made Practicable," by John E. Goldberg, *Engineering News-Record*, November 12, 1931, pp. 770–772.